——————Stanley Gibbons

GREAT BRITAIN
CONCISE
STAMP CATALOGUE

Third edition, 1988

Stanley Gibbons Publications Ltd
London and Ringwood

By Appointment to Her Majesty The Queen
Stanley Gibbons Ltd., London
Philatelists

Published by **Stanley Gibbons Publications Ltd**
Editorial, Sales Offices and Distribution Centre:
5 Parkside, Christchurch Road, Ringwood,
Hants BH24 3SH

First Edition — May 1986
Second Edition — May 1987
Third Edition — May 1988

© Stanley Gibbons Publications 1988

ISBN: 0-85259-189-6

Item No. 2887 (88)

Printed in Great Britain by
Pardy Printers, Ringwood, Hampshire

THE GREAT BRITAIN CONCISE CATALOGUE

Third Edition

The *Concise Catalogue*, now in its third year of publication, has rapidly established itself as an essential guide for the "one-country" collector of Great Britain. Both the previous editions have sold out and we continue to receive many letters making suggestions for further improvements.

The popularity of Great Britain stamps continues to grow – the *Concise Catalogue* supplies the information to enhance your collection.

The *Concise* listings are based on the Great Britain section of our *Part 1 (British Commonwealth) Catalogue*, but there is much more additional material within its pages:

- All issues from the Penny Black of 1840 to the latest 1988 Sports commemorative, including Regional, Postage Due, Official and Postal Fiscal stamps.
- All different stamp designs are illustrated.
- Every basic stamp listed, including those with different watermarks or perforations and those showing graphite lines or phosphor bands.
- Missing colours, missing embossing, watermark errors, imperforate errors and phosphor omitted varieties from those stamps normally issued with phosphor bands.
- Gutter Pairs and "Traffic light" Gutter Pairs listed in mint sets.
- First Day Covers for all Special Issues and for definitives, including Regionals, of the present reign. All British Post Office special First Day of Issue postmarks are illustrated and priced on cover.
- Post Office Picture Cards (PHQ cards) are priced as sets, both mint and used with First Day of Issue postmarks.
- Presentation, Collector and Gift Packs, including the scarce versions with foreign inscriptions.
- Quick-reference diagrams for Machin decimal booklet panes.
- Machin and commemorative underprints given separate catalogue numbers.
- Post Office Yearbooks.
- Royal Mail Postage Labels priced in mint or used sets and on British Post Office First Day Covers.
- Wartime issues for the Channel Islands.
- Separate section for Post Office Stamp Booklets with dated editions of King George VI listed separately.
- Helpful Introductory section providing definitions and guidance for the collector and including all watermark illustrations shown together to assist identification.
- Addresses for specialist philatelic societies covering Great Britain stamps.

NEW FEATURES for this edition include:

- Recently discovered errors and varieties listed. See Nos. 64a, 73Wk, 178Wi, 724c, 767Ey, X845nEy, X856Egy, X864lEy, X875a, X886lEy, X888mEy, X943a, X951a, 1232a, 1332a, 1334a, 1349a, 1357a, NI11Ey, NI50Ea, W38Ea, Jersey 12Ey.
- Decimal Machin and Regional Presentation Packs listing improved.
- New section for Postmaster and U.P.U. Specimen overprints.

David J. Aggersberg

Stanley Gibbons International Ltd.

HEAD OFFICE, 399 STRAND, LONDON WC2R 0LX

Auction Room and Specialist Departments. Open Monday–Friday, 9.30 a.m. to 5 p.m.

Shop: Open Monday–Friday 9.30 a.m. to 6 p.m. and Saturday 10 a.m. to 4.00 p.m.
 Telephone 01-836 8444 and Telex 28883 for all departments.

RINGWOOD OFFICE

Stanley Gibbons Publications and Promotions, Parkside, Christchurch Road, Ringwood, Hants BH24 3SH.
 Telephone 04254 2363. Telex 41271.

OVERSEAS BRANCHES

Stanley Gibbons (Australia) Pty. Ltd., P.O. Box 863J, Melbourne 3001, Australia.
Telephone (010 613) 670-3332 and Telex AA 37223.

Stanley Gibbons (Pty.) Ltd., P.O. Box 930, Parklands 2121, Republic of South Africa.

Stanley Gibbons (Singapore) Pte Ltd., Maxwell Road, P.O. Box 1372, Singapore 9027, Republic of Singapore.

Contents

For the Great Britain specialist collector . . .

Stanley Gibbons Great Britain Specialised Catalogue in five volumes. Recognised as leading publications of their kind, and spanning British stamp issues from the 1840s to the 1980s.

Item 0285 Volume 1 (Queen Victoria)
Item 0286 Volume 2 (King Edward VII to King George VI)
Item 2810 Volume 3 (Queen Elizabeth II Pre-decimal issues)
Item 2820 Volume 4 (Queen Elizabeth II Decimal Definitive issues)
Item 2891 Volume 5 (Queen Elizabeth II Decimal Commemorative issues)

Great Britain Checklist

Printed in colour, published annually, this handy size checklist provides a clear update on GB stamp prices.

Item 0289 Collect British Stamps

For details of these and other S.G. Publications write for free Mail Order catalogue.

Great Britain Philatelic Societies

The Great Britain Philatelic Society. Hon. Membership Secretary: A. J. Walker, 42 Jesmond Road, Newcastle-upon-Tyne, Tyne & Wear, NE2 4PQ.

The British Decimal Stamps Study Circle. The Secretary: P. Daniels, 70 Moor Park Close, Rainham, Gillingham, Kent, ME8 8QT.

The Great Britain Decimal Stamp Book Study Circle. Hon. Membership Secretary: A. J. Wilkins, 3 Buttermere Close, Brierley Hill, West Midlands, DY5 3SD.

STANLEY GIBBONS PUBLICATIONS LIMITED
OVERSEAS REPRESENTATION

Stanley Gibbons Publications Ltd. are represented overseas by the following sole distributors (*) and main agents (**)

Australia*
Lighthouse Philatelic (Aust.) Pty Ltd
Box 62
Chippendale 2008
New South Wales
Australia

Belgium and Luxembourg**
Philac
Rue du Midi 48
Bruxelles
Belgium 1000

Canada*
Unitrade Associates
127 Cartwright Avenue
Toronto
Ontario
Canada M6A 1V4

Denmark**
Nordfrim
DK 5450
Otterup
Denmark

Finland**
Suomen Poskimerkkeily OY
Ludvigin Katu 5
SF-00130 Helsinki
Finland

France*
Davo France SARL
30 Rue de Gren Elle
75007 Paris
France

West Germany (incl. West Berlin
and Austria)*
Ka-Be Briefmarkenalben-Verlag
Volkhardt GMBH
Daimlerstrasse 15
Goppingen-Ursenwang
West Germany

Hong Kong**
Po-on Stamp Service
GPO Box 2498
Hong Kong

Israel**
Capital Stamps
PO Box 3749
Jerusalem 91036
Israel

Japan**
Japan Philatelic Co Ltd
PO Box 2
Suginami-Minami
Tokyo
Japan

Netherlands*
Davo Publications
PO Box 411
7400 AK Deventer
Netherlands

New Zealand*
Philatelic Distributors Ltd
PO Box 863
New Plymouth
New Zealand

Norway**
Wennergren-Cappelen AS
Nedre Vollgate 4
PO Box 738
Sentrum N-0105
Oslo 1
Norway

Sweden*
Frimarkshuset AB
S-793 01
Leksand
Sweden

Switzerland**
Dove of Basle
Birsigstrasse 111
4011 Basle
Switzerland

USA*
Subway Stamp Shop Inc
111 Nassau Street
New York
NY 10038
USA

West Indies/Caribbean**
Hugh Dunphy
PO Box 413
Kingston 10
Jamaica
West Indies

PRICES

The prices quoted in this catalogue are the estimated selling prices of Stanley Gibbons Ltd at the time of publication. They are, *unless it is specifically stated otherwise*, for examples in fine condition for the issue concerned. Superb examples are worth more; those of a lower quality considerably less.

All prices are subject to change without prior notice and Stanley Gibbons Ltd may from time to time offer stamps below catalogue price in consequence of special purchases or particular promotions.

No guarantee is given to supply all stamps priced, since it is not possible to keep every catalogued item in stock.

Quotation of prices. The prices in the left-hand column are for unused stamps and those in the right-hand column are for used.

A dagger (†) denotes that the item listed does not exist in that condition and a blank, or dash, that it exists, or may exist, but no market price is known.

Prices are expressed in pounds and pence sterling. One pound comprises 100 pence (£1 = 100p).

The method of notation is as follows: pence in numerals (e.g. 5 denotes five pence); pounds and pence up to £100, in numerals (e.g. 4.25 denotes four pounds and twenty-five pence); prices above £100 expressed in whole pounds with the "£" sign shown.

Unused and Used stamps. The prices for unused stamps of Queen Victoria to King George V are for lightly hinged examples. In addition prices are quoted for King George V commemorative sets in unmounted mint condition. Unused prices for Edward VIII to Queen Elizabeth II issues are for unmounted mint (though when not available, mounted mint stamps are often supplied at a lower price). Prices for used stamps are for postally used examples.

Prices quoted for bisects on cover or on large piece are for those dated during the period officially authorised.

Minimum price. The minimum price quoted is five pence. This represents a handling charge rather than a basis for valuing common stamps, for which the 5p price should not be reckoned automatically, since it covers a variation in real scarcity.

Set prices. Set prices are generally for one of each value, excluding shades and varieties, but including major colour changes. Where there are alternative shades, etc., the cheapest is usually included. The number of stamps in the set is always stated for clarity.

The mint prices for sets containing *se-tenant* pieces are based on the prices quoted for such combinations, and not on those for the individual stamps. The used set price is for single stamps.

Gutter Pairs. These, and traffic-light gutter pairs, are priced as complete sets.

Used on Cover prices. To assist collectors, cover prices are quoted in a third column for postage and Official stamps issued in the reigns of Queen Victoria and King Edward VII.

The cover should be of non-philatelic origin, bearing the correct postal rate for the period and distance involved and cancelled with the markings normal to the offices concerned. Purely philatelic items have a cover value only

slightly greater than the catalogue value for the corresponding used stamps. This applies generally to those high-value stamps used philatelically rather than in the normal course of commerce.

Oversized covers, difficult to accommodate on an album page, should be reckoned as worth little more than the corresponding value of the used stamps. The condition of a cover affects its value. Except for "wreck covers", serious damage or soiling reduce the value where the postal markings and stamps are ordinary ones. Conversely, visual appeal adds to the value and this can include freshness of appearance, important addresses, old-fashioned but legible handwriting, historic town-names, etc. The prices quoted are a base on which further value would be added to take account of the cover's postal historical importance in demonstrating such things as unusual, scarce or emergency cancels, interesting routes, significant postal markings, combination usage, the development of postal rates, and so on.

First Day Cover prices. Prices are quoted for commemorative first day covers from 1924 British Empire Exhibition pair onwards. These prices are for special covers (from 1937) franked with complete sets and cancelled by ordinary operational postmarks to the end of 1962 or the various standard "First Day of Issue" markings from 1963.

The Philatelic Bureau and other special "First Day of Issue" postmarks provided by the Post Office since 1963 are listed under each issue. Prices quoted are for these postmarks used on illustrated covers (from 1964 those produced by the Post Office), franked with complete sets.

The British Post Office did not introduce special First Day of Issue postmarks for definitive issues until the first instalment of the Machin £sd series, issued 5 June 1967, although "First Day" treatment had been provided for some Regional stamps from 8 June 1964 onwards. Prices for the First Day Covers from 1952 to 1966, showing definitive stamps are for the stamps indicated, used on illustrated envelopes and postmarked with operational cancellations.

From 1967 onwards the prices quoted are for stamps as indicated, used on illustrated envelopes and postmarked with special First Day of Issue handstamps. Other definitives issued during this period were not accepted for "First Day" treatment by the British Post Office.

Guarantee

All stamps are guaranteed genuine originals in the following terms:

If not as described, and returned by the purchaser, we undertake to refund the price paid to us in the original transaction. If any stamp is certified as genuine by the Expert Committee of the Royal Philatelic Society, London, or by B.P.A. Expertising Ltd, the purchaser shall not be entitled to make any claim against us for any error, omission or mistake in such certificate.

Consumers' statutory rights are not affected by the above guarantee.

The recognised Expert Committees in this country are those of the Royal Philatelic Society, 41 Devonshire Place, London W1N 1PE, and B.P.A. Expertising Ltd, P.O. Box 163, Carshalton Beeches, Surrey SM5 4QR. They do not undertake valuations under any circumstances and fees are payable for their services.

CONTACTING THE CATALOGUE EDITOR

The Editor is always interested in hearing from people who have new information which will improve or correct the Catalogue. As a general rule he must see and examine the actual stamps before they can be considered for listing; photographs or photocopies are insufficient evidence.

Submissions should be made in writing to the Catalogue Editor, Stanley Gibbons Publications Ltd. The cost of return postage for items submitted is appreciated, and this should include the registration fee if required.

Where information is solicited purely for the benefit of the enquirer, the Editor cannot undertake to reply if the answer is already contained in these published notes or if return postage is omitted. Written communications are greatly preferred to enquiries by telephone and the Editor regrets that he or his staff cannot see personal callers without a prior appointment being made. Correspondence may be subject to delay during the production period of each new edition.

Please note that the following classes of material are outside the scope of this Catalogue:

(a) Non-postal revenue or fiscal stamps.
(b) Postage stamps used fiscally.
(c) Local carriage labels and private local issues.
(d) Punctured postage stamps (perfins).
(e) Telegraph stamps.
(f) Bogus or phantom stamps.
(g) Railway or airline letter fee stamps, bus or road transport company labels.
(h) Postal stationery cut-outs.
(i) All types of non-postal labels and souvenirs.
(j) Documentary labels for the postal service, e.g. registration, recorded delivery, airmail etiquettes, etc.
(k) Privately applied embellishments to official issues and privately commissioned items generally.
(l) Stamps for training postal staff.

> **We regret we do not give opinions as to the genuineness of stamps, nor do we identify stamps or number them by our Catalogue.**

Stanley Gibbons Stamp Collecting Series

A well illustrated series of handbooks, packed with essential information for all collectors.

Item 2760 Stamp Collecting: How to Start – Especially for the beginner. A clear outline of the basic elements.

Item 2762 Stamp Collecting: Collecting by Theme – Sound practical advice on how to form and develop a thematic collection, including an A–Z of collecting subjects.

Item 2764 Stamp Collecting: A Guide to Modern Philately – A philatelic classic! The story of the post, stamp design, printing – in fact everything you need to know about this fascinating hobby.

GENERAL ABBREVIATIONS

Alph	Alphabet
Anniv	Anniversary
Brt	Bright (colour)
C, c	Chalky paper
C.	Overprinted in carmine
Des	Designer; designed
Dp	Deep (colour)
Eng	Engraver; engraved
Horiz	Horizontal; horizontally
Imp, Imperf	Imperforate
Inscr	Inscribed
L	Left
Litho	Lithographed
Lt	Light (colour)
mm	Millimetres
MS	Miniature sheet
O, o	Ordinary paper
Opt(d)	Overprint(ed)
P, Pf or Perf	Perforated
Photo	Photogravure
Pl	Plate
Pr	Pair
Ptd	Printed
Ptg	Printing
PVA	Polyvinyl alcohol (gum)
R	Right
R.	Row
Recess	Recess-printed
T	Type
Typo	Typographed
Un	Unused
Us	Used
Vert	Vertical; vertically
W or wmk	Watermark
Wmk s	Watermark sideways

(†) = Does not exist.
(—) (or blank price column) = Exists, or may exist, but no market price is known.
/ between colours means "on" and the colour following is that of the paper on which the stamp is printed.

PRINTERS

B.W.	Bradbury Wilkinson & Co, Ltd.
D.L.R.	De La Rue & Co, Ltd, London, and (from 1961) Bogota, Colombia.
Enschedé	Joh. Enschedé en Zonen, Haarlem, Netherlands.
Harrison	Harrison & Sons, Ltd, High Wycombe.
J.W.	John Waddington Security Print, Ltd, Leeds
P.B.	Perkins Bacon Ltd, London.
Questa	Questa Colour Security Printers, Ltd.
Waterlow	Waterlow & Sons, Ltd, London.

PHILATELIC INFORMATION

Catalogue Numbers

The catalogue number appears in the extreme left column. The boldface Type numbers in the next column are merely cross-reference to illustrations. Catalogue numbers in the Gibbons *Stamp Monthly* Supplement are provisional only and may need to be altered when the lists are consolidated.

Our catalogue numbers are universally recognised in specifying stamps and as a hallmark of status.

Catalogue Illustrations

Stamps and first day postmarks are illustrated at three-quarters linear size. Stamps not illustrated are the same size and format as the value shown, unless otherwise indicated. Overprints, surcharges and watermarks are normally actual size. Illustrations of varieties are often enlarged to show the detail.

Designers

Designers' names are quoted where known, though space precludes naming every individual concerned in the production of a set. In particular, photographers supplying material are usually named only when they also make an active contribution in the design stage; posed photographs of reigning monarchs are, however, an exception to this rule.

Printing Errors

Errors in printing are of major interest to the Catalogue. Authenticated items meriting consideration would include: background, centre or frame inverted or omitted; centre or subject transposed; error of colour; error or omission of value; double prints and impressions; printed both sides; and so on. Designs *tête-bêche*, whether intentionally or by accident, are listable. Colours only partially omitted are not listed. However, stamps with embossing, phosphor or both omitted and stamps printed on the gummed side are included.

Printing technology has radically improved over the years, during which time photogravure and lithography have become predominant. Varieties nowadays are more in the nature of flaws which are almost always outside the scope of this book.

In no catalogue, however, do we list such items as: dry prints, kiss prints, doctor-blade flaws, colour shifts or registration flaws (unless they lead to the complete omission of a colour from an individual stamp), lithographic ring flaws, and so on. Neither do we recognise fortuitous happenings like paper creases or confetti flaws.

Paper Types

All stamps listed are deemed to be on "ordinary" paper of the wove type and white in colour; only departures from this are normally mentioned.

A coloured paper is one that is coloured right through (front and back of the stamp). In the Catalogue the colour of the paper is given in *italics*, thus:

purple/*yellow* = purple design on yellow paper.

Papers have been made specially white in recent years by, for example, a very heavy coating of chalk. We do not classify shades of whiteness of paper as distinct varieties.

The availability of many postage stamps for revenue purposes made necessary some safeguard against the illegitimate re-use of stamps with removable cancellations. This was at first secured by using fugitive inks and later by printing on chalky (chalk-surfaced) paper, both of which made it difficult to remove any form of obliteration without also damaging the stamp design. We have indicated the existence of the papers by the letters "O" (ordinary) and "C" (chalky) after the description of all stamps where the chalky paper may be found. Where no indication is given the paper is "ordinary".

Our chalky paper is specifically one which shows a black mark when touched with a silver wire. Stamps on chalk-surfaced paper can easily lose this coating through immersion in water.

Perforation Measurement

The gauge of a perforation is the number of holes in a length of 2 cm.

The Gibbons *Instanta* gauge is the standard for measuring perforations. The stamp is viewed against a dark background with the transparent gauge put on top of it. Though the gauge measures to decimal accuracy, perforations read from it are generally quoted in the Catalogue to the nearest half. For example:

Just over perf 12¾ to just under 13¼   = perf 13
Perf 13¼ exactly, rounded up   = perf 13½
Just over perf 13¼ to just under 13¾   = perf 13½
Perf 13¾ exactly, rounded up   = perf 14

However, where classification depends on it, actual quarter-perforations are quoted. Perforations are usually abbreviated (and spoken) as follows, though sometimes they may be spelled out for clarity.

P 14: perforated alike on all sides (read: "perf 14").

P 14 × 15: the first figure refers to top and bottom, the second to left and right sides (read: "perf 14 by 15"). This is a compound perforation.

Such headings as "P 13 × 14 (vert) and P 14 × 13 (horiz)" indicate which perforations apply to which stamp format—vertical or horizontal.

Perforation Errors

Authenticated errors, where a stamp normally perforated is accidentally issued imperforate, are listed provided no traces of perforation (blind holes or indentations) remain. They must be provided as pairs, both stamps wholly imperforate, and are only priced in that form.

Numerous part-perforated stamps have arisen from the introduction of the Jumelle Press. This has a rotary perforator with rows of pins on one drum engaging with holes on another. Engagement is only gradual when the perforating unit is started up or stopped, giving rise to perforations "fading out", a variety mentioned above as not listed.

Stamps from the Jumelle printings sometimes occur imperforate between stamp and sheet margin. Such errors are not listed in this catalogue, but are covered by the fourth volume of the *Great Britain Specialised Catalogue*.

Pairs described as "imperforate between" have the line of perforations between the two stamps omitted.

Imperf between (*horiz pair*): a horizontal pair of stamps with perfs all around the edges but none between the stamps.

Imperf between (*vert pair*): a vertical pair of stamps with perfs all around the edges but none between the stamps.

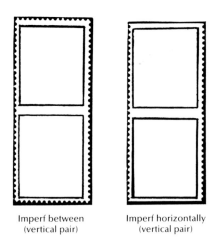

Imperf between
(vertical pair)

Imperf horizontally
(vertical pair)

Where several of the rows have escaped perforation the resulting varieties are listable. Thus:

Imperf vert (*horiz pair*): a horizontal pair of stamps perforated at top and bottom; all three vertical directions are imperf—the two outer edges and between the stamps.

Imperf horiz (*vert pair*): a vertical pair perforated at left and right edges; all three horizontal directions are imperf—the top, bottom and between the stamps.

Varieties of double, misplaced or partial perforation caused by error or machine malfunction are not listable, neither are freaks, such as perforations placed diagonally from paper folds, nor missing holes caused by broken pins.

Phosphor Issues

Machines which sort mail electronically have been introduced progressively and the British Post Office issued the first stamps specially marked for electronic sorting in 1957. This first issue had easily visible graphite lines printed on the back beneath the gum (see Nos. 561/6). They were issued in the Southampton area where the experiment was carried out.

The graphite lines were replaced by phosphor bands, activated by ultra-violet light. The bands are printed on the front of the stamps and show as a matt surface against the usual smooth or shiny appearance of the untreated surface of the paper. The bands show clearly in the top or bottom horizontal margins of the sheet.

The first phosphor issues appeared in 1959 (see Nos. 599/609) and these stamps also had graphite lines on the back. Further details will be found in the listings above Nos. 599 and 619. From 1962 onwards most commemoratives were issued in versions with or without bands. From 1967 all commemorative stamps had phosphor bands, but from 1972 they were replaced by "all-over" phosphor covering the entire area of the stamp.

After a considerable period of development a special paper was produced in which the phosphor had been incorporated into the coating. From 15 August 1979 phosphorised paper was accepted for use generally, this paper replacing phosphor bands on most values. Phosphorised paper can only be identified by ultra-violet light. The Stanley Gibbons Uvitec Micro ultra-violet lamp is firmly recommended for use in identifying the phosphor stamps listed in this Catalogue. *Warning.* Never stare at the lighted lamp but follow the manufacturer's instructions.

During the years, 1967 to 1972, when all issues, except the high values, should have shown phosphor bands, a number of stamps appeared with them omitted in error. These varieties are listed in this Catalogue. Stamps with "all-over" phosphor omitted can only be detected by the use of an ultra-violet lamp and these varieties are listed in the Stanley Gibbons *Great Britain Specialised Catalogue*. Note that prices are for unmounted mint examples only. Varieties such as double bands, misplaced or printed on the back are not listed in this Catalogue.

Gum Description

All stamps listed are assumed to have gum of some kind and original gum (o.g.) means that which was present on the stamp as issued to the public. Deleterious climates and the presence of certain chemicals can cause gum to crack and, with early stamps, even make the paper deteriorate. Unscrupulous fakers are adept in removing it and regumming the stamp to meet the unreasoning demand often made for "full o.g." in cases where such a thing is virtually impossible.

The gum normally used on stamps has been gum arabic until the late 1960s when synthetic adhesives were introduced. Harrison and Sons Ltd for instance use *polyvinyl alcohol*, known to philatelists as PVA (see note above SG723).

Colour Identification

The 100 colours most used for stamp identification are given in the Stanley Gibbons Colour Guide; these, plus a further 100 variations for more specialised use, are included in the Stanley Gibbons Stamp Colour Key. The Catalogue has used the Guide and Key as standards for describing new issues for some years. The names are also introduced as lists are rewritten, though exceptions are made for those early issues where traditional names have become universally established.

In compound colour names the second is the predominant one, thus:

orange-red = a red tending towards orange;
red-orange = an orange containing more red than usual.

When comparing actual stamps with colour samples in the Guide or Key, view in a good north daylight (or its best substitute: fluorescent "colour-matching" light). Sunshine is not recommended. Choose a solid portion of the stamp design; if available, marginal markings such as solid bars of colour or colour check dots are helpful. Shading lines in the design can be misleading as they appear lighter than solid colour. Furthermore, the listings refer to colours as issued: they may deteriorate into something different through the passage of time.

Shades are particularly significant when they can be linked to specific printings. In general, shades need to be quite marked to fall within the scope of this Catalogue.

Modern colour printing by lithography is prone to marked differences of shade, even within a single run, and variations can occur within the same sheet. Such shades are not listed.

Errors of Colour

Major colour errors in stamps or overprints which qualify for listing are: wrong colours; albinos (colourless impressions), where these have Expert Committee certificates; colours completely omitted, but only on unused stamps (if found on used stamps the information is usually footnoted) and with good credentials, missing colours being frequently faked.

Colours only partially omitted are not recognised. Colour shifts, however spectacular, are not listed.

Booklet Stamps

Single stamps from booklets are listed if they are distinguishable in some way (such as watermark or phosphor bands) from similar sheet stamps.

Booklet Pane with Printed Labels   *Se-tenant* Pane of Four

Booklet panes are listed where they contain stamps of different denominations *se-tenant*, where stamp-size labels are included, or where such panes are otherwise identifiable. Booklet panes are placed in the listing under the lowest denomination present.

In the listing of complete booklets the numbers and prefix letters are the same as used in the Stanley Gibbons *Great Britain Specialised Catalogue*.

Coil Stamps

Stamps only issued in coil form are given full listing. If stamps are issued in both sheets and coils, the coil stamps are listed separately only where there is some feature (e.g. watermark sideways or gum change) by which single stamps can be distinguished. Coil strips containing different values *se-tenant* are also listed.

Multi-value Coil Strip

Coil join pairs are generally too random and easily faked to permit listing; similarly ignored are coil stamps which have accidentally suffered an extra row of perforations from the claw mechanism in a malfunctioning vending machine.

Gutter Pairs

All modern Great Britain commemoratives and special stamps are produced in sheets containing two panes separated by a blank horizontal or vertical margin known as a gutter. This feature first made its appearance on some supplies of the 1972 Royal Silver Wedding 3p and marked the introduction of Harrison & Sons' new "Jumelle" stamp-printing press. There are advantages for both the printer and the Post Office in such a layout which has now been used for all commemorative issues since 1974.

The term "gutter pair" is used for a pair of stamps separated by part of the blank gutter margin.

Most printers include some form of colour check device on the sheet margins, in addition to the cylinder or plate numbers. Harrison & Sons use round "dabs", or spots of colour, resembling traffic lights. For the period from the 1972 Royal Silver Wedding until the end of 1979 these colour dabs appeared in the gutter margin. There was always one example to every double

Gutter Pair   Traffic Light Gutter Pair

pane sheet of stamps. Although they no longer appear in the commemorative issues they can still be found in the high value Machin issue. Gutter pairs showing these "traffic lights" are worth considerably more than the normal version.

Miniature Sheets

A miniature sheet contains a single stamp or set with wide inscribed or decorated margins. The stamps usually also exist in normal sheet format. This Catalogue lists, with **MS** prefix, complete miniature sheets which have been issued by the Post Office and which are valid for postal purposes.

Miniature Sheet containing a set of stamps

Se-tenant Combinations

Se-tenant means "joined together". Some sets include stamps of different design arranged *se-tenant* as blocks or strips and, in mint condition, these are usually collected unsevered as issued. Such *se-tenant* combinations can often be supplied in used condition at a premium over the used prices of the individual stamps. See also the note on Set Prices.

Specimen Stamps

Stamps of Great Britain overprinted "SPECIMEN" for circulation to postmasters and the Universal Postal Union are listed in a special section following the Postal Fiscal stamps. For other "SPECIMEN" overprints see Stanley Gibbons *Great Britain Specialised Catalogue*.

Presentation and Souvenir Books

Special Packs comprising slip-in cards with printed commemorative inscriptions and notes on the back and with protective covering, were introduced in 1964 for the Shakespeare issue. Definitive issues first appeared in Presentation Packs in 1960. Notes will be found in the listings to describe souvenir books issued on special occasions.

Issues of 1968–69 (British Paintings to the Prince of Wales Investiture) were also issued in packs with text in German for sale through the Post Office's German Agency and these are also included.

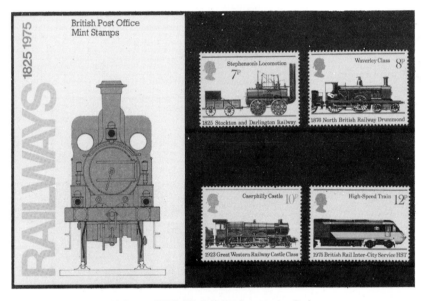

13 August 1975 Public Railways Presentation Pack

Collectors packs, first called gift packs, containing commemoratives issued in the preceeding twelve months, first appeared in 1967. These are listed and priced.

Yearbooks

Special Post Office Yearbooks were first available in 1984. They contain all of the commemorative issues for one year in a hardbound book, illustrated in colour complete with slip case. These are listed and priced.

Commemorative First Day Covers

Until 1963 the Post Office did not provide any special first day of issue postmark facilities for collectors. Several philatelic organisations and stamp dealers did produce pictorial covers for the various commemorative issues and collectors serviced these to receive ordinary operational postmarks. Occasionally a special handstamp was produced which coincided with a new stamp issue, or relevant slogan postmarks, like the 1953 'Long Live the Queen' type, were in general use at the time.

On 21 March 1963 the Post Office installed special posting boxes at eleven main offices so that collectors could obtain 'uniformly high standard' impressions, from normal operational postmarks, for their first day covers. From 7 May 1963 special 'First Day of Issue' slogans (Type A) were applied to mail posted in these special boxes, whose number had, by then, risen to thirty. The Philatelic Bureau accepted orders by post for such covers from the issue of 16 May 1963 onwards.

The slogan type was replaced on 23 April 1964 by 'First Day of Issue' handstamps (Type B). These were, initially, of considerable size, but were later replaced by smaller versions (Type C) which remain in service today at nearly 200 principal offices.

Since 1972 the Post Office has provided pictorial cancellations at the Philatelic Bureau and, often, at one or more towns connected with each issue.

From time to time 'First Day of Issue' handstamps in the standard type have been provided on a temporary basis for offices which had a link with a particular stamp issue. Such postmarks could not be ordered through the Philatelic Bureau.

Other special handstamps sponsored by organisations or individuals also exist, but are not listed.

Type A. First Day of Issue Slogan   **Type B.** Large Handstamp   **Type C.** Small Handstamp

First Day Cover with a Special Postmark

PHQ Cards

From 1973 the Post Office produced sets of picture cards to accompany commemorative issues which can be sent through the post as postcards. Each card shows an enlarged colour reproduction of one stamp, initially of a single value from one set and subsequently of all values. The Post Office gives each card a "PHQ" serial number, hence the term. The cards are usually on sale shortly before the date of issue of the stamps, but there is no officially designated "first day".

PHQ Card with appropriate stamp
cancelled on First Day of Issue

Cards are priced in fine mint condition for complete sets as issued. Used prices are for sets of cards, each franked with the appropriate stamp depicted and cancelled with an official postmark for first day of issue.

Watermark Types

Stamps are on unwatermarked paper except where the heading to the set states otherwise.

Watermarks are detected for Catalogue description by one of four methods: (1) holding stamps to the light; (2) laying stamps face down on a dark background; (3) by use of the Morley-Bright Detector, which works by revealing the thinning of the paper at the watermark; or (4) by the more complex electric watermark detectors such as the Signoscope.

The diagram below shows how watermark position is described in the Catalogue. Watermarks are usually impressed so that they read normally when looked through from the printed side. However, since philatelists customarily detect watermarks by looking at the back of the stamp, the watermark diagram also makes clear what is actually seen. Note that "G v R" is only an example and illustrations of the different watermarks employed are shown in the listings. The illustrations are actual size and shown in normal positions (from the front of the stamps).

AS DESCRIBED (Read through front of stamp)		AS SEEN DURING WATERMARK DETECTION (Stamp face down and back examined)
GvR	Normal	ꓤvƆ
ꓤ∧Ɔ	Inverted	ꓯ∧ꓤ
ꓤvƆ	Reversed	GvR
Ɔ∧ꓤ	Reversed and inverted	ꓤ∧Ɔ
GvR (sideways)	Sideways	ꓤvƆ (sideways)
GvR (sideways inverted)	Sideways inverted	ꓤvƆ (sideways inverted)

Philatelic Information

General Types of watermark as seen through the front side of the stamp.

2 Small Crown

4 Large Crown

9 (Extends over three stamps)

13 V R

15 Small Garter

16 Medium Garter

17 Large Garter

20 Emblems

33 Spray of Rose

39 Maltese Cross

40 Large Anchor

47 Small Anchor

48 Orb

49 Imperial Crown

100 Simple Cypher

103 Multiple Cypher

110 Single Cypher

111 Block Cypher

117 PUC £1

125 E8R

127

133

153 Tudor Crown

Postal Fiscals

165 St. Edward's Crown

179 Multiple Crowns

F5 Double-lined Anchor

F6 Single-lined Anchor

Watermark Errors and Varieties

Watermark errors are recognised as of major importance. They comprise stamps showing the wrong watermark devices or stamps printed on paper with the wrong watermark. Stamps printed on paper showing broken or deformed bits on the dandy roll, are not listable.

Underprints

From 1982 various values appeared with underprints, printed on the reverse, in blue, over the gum. These were usually from special stamp booklets, sold at a discount by the Post Office, but in 1985 surplus stocks of such underprinted paper were used for other purposes.

In this Catalogue stamps showing underprints are priced mint only. Used examples can be obtained, but care has to be taken in floating the stamps since the ink employed to print the device is solvent in water.

Underprint Types

1 Star with central dot

2 Double-lined Star

3 Double-lined "D"

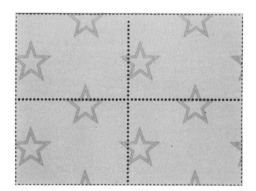

4 Multiple double-lined Stars

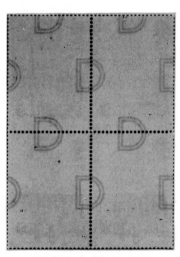

5 Multiple double-lined "D"

*(Types **4/5** are shown ¾ actual size)*

Note: Types **4/5** are arranged in a random pattern so that stamps from the same sheet or booklet pane will show the underprint in a slightly different position to the above. Stamps, when inspected, should be placed the correct way up, face down, when comparing with the illustrations.

QUEEN VICTORIA
20 June 1837—22 January 1901

MULREADY ENVELOPES AND LETTER SHEETS, so called from the name of the designer, William Mulready, were issued concurrently with the first British adhesive stamps.

1d. black

Envelopes: ....£100 *unused*; £130 *used*.
Letter Sheets: ...... £90 *unused*; £110 *used*.

2d. blue

Envelopes: ....£150 *unused*; £500 *used*.
Letter Sheets: ......£130 *unused*; £450 *used*.

LINE–ENGRAVED ISSUES

GENERAL NOTES

Brief notes on some aspects of the line-engraved stamps follow, but for further information and a full specialist treatment of these issues collectors are recommended to consult Volume I of the Stanley Gibbons *Great Britain Specialised Catalogue*.

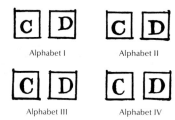

Alphabet I   Alphabet II

Alphabet III   Alphabet IV

Typical Corner Letters of the four Alphabets

Alphabets. Four different letterings were used for the corner letters on stamps prior to the issue with letters in all four corners, these being known to collectors as:

Alphabet I. Used for all plates made from 1840 to the end of 1851. Letters small.

Alphabet II. Plates from 1852 to mid-1855. Letters larger, heavier and broader.

Alphabet III. Plates from mid-1855 to end of period. Letters tall and more slender.

Alphabet IV. 1861. 1d. Die II, Plates 50 and 51 only. Letters were hand-engraved instead of being punched on the plate. They are therefore inconsistent in shape and size but generally larger and outstanding.

While the general descriptions and the illustrations of typical letters given above may be of some assistance, only long experience and published aids can enable every stamp to be allocated to its particular Alphabet without hesitation, as certain letters in each are similar to those in one of the others.

Blued Paper. The blueing of the paper of the earlier issues is believed to be due to the presence of prussiate of potash in the printing ink, or in the paper, which, under certain conditions, tended to colour the paper when the sheets were damped for printing. An alternative term is bleuté paper.

Corner Letters. The corner letters on the early British stamps were intended as a safeguard against forgery, each stamp in the sheet having

a different combination of letters. Taking the first 1d. stamp, printed in 20 horizontal rows of 12, as an example, the lettering is as follows:

Row. 1.   A A, A B, A C, etc. to A L.

Row. 2.   B A, B B, B C, etc. to B L.

and so on to

Row. 20.   T A, T B, T C, etc. to T L.

On the stamps with four corner letters, those in the upper corners are in the reverse positions to those in the lower corners. Thus in a sheet of 240 (12 ×20) the sequence is:

Row 1.   A A   B A   C A etc. to L A
          A A   A B   A C   A L

Row 2.   A B   B B   C B etc. to L B
          B A   B B   B C   B L

and so on to

Row 20.   A T   B T   C T etc. to L T
          T A   T B   T C   T L

Placing letters in all four corners was not only an added precaution against forgery but was meant to deter unmarked parts of used stamps being pieced together and passed off as an unused whole.

Dies. The first die of the 1d. was used for making the original die of the 2d., both the No Lines and White Lines issues. In 1855 the 1d. Die I was amended by retouching the head and deepening the lines on a transferred impression of the original. This later version, known to collectors as Die II, was used for making the dies for the 1d. and 2d. with letters in all four corners and also for the 1½d.

The two dies are illustrated above No. 17 in the catalogue.

Double letter

Guide line in corner

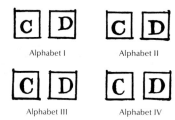

Guide line through value

Double Corner Letters. These are due to the workman placing his letter-punch in the wrong position at the first attempt, when lettering the plate, and then correcting the mistake; or to a slight shifting of the punch when struck. If a wrong letter was struck in the first instance, traces of a wrong letter may appear in a corner in addition to the correct one. A typical example is illustrated.

Guide Lines and Dots. When laying down the impressions of the design on the early plates, fine vertical and horizontal guide lines were marked on the plates to assist the operative. These were usually removed from the gutter margins, but could not be removed from the stamp impressions without damage to the plate, so that in such cases they appear on the printed stamps, sometimes in the corners, sometimes through "POSTAGE" or the value. Typical examples are illustrated.

Guide dots or cuts were similarly made to indicate the spacing of the guide lines. These too sometimes appear on the stamps.

Ivory Head

"Ivory Head". The so-called "ivory head" variety is one in which the Queen's Head shows white on the back of the stamp. It arises from the comparative absence of ink in the head portion of the design, with consequent absence of blueing. (*See* "Blued Paper", on page 1).

Line-engraving. In this context "line-engraved" is synonymous with recess-printing, in which the engraver cuts recesses in a plate and printing (the coloured areas) is from these recesses. "Line-engraved" is the traditional philatelic description for these stamps; other equivalent terms found are "engraving in *taille-douce*" (French) or "in *intaglio*" (Italian).

Plates. Until the introduction of the stamps with letters in all four corners, the number of the plate was not indicated in the design of the stamp, but was printed on the sheet margin. By long study of indentifiable blocks and the minor variation in the design, coupled with the position of the corner letters, philatelists are now able to allot many of these stamps to their respective plates. Specialist collectors often endeavour to obtain examples of a given stamp printed from its different plates and our catalogue accordingly reflects this depth of detail.

Maltese Cross   Type of Town postmark

Type of Penny Post cancellation

Example of 1844 type postmark

Postmarks. The so-called "Maltese Cross" design was the first employed for obliterating British postage stamps and was in use from 1840 to 1844. Being hand-cut, the obliterating stamps varied greatly in detail and some distinctive types can be allotted to particular towns or offices. Local types, such as those used at Manchester, Norwich, Leeds, etc., are keenly sought. A red ink was first employed, but was superseded by black, after some earlier experiments, in February 1841. Maltese Cross obliterations in other colours are rare.

Obliterations of this type, numbered 1 to 12 in the centre, were used at the London Chief Office in 1843 and 1844.

Some straight-line cancellations were in use in 1840 at the Penny Post receiving offices, normally applied on the envelope, the adhesives then being obliterated at the Head Office. They are nevertheless known, with or without Maltese Cross, on the early postage stamps.

In 1842 some offices in S.W. England used dated postmarks in place of the Maltese Cross, usually on the back of the letter since they were not originally intended as obliterators. These town postmarks have likewise been found on adhesives.

In 1844 the Maltese Cross design was superseded by numbered obliterators of varied type, one of which is illustrated. They are naturally comparatively scarce on the first 1d. and 2d. stamps. Like the Maltese Cross they are found in various colours, some of which are rare.

Re-entry

"Union Jack" re-entry

Re-entries. Re-entries on the plate show as a doubling of part of the design of the stamp generally at top or bottom. Many re-entries are very slight while others are most marked. A typical one is illustrated.

The *"Union Jack" re-entry*, so-called owing to the effect of the re-entry on the appearance of the corner stars (*see illustration*) occurs on stamp L K of Plate 75 of the 1d. red, Die I.

T A (T L)   M A (M L)
Varieties of Large Crown Watermark

I   Two states of Large Crown Watermark   II

Watermarks. Two watermark varieties, as illustrated, consisting of crowns of entirely different shape, are found in sheets of the Large Crown paper and fall on stamps lettered M A and T A (or M L and T L when the paper is printed on the wrong side). Both varieties are found on the 1d. rose-red of 1857, while the M A (M L) variety comes also on some plates of the 1d. of 1864 (Nos. 43, 44) up to about Plate 96. On the 2d. the T A (T L) variety is known on plates 8 and 9, and the M A (M L) on later prints of plate 9. These varieties may exist inverted, or inverted reversed on stamps lettered A A and A L and H A and H L, and some are known.

In 1861 a minor alteration was made in the Large Crown watermark by the removal of the two vertical strokes, representing *fleurs-de-lis*, which projected upwards from the uppermost of the three horizontal curves at the base of the Crown. Hence two states are distinguishable, as illustrated.

CONDITION—IMPERFORATE LINE–ENGRAVED ISSUES

The prices quoted for the 1840 and 1841 imperforate Line-engraved issues are for "fine" examples. As condition is most important in assessing the value of a stamp, the following definitions will assist collectors in the evaluation of individual examples.

Four main factors are relevant when considering quality.

(a) **Impression.** This should be clean and the surface free of any rubbing or unnatural blurring which would detract from the appearance.

(b) **Margins.** This is perhaps the most difficult factor to evaluate. Stamps described as "fine", the standard adopted in this catalogue for pricing purposes, should have margins of the recognised width, defined as approximately one half of the distance between two adjoining unsevered stamps. Stamps described as "very fine" or "superb" should have margins which are proportionately larger than those of a "fine" stamp. Examples with close margins should not, generally, be classified as "fine".

(c) **Cancellation.** On a "fine" stamp this should be reasonably clear and not noticeably smudged. A stamp described as "superb" should have a neat cancellation, preferably centrally placed or to the right.

(d) **Appearance.** Stamps, at the prices quoted, should always be without any tears, creases, bends or thins and should not be toned on either the front or back. Stamps with such defects are worth only a proportion of the catalogue price.

Good

Fine

Very Fine

Superb

The actual size illustrations of 1840 1d. blacks show the various grades of quality. When comparing these illustrations it should be assumed that they are all from the same plate and that they are free of any hidden defects.

PRINTERS. Nos. 1/53a were recess-printed by Perkins, Bacon & Petch, known from 1852 as Perkins, Bacon & Co.

STAMPS ON COVER. Prices are quoted, as a third price column, for those Victorian and Edwardian issues usually found used on cover. In general these prices refer to the cheapest version of each basic stamp with other shades, plates or varieties, together with unusual frankings and postmarks, being worth more.

1   **1a**   **2** Small Crown

(Eng Charles and Frederick Heath)

1840 (6–8 May). *Letters in lower corners. Wmk Small Crown. W* **2.** *Imperf.*

No.	Type			Un	Used	Used on cover
1	1	1d.	intense black	£3250	£190	
2		1d.	black	£2750	£140	£225
			Wi. Watermark inverted	£3750	£350	
3		1d.	grey-black (worn plate)	£3000	£180	
4	1a	2d.	dp full blue (8.5.40)	£7000	£375	
5		2d.	blue	£5500	£300	£550
			Wi. Watermark inverted	£7000	£650	
6		2d.	pale blue	£7000	£350	

The 1d. stamp in black was printed from Plates 1 to 11. Plate 1 exists in two states (known to collectors as 1a and 1b), the latter being the result of extensive repairs.

Repairs were also made to plates 2, 5, 6, 8, 9, 10 and 11, and certain impressions exist in two or more states.

The so-called "Royal reprint" of the 1d. black was made in 1864, from Plate 66, Die II, on paper with Large Crown watermark, inverted. A printing was also made in carmine, on paper with the same watermark, normal.

For 1d. black with "VR" in upper corners *see* No. V1 under Official Stamps.

The 2d. stamps were printed from Plates 1 and 2.

Plates of 1d. black

Plate	Un	Used	Used on Cover
1a	£4500	£175	£300
1b	£2750	£140	£225
2	£2750	£140	£225
3	£3500	£190	£300
4	£3000	£160	£225
5	£2750	£150	£225
6	£2750	£140	£225
7	£3250	£180	£300
8	£3500	£190	£350
9	£4000	£225	£400
10	£4500	£300	£450
11	£4500	£1600	£2750

Varieties of 1d. black

		Un	Used
a.	On *bleuté* paper (Plates 1 to 8) .... *from*	—	£175
b.	Double letter in corner .... *from*	£3000	£160
bb.	Re-entry .... *from*	£3250	£180
bc.	"PB" re-entry (Plate 5, 3rd state)	—	£3500
cc.	Large letters in each corner (E J, I L, J C and P A) (Plate 1b) .... *from*	£3500	£300
c.	Guide line in corner	£3000	£160
d.	Guide line through value	£3000	£160
g.	Obliterated by Maltese Cross		
	In red	—	£140
	In black	—	£140
	In blue	—	£1200
	In magenta	—	£500
	In yellow	—	£3000
h.	Obliterated by Maltese Cross with number in centre		
	No. 1	—	£1800
	No. 2	—	£1000
	No. 3	—	£1000
	No. 4	—	£1000
	No. 5	—	£1000
	No. 6	—	£1000
	No. 7	—	£1000
	No. 8	—	£1000
	No. 9	—	£1000
	No. 10	—	£1000
	No. 11	—	—
	No. 12	—	£1000
i.	Obliterated "Penny Post" in black .... *from*	—	£950
j.	Obliterated by town postmark (without Maltese Cross)		
	In black .... *from*	—	£900
	In yellow .... *from*	—	£3750
	In red .... *from*	—	£950
k.	Obliterated by 1844 type postmark in black *from*	—	£400

Plates of 2d. blue

Plate		Un	Used	Used on Cover
1	.... Shades *from*	£5500	£300	£550
2	.... Shades *from*	£6500	£375	£550

Varieties of 2d. blue

		Un	Used
a.	Double letter in corner	—	£400
aa.	Re-entry	—	£450
b.	Guide line in corner	—	£350
c.	Guide line through value	—	£350
e.	Obliterated by Maltese Cross		
	In red	—	£300
	In black	—	£300
	In blue	—	£1700
	In magenta	—	£1500
f.	Obliterated by Maltese Cross with number in centre		
	No. 1	—	£2250
	No. 2	—	£2250
	No. 3	—	—
	No. 4	—	£2250
	No. 5	—	£2500
	No. 6	—	£2250
	No. 7	—	£2250
	No. 8	—	£2750
	No. 9	—	£2500
	No. 10	—	£2500
	No. 11	—	—
	No. 12	—	£2250
g.	Obliterated "Penny Post" in black .... *from*	—	£1100

		Un	Used
h.	Obliterated by town postmark (without Maltese Cross) in black .... *from*	—	£950
i.	Obliterated by 1844 type postmark		
	In black ....*from*	—	£500
	In blue ....*from*	—	£1100

1841 (10 Feb). *Printed from "black" plates. Wmk W 2. Paper more or less blued. Imperf.*

No.	Type		Un	Used	Used on cover
7	**1**	1d. red-brown (*shades*)	£450	30.00	50.00
		a. "PB" re-entry (Plate 5, 3rd state)	—	£1000	

The first printings of the 1d. in red were made from Plates 1b, 2, 5 and 8 to 11 used for the 1d. black.

1d. red-brown from "black" plates

Plate	Un	Used	Used on cover
1b	£2750	£140	£250
2	£1600	90.00	£140
5	£600	40.00	65.00
8	£475	32.00	60.00
9	£450	30.00	50.00
10	£475	32.00	60.00
11	£500	30.00	50.00

1841 (late Feb). *Plate 12 onwards. Wmk W 2. Paper more or less blued. Imperf.*

No.	Type		Un	Used	Used on cover
8	**1**	1d. red-brown	£110	2.50	6.00
		Wi. Watermark inverted.............	£325	35.00	
8a		1d. red-brown on very blue paper	£130	2.50	
9		1d. pale red-brown (worn plates)	£170	8.00	
10		1d. deep red-brown..................	£140	5.50	
11		1d. lake-red	£500	£180	
12		1d. orange-brown	£250	45.00	

Error. No letter "A" in right lower corner (Stamp B (A), Plate 77)

No.	Type		Un	Used	Used on cover
12a	**1**	1d. red-brown	—	£3500	

The error "No letter A in right corner" was due to the omission to insert this letter on stamp B A of Plate 77. The error was discovered some months after the plate was registered and was then corrected.

There are innumerable variations in the colour and shade of the 1d. "red" and those given in the above list represent colour groups each covering a wide range.

Varieties of 1d. red-brown, etc.

		Un	Used
b.	Re-entry .... *from*	—	17.00
c.	Double letter in corner .... *from*	—	8.00
d.	Double Star (Plate 75) "Union Jack" re-entry	—	£350
e.	Guide line in corner	—	3.00
f.	Guide line through value	—	8.50
g.	Thick outer frame to stamp	—	7.00
h.	Ivory head	£160	5.00
j.	Left corner letter "S" inverted (Plates 78, 105, 107) .... *from*	—	30.00
k.	P converted to R (Plates 30, 33, 83, 86) ...... *from*	—	20.00
l.	Obliterated by Maltese Cross		
	In red	—	£600
	In black	—	6.00
	In blue	—	80.00
m.	Obliterated by Maltese Cross with number in centre.		
	No. 1	—	24.00
	No. 2	—	24.00
	No. 3	—	38.00

No. 4	—	70.00
No. 5	—	24.00
No. 6	—	20.00
No. 7	—	18.00
No. 8	—	18.00
No. 9	—	27.00
No. 10	—	35.00
No. 11	—	40.00
No. 12	—	60.00

n.   Obliterated "Penny Post" in black .... — £150

o.   Obliterated by town postmark (without Maltese Cross)

In black ....*from*	—	£100
In blue ....*from*	—	£200
In green ....*from*	—	£350
In yellow ....*from*	—	£3250
In red ....*from*	—	£1300

p.   Obliterated by 1844 type postmark

In blue ....*from*	—	30.00
In red ....*from*	—	£600
In green ....*from*	—	60.00
In violet ....*from*	—	£300
In black ....*from*	—	2.50

Stamps with thick outer frame to the design are from plates on which the frame-lines have been straightened or recut, particularly Plates 76 and 90.

For "Union Jack" re-entry *see* General Notes to Line-engraved Issues.

In "P converted to R" the corner letter "R" is formed from the "P", the distinctive long tail having been hand-cut.

KEY TO LINE–ENGRAVED ISSUES

S.G. Nos.	Description	Date	Wmk	Perf	Die	Alphabet
	THE IMPERFORATE ISSUES					
1/3	1d. black	6.5.40	SC	Imp	I	I
4/6	2d. no lines	8.5.40	SC	Imp	I	I
	PAPER MORE OR LESS BLUED					
7	1d. red-brown	10.2.41	SC	Imp	I	I
8/12	1d. red-brown	10.2.41	SC	Imp	I	I
8/12	1d. red-brown	6.2.52	SC	Imp	I	II
13/15	2d. white lines	13.3.41	SC	Imp	I	I
	THE PERFORATED ISSUES					
	ONE PENNY VALUE					
16a	1d. red-brown	1848	SC	Roul	I	I
16b	1d. red-brown	1850	SC	16	I	I
16c	1d. red-brown	1853	SC	16	I	II
16d	1d. red-brown	1854	SC	14	I	I
17/18	1d. red-brown	Feb 1854	SC	16	I	II
22	1d. red-brown	Jan 1855	SC	14	I	II
24/5	1d. red-brown	28.2.55	SC	14	II	II
21	1d. red-brown	1.3.55	SC	16	II	II
26	1d. red-brown	15.5.55	LC	16	II	II
29/33	1d. red-brown	Aug 1855	LC	14	II	III
	NEW COLOURS ON WHITE PAPER					
37/41	1d. rose-red	Nov 1856	LC	14	II	III
36	1d. rose-red	26.12.57	LC	16	II	III
42	1d. rose-red	1861	LC	14	II	IV
40b	1d. rose-red	1862	LC	14	II	II
	TWO PENCE VALUE					
19, 20	2d. blue	1.3.54	SC	16	I	I
23	2d. blue	22.2.55	SC	14	I	I
23a	2d. blue	5.7.55	SC	14	I	II
20a	2d. blue	18.8.55	SC	16	I	II
27	2d. blue	20.7.55	LC	16	I	II
34	2d. blue	20.7.55	LC	14	I	II
35	2d. blue	2.7.57	LC	14	I	III
36a	2d. blue	1.2.58	LC	16	I	III
	LETTERS IN ALL FOUR CORNERS					
48/9	½d. rose-red	1.10.70	W **9**	14		—
43/4	1d. rose-red	1.4.64	LC	14		II
53a	1½d. rosy mauve	1860	LC	14		II
51/3	1½d. rose-red	1.10.70	LC	14		II
45	2d. blue	July 1858	LC	14		II
46/7	2d. thinner lines	7.7.69	LC	14		II

Watermarks: SC = Small Crown, T **2**. LC = Large Crown, T **4**.

Dies: See notes above No. 17 in the catalogue.

Alphabets: See General Notes to this section.

3 White lines added

1841 (13 Mar). *White lines added. Wmk W* **2**. *Paper more or less blued. Imperf.*

			Un	Used	Used on cover
13	**3**	2d. pale blue	£1300	40.00	
14		2d. blue	£1000	30.00	£120
	Wi.	Watermark inverted	£2250	£180	
15		2d. dp full blue	£1300	45.00	
15aa		2d. violet-blue	£6000	£400	

The 2d. stamp with white lines was printed from Plates 3 and 4.

Plates of 2d. blue

Plate	Un	Used
3 .... *Shades from*	£1000	35.00
4 .... *Shades from*	£1200	30.00

Varieties of 2d. blue

		Un	Used
a.	Guide line in corner	—	32.00
b.	Guide line through value	£1500	32.00
bb.	Double letter in corner	—	40.00
be.	Re-entry	£1800	50.00
c.	Ivory head	£1600	35.00
e.	Obliterated by Maltese Cross		
	In red	—	£3000
	In black	—	50.00
	In blue	—	£550
f.	Obliterated by Maltese Cross with number in centre		
	No. 1	—	£160
	No. 2	—	£160
	No. 3	—	£160
	No. 4	—	£150
	No. 5	—	£200
	No. 6	—	£150
	No. 7	—	£300
	No. 8	—	£200
	No. 9	—	£300
	No. 10	—	£350
	No. 11	—	£200
	No. 12	—	£110
g.	Obliterated by town postmark (without Maltese Cross)		
	In black ....*from*	—	£300
	In blue ....*from*	—	£550

				Un	Used	Used on cover

h. Obliterated by 1844 type postmark
In black .... *from* — 30.00
In blue .... *from* — £300
In red .... *from* — £3250
In green .... *from* — £400

1841 (April). *Trial printing (unissued) on Dickinson silk-thread paper. Imperf.*
16 **1** 1d. red-brown (Plate 11)................................. £1750
Eight sheets were printed on this paper, six being gummed, two ungummed, but we have only seen examples without gum.

1848. *Rouletted approx 11½ by Henry Archer.*
16a **1** 1d. red-brown (Plates 70, 71) £3250

1850. *P 16, by Henry Archer.*
16b **1** 1d. red-brown (Alph I) (from Plates 71, 79, 90–101
& 105. Also Plate 8, unused only) ....*from* £500 £130
bWi. Watermark inverted.................................. — £225
Stamp on cover, dated prior to February 1854 (*price* £300); dated February and after 1854 (*price* £200).

1853. *Government Trial Perforations.*
16c **1** 1d. red-brown (*p* 16) (Alph II) (*on cover*) .... † £4250
16d 1d. red-brown (*p* 14) (Alph I) £3500

SEPARATION TRIALS. Although the various trials of machines for rouletting and perforating were unofficial, Archer had the consent of the authorities in making his experiments, and sheets so experimented upon were afterwards used by the Post Office.
As Archer ended his experiments in 1850 and plates with corner letters Alphabet II did not come into issue until 1852, perforated stamps with corner letters of Alphabet I may safely be assumed to be Archer productions, if genuine.
The Government trial perforations were done on Napier machines in 1853. As Alphabet II was by that time in use, the trials can be distinguished from the perforated stamps listed below by being dated prior to 28 January 1854, the date when the perforated stamps were officially issued.

Die I	Die II	**4** Large Crown

Die I: The features of the portrait are lightly shaded and consequently lack emphasis.
Die II (Die I retouched): The lines of the features have been deepened and appear stronger.
The eye is deeply shaded and made more lifelike. The nostril and lips are more clearly defined, the latter appearing much thicker. A strong downward stroke of colour marks the corner of the mouth. There is a deep indentation of colour between lower lip and chin. The band running from the back of the ear to the chignon has a bolder horizontal line below it than in Die I.

1854–57. *Paper more or less blued. (a) Wmk Small Crown, W **2**. P 16.*

				Un	Used	★ Used on cover
17	**1**		1d. red-brown (Die I) (2.54)........	£100	2.50	7.00
		Wi.	Watermark inverted.............	—	18.00	
18			1d. yellow-brown (Die I)............	£120	8.00	

				Un	Used	Used on cover
19	**3**	2d. dp blue (Plate 4) (1.3.54).......	£1250	30.00	50.00
		a. Imperf three sides (horiz pair)	†	—	
		Wi. Watermark inverted............	—	50.00	
20		2d. pale blue (Plate 4)................	£1300	45.00	
20a		2d. blue (Plate 5) (18.8.55).........	£1600	£125	£200
		aWi. Watermark inverted............	£1800	£250	
21	**1**	1d. red-brown (Die II) (1.3.55)	£120	10.00	20.00
		a. Imperf			
		Wi. Watermark inverted............	£350	25.00	

*(b) Wmk Small Crown, W **2**. P 14*

22	**1**	1d. red-brown (Die I) (1.55)........	£225	16.00	25.00
		Wi. Watermark inverted............	—	55.00	
23	**3**	2d. blue (Plate 4) (22.2.55).........	£1600	£110	£150
		Wi. Watermark inverted............	—	£175	
23a		2d. blue (Plate 5) (5.7.55)	£1600	£100	£140
		b. Imperf (Plate 5)			
		aWi. Watermark inverted............	—	£225	
24	**1**	1d. red-brown (Die II) (28.2.55)...	£225	15.00	22.00
		Wi. Watermark inverted............	£400	35.00	
24a		1d. dp red-brown (very blue paper) (Die II).....................	£200	18.00	
25		1d. orange-brown (Die II)	£500	40.00	

*(c) Wmk Large Crown, W **4**, P 16*

26	**1**	1d. red-brown (Die II) (15.5.55)...	£400	28.00	40.00
		a. Imperf (Plate 7)			
		Wi. Watermark inverted............	—	60.00	
27	**3**	2d. blue (Plate 5) (20.7.55)	£2000	£125	£200
		a. Imperf	—	£2000	
		Wi. Watermark inverted............	—	£275	

*(d) Wmk Large Crown, W **4**. P 14*

29	**1**	1d. red-brown (Die II) (18.8.55)...	£100	80	5.50
		a. Imperf (*shades*) (Plates 22, 25, 43)	£750	£600	
		Wi. Watermark inverted............	£350	16.00	
30		1d. brick-red (Die II)	£130	12.00	
31		1d. plum (Die II) (2.56)	£750	£200	
32		1d. brown-rose (Die II)	£150	12.00	
33		1d. orange-brown (Die II) (3.57)..	£225	15.00	
34	**3**	2d. blue (Plate 5) (20.7.55)	£1000	18.00	45.00
		Wi. Watermark inverted............	—	90.00	
35		2d. blue (Plate 6) (2.7.57)	£1100	20.00	60.00
		a. Imperf	—	£2000	
		Wi. Watermark inverted............	—	65.00	
★17/35a		**For well-centred, lightly used**		+125%	

1856–62. *Paper no longer blued. (a) Wmk Large Crown, W **4**. P 16.*

36	**1**	1d. rose-red (Die II) (26.12.57)	£500	20.00	32.00
36a	**3**	2d. blue (Plate 6) (1.2.58)	£2750	£100	£200
		aWi. Watermark inverted............	—	£275	

*(b) (Die II) Wmk Large Crown, W **4**. P 14*

37	**1**	1d. red-brown (11.56)................	£225	50.00	
38		1d. pale red (9.4.57)	40.00	1.75	
		a. Imperf	£425	£350	
39		1d. pale rose (3.57)	40.00	6.00	
40		1d. rose-red (9.57)	25.00	60	1.00
		a. Imperf	£475	£350	
		Wi. Watermark inverted............	40.00	18.00	
41		1d. dp rose-red (7.57)................	40.00	2.00	

1861. *Letters engraved on plate instead of punched (Alphabet IV).*

42	**1**	1d. rose-red (Die II) (Plates 50 & 51)	95.00	5.00	18.00
		a. Imperf	—	£1500	
		Wi. Watermark inverted............	£170	8.00	
★36/42a		**For well-centred, lightly used**		+125%	

The original die (Die I) was used to provide roller dies for the laying down of all the line-engraved stamps from 1840 to 1855. In that year a new master die was laid down (by means of a Die I roller die) and the impression was retouched by hand engraving by William Humphrys. This retouched die, always known to philatelists as Die II, was from that time used for preparing all new roller dies.

One Penny. The numbering of the 1d. plates recommenced at 1 on the introduction of Die II. Plates 1 to 21 were Alphabet II from which a scarce plum shade exists. Corner letters of Alphabet III appear on Plate 22 and onwards.

As an experiment, the corner letters were engraved by hand on Plates 50 and 51 in 1856, instead of being punched (Alphabet IV), but punching was again resorted to from Plate 52 onwards. Plates 50 and 51 were not put into use until 1861.

Two Pence. Unlike the 1d. the old sequence of plate numbers continued. Plates 3 and 4 of the 2d. had corner letters of Alphabet I, Plate 5 Alphabet II and Plate 6 Alphabet III. In Plate 6 the white lines are thinner than before.

In both values, varieties may be found as described in the preceding issues—ivory heads, inverted watermarks, re-entries, and double letters in corners.

The change of perforation from 16 to 14 was decided upon late in 1854 since the closer holes of the former gauge tended to cause the sheets of stamps to break up when handled, but for a time both gauges were in concurrent use. Owing to faulty alignment of the impressions on the plates and to shrinkage of the paper when damped, badly perforated stamps are plentiful in the line-engraved issues.

5

6

Showing position of the plate number on the 1d. and 2d. values. (Plate 170 shown)

1858–79. *Letters in all four corners. Wmk Large Crown, W 4. Die II (1d. and 2d.).* P 14.

			Un	Used	★ Used on cover
43	5	1d. rose-red (1.4.64)	9.00	60	1.25
44		1d. lake-red	9.00	60	
		a. Imperf	from £600	£500	
		Wi. Watermark inverted	50.00	5.00	
★43/4a		**For well-centred, lightly used**		+125%	

Plate		Un	Used	Plate		Un	Used
71	....	22.00	3.00	88	....	£160	8.00
72	....	35.00	3.50	89	....	40.00	75
73	....	25.00	3.00	90	....	28.00	75
74	....	20.00	75	91	....	40.00	5.00
76	....	40.00	75	92	....	15.00	75
77	....	£50000	£30000	93	....	40.00	75
78	....	£100	75	94	....	40.00	4.00
79	....	30.00	60	95	....	25.00	75
80	....	20.00	1.25	96	....	28.00	60
81	....	60.00	1.50	97	....	15.00	2.50
82	....	£120	3.50	98	....	15.00	5.00
83	....	£140	5.00	99	....	25.00	4.00
84	....	60.00	1.50	100	....	35.00	1.50
85	....	25.00	1.50	101	....	50.00	8.00
86	....	30.00	3.50	102	....	20.00	80
87	....	9.00	1.00	103	....	19.00	2.00

Plate		Un	Used	Plate		Un	Used
104	....	28.00	4.00	166	....	15.00	5.00
105		65.00	6.00	167		10.00	70
106		30.00	80	168		12.00	7.00
107		40.00	5.50	169		30.00	6.00
108		30.00	1.50	170		11.00	60
109		75.00	2.50	171		9.00	60
110		19.00	8.00	172		9.00	1.25
111		35.00	1.50	173		50.00	9.00
112		60.00	1.50	174		9.00	60
113		15.00	11.00	175		35.00	2.50
114		£350	12.00	176		25.00	1.25
115		£100	1.50	177		10.00	75
116		75.00	9.00	178		15.00	3.00
117		16.00	60	179		16.00	1.50
118		25.00	75	180		16.00	4.00
119		10.00	1.00	181		15.00	75
120		9.00	60	182		£100	3.00
121		40.00	9.00	183		25.00	2.00
122		9.00	60	184		9.00	1.00
123		12.00	1.00	185		15.00	2.00
124		12.00	60	186		30.00	1.50
125		15.00	2.00	187		11.00	75
127		35.00	2.00	188		20.00	10.00
129		11.00	7.00	189		35.00	6.00
130		18.00	1.50	190		10.00	5.00
131		75.00	16.00	191		9.00	6.00
132		£100	24.00	192		25.00	75
133		90.00	9.00	193		9.00	75
134		9.00	60	194		15.00	7.00
135		£100	30.00	195		15.00	7.00
136		£100	20.00	196		10.00	4.00
137		15.00	1.25	197		16.00	12.00
138		9.00	60	198		9.00	5.00
139		20.00	16.00	199		20.00	5.00
140		9.00	60	200		20.00	75
141		£150	9.00	201		9.00	6.00
142		50.00	25.00	202		15.00	7.00
143		30.00	15.00	203		9.00	15.00
144		£100	20.00	204		12.00	1.00
145		9.00	1.50	205		11.00	3.00
146		10.00	5.00	206		11.00	11.00
147		18.00	3.00	207		12.00	12.00
148		20.00	2.50	208		11.00	15.00
149		15.00	5.00	209		15.00	12.00
150		9.00	60	210		20.00	18.00
151		25.00	9.00	211		42.00	25.00
152		18.00	4.50	212		15.00	15.00
153		70.00	8.00	213		15.00	15.00
154		15.00	60	214		25.00	25.00
155		16.00	1.00	215		25.00	25.00
156		15.00	75	216		25.00	25.00
157		15.00	75	217		15.00	5.00
158		9.00	75	218		11.00	7.00
159		9.00	75	219		60.00	75.00
160		9.00	60	220		9.00	7.00
161		29.00	6.00	221		29.00	20.00
162		16.00	6.00	222		35.00	40.00
163		15.00	2.00	223		50.00	70.00
164		15.00	3.00	224		65.00	65.00
165		20.00	75	225		£1500	£400

Error. Imperf. Issued at Cardiff (Plate 116)

			Un	Used
44b	5	1d. rose-red (18.1.70)	£900	£750

The following plate numbers are also known imperf and used (No. 44a): 72, 79, 80, 81, 82, 83, 86, 87, 88, 90, 91, 92, 93, 96, 97, 100, 102, 103, 104, 105, 107, 108, 109, 112, 114, 117, 120, 121, 122, 136, 137, 142, 146, 148, 158, 162, 164, 166, 171, 174, 191 and 202.

The numbering of this series of 1d. red plates follows after that of the previous 1d. stamp, last printed from Plate 68.

Plates 69, 70, 75, 126 and 128 were prepared for this issue but rejected owing to defects, and stamps from these plates do not exist, so that specimens which appear to be from these plates (like many of those which optimistic collectors believe to be from Plate 77) bear other plate numbers. Owing to faulty engraving or printing it is not always easy to identify the plate number. Plate 77 was also rejected but some stamps printed from it were used. One specimen is in the Tapling Collection and six or seven others are known. Plates 226 to 228 were made but not used.

Specimens from most of the plates are known with inverted watermark. The variety of watermark described in the General Notes to this section occurs on stamp M A (or M L) on plates up to about 96 (*Prices from £85 used*).

Re-entries in this issue are few, the best being on stamps M K and T K of Plate 71 and on S L and T L, Plate 83.

			Un	Used	★ Used on cover
45	**6**	2d. blue (thick lines) (7.58)	£150	2.50	15.00
		a. Imperf (Plate 9)	—	£2500	
		Wi. Watermark inverted	£250	50.00	
		Plate			
		7	£400	15.00	
		8	£450	11.00	
		9	£150	2.50	
		12	£700	30.00	
46		2d. blue (thin lines) (1.7.69)	£140	5.50	14.00
		Wi. Watermark inverted	£225	50.00	
47		2d. dp blue (thin lines)	£140	5.50	
		a. Imperf (Plate 13)	£1100		
		Plate			
		13	£175	5.50	
		14	£200	7.50	
		15	£140	7.50	
★45/7		**For well-centred, lightly used**	+**125**%		

Plates 10 and 11 of the 2d. were prepared but rejected. Plates 13 to 15 were laid down from a new roller impression on which the white lines were thinner.

There are some marked re-entries and repairs, particularly on Plates 7, 8, 9 and 12.

Stamps with inverted watermark may be found and also the T A (T L) and M A (M L) watermark varieties (*see* General Notes to this section).

Though the paper is normally white, some printings showed blueing and stamps showing the "ivory head" may therefore be found.

7
Showing the plate number (9)

9

1870 (1 Oct). *Wmk W **9**, extending over three stamps. P 14.*

			Un	Used	★ Used on cover
48	**7**	½d. rose-red	40.00	5.00	22.00
49		½d. rose	40.00	5.00	
		a. Imperf (Plates 1, 4, 5, 6, 8, 14) *from*	£950	£575	
		Wi. Watermark inverted	—	55.00	
		Wj. Watermark reversed	—	45.00	

(49)		Wk. Watermark inverted & reversed	£120	35.00
		Plate		
		1	90.00	25.00
		3	55.00	9.00
		4	70.00	7.00
		5	50.00	5.00
		6	40.00	5.00
		8	80.00	25.00
		9	£1700	£250
		10	70.00	5.00
		11	40.00	5.00
		12	40.00	5.00
		13	40.00	5.00
		14	40.00	5.00
		15	55.00	7.00
		19	85.00	13.00
		20	90.00	18.00
★48/9a		**For well-centred, lightly used**	+**200**%	

The ½d. was printed in sheets of 480 (24 ×20) so that the check letters

run from   A A   to   X T
            A A   T X

Plates 2, 7, 16, 17 and 18 were not completed while plates 21 and 22, though made, were not used.

Owing to the method of perforating, the outer side of stamps in either the A or X row (ie the left or right side of the sheet) is imperf.

Stamps may be found with watermark inverted or reversed, or without watermark, the latter due to misplacement of the paper when printing.

8   Position of plate Number

1870 (1 Oct). *Wmk W **4**. P 14.*

			Un	Used	★ Used on cover
51	**8**	1½d. rose-red	£150	16.00	£120
52		1½d. lake-red	£150	16.00	
		a. Imperf (Plates 1 & 3) *from*	£1500	†	
		Wi. Watermark inverted	—	£100	
		Plate			
		(1)	£350	20.00	
		3	£150	16.00	

Error of lettering. OP–PC for CP–PC (*Plate 1*)

53	**8**	1½d. rose-red	£3500	£550
★51/3		**For well-centred, lightly used**	+**125**%	

1860. *Prepared for use but not issued; blued paper. Wmk W **4**. P 14.*

			Un	Used
53a	**8**	1½d. rosy mauve (Plate 1)		£1750
		b. Error of lettering, OP–PC for CP–PC		

Owing to a proposed change in the postal rates, 1½d. stamps were first printed in 1860, in rosy mauve, No. 53a, but the change was not approved and the greater part of the stock was destroyed.

In 1870 a 1½d. stamp was required and was issued in rose-red.

Plate 1 did not have the plate number in the design of the stamps, but on stamps from Plate 3 the number will be found in the frame as shown above.

Plate 2 was defective and was not used.

The error of lettering OP–PC on Plate 1 was apparently not noticed by the printer, and therefore not corrected.

EMBOSSED ISSUES

Volume 1 of the Stanley Gibbons *Great Britain Specialised Catalogue* gives further detailed information on the embossed issues.

PRICES. The prices quoted are for cut-square stamps with average to fine embossing. Stamps with exceptionally clear embossing are worth more.

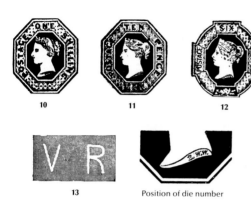

10   11   12

13   Position of die number

(Primary die engraved at the Royal Mint by William Wyon. Stamps printed at Somerset House)

1847–54. *Imperf* (For paper and wmk see footnote.)

			Un	Used	Used on cover
54	**10**	1s. pale green (11.9.47)	£2750	£325	£450
55		1s. green	£2750	£375	
56		1s. dp green	£3250	£450	
		Die 1 (1847)	£2750	£325	
		Die 2 (1854)	£3250	£375	
57	**11**	10d. brown (6.11.48)	£2250	£500	£900
		Die 1 (1848)	£2500	£550	
		Die 2 (1850)	£2250	£500	
		Die 3 (1853)	£2250	£500	
		Die 4 (1854)	£2500	£550	
		Die 5	£16000		
58	**12**	6d. mauve (1.3.54)	£2500	£425	
59		6d. dull lilac	£2500	£375	£375
60		6d. purple	£2500	£375	
		Wi. Watermark inverted	—	£325	
		Wj. Watermark reversed	£2500	£325	
		Wk. Watermark inverted & reversed	£2500	£325	
61		6d. violet	£3250	£600	

The 1s. and 10d. are on "Dickinson" paper with silk threads. The 6d. is on paper watermarked V R in single-lined letters, W **13**, which may be found in four ways—upright, inverted, upright reversed, and inverted reversed; upright reversed being the commonest.

The die numbers are indicated on the base of the bust. Only Die 1 (1 W W) of the 6d. was used for the adhesive stamps. The 10d. is from Die 1 (W.W.1 on stamps), and Dies 2 to 5 (2W.W., 3W.W., 4W.W. and 5W.W.) but the number and letters on stamps from Die 1 are seldom clear and many specimens are known without any trace of them. Because of this the stamp we previously listed as "No die number" has been deleted. That they are from Die 1 is proved by the existence of blocks showing stamps with and without the die number. The 1s. is from Dies 1 and 2 (W.W.1, W.W.2).

The normal arrangement of the silk threads in the paper was in pairs running down each vertical row of the sheet, the space between the threads of each pair being approximately 5 mm and between pairs of threads 20 mm. Varieties due to misplacement of the paper in printing show a single thread on the first stamp from the sheet margin and two threads 20 mm apart on the other stamps of the row. Faulty manufacture is the cause of stamps with a single thread in the middle.

Through bad spacing of the impressions, which were handstruck, all values may be found with two impressions more or less overlapping. Owing to the small margin allowed for variation of spacing, specimens with good margins on all sides are not common.

Double impressions are known of all values.

Later printings of the 6d. had the gum tinted green to enable the printer to distinguish the gummed side of the paper.

SURFACE–PRINTED ISSUES

GENERAL NOTES

Volume 1 of the Stanley Gibbons *Great Britain Specialised Catalogue* gives further detailed information on the surface-printed issues.

"Abnormals". The majority of the great rarities in the surface-printed group of issues are the so-called "abnormals", whose existence is due to the practice of printing six sheets from every plate as soon as it was made, one of which was kept for record purposes at Somerset House, while the others were perforated and usually issued. If such plates were not used for general production or if, before they came into full use, a change of watermark or colour took place, the six sheets originally printed would differ from the main issue in plate, colour or watermark and, if issued, would be extremely rare.

The abnormal stamps of this class listed in this Catalogue and distinguished, where not priced, by an asterisk (*) are:

No.	
78	3d. Plate 3 (with white dots)
152	4d. vermilion, Plate 16
153	4d. sage-green, Plate 17
109	6d. mauve, Plate 10
122/4	6d. pale chestnut & 6d. chestnut, Plate 12
145	6d. pale buff, Plate 13
88	9d. Plate 3 (hair lines)
98	9d. Plate 5 (see footnote to No. 98)
113	10d. Plate 2
91	1s. Plate 3 ("Plate 2")
148/50	1s. green, Plate 14
120	2s. blue, Plate 3

Those which may have been issued, but of which no specimens are known, are 2½d. wmk. Anchor, Plates 4 and 5; 3d. wmk Emblems, Plate 5; 3d. wmk Spray, Plate 21; 6d. grey, wmk Spray, Plate 18; 8d. orange, Plate 2; 1s. wmk Emblems, Plate 5. 5s. wmk Maltese Cross, Plate 4.

The 10d. Plate 1, wmk Emblems (No. 99), is sometimes reckoned among the abnormals, but was an error, due to the use of the wrong paper.

Corner Letters. With the exception of the 4d., 6d. and 1s. of 1855–57, the ½d., 1½d., 2d. and 5d. of 1880, the 1d. lilac of 1881 and the £5 (which had letters in lower corners only, and in the reverse order to the normal), all the surface-printed stamps issued prior to 1887 had letters in all four corners, as in the later line-engraved stamps. The arrangement is the same, the letters running in sequence right across and down the sheets, whether these were divided into panes or not. The corner letters existing naturally depend on the number of stamps in the sheet and their arrangement.

Imprimaturs and Imperforate Stamps. The Post Office retained in their records (now in the National Postal Museum) one imperforate sheet from each plate, known as the Imprimatur (or officially approved) sheet. Some stamps were removed from time to time for presentation purposes and have come on to the market, but these imperforates are not listed as they were not issued. Full details can be found in Volume I of the *Great Britain Specialised Catalogue.*

However, other imperforate stamps are known to have been issued and these are listed where it has been possible to prove that they do not come from the Imprimatur sheets. It is therefore advisable to purchase these only when accompanied by an Expert Committee certificate of genuineness.

Plate Numbers. All stamps from No. 75 to No. 163 bear in their designs either the plate number or, in one or two earlier instances, some other indication by which one plate can be distinguished from another. With the aid of these and of the corner letters it is thus possible to "reconstruct" a sheet of stamps from any plate of any issue or denomination.

Surface-printing. In this context the traditional designation "sur-face-printing" is synonymous with typo(graphy)—a philatelic term—or letterpress—the printers' term—as meaning printing from (the surface of) raised type. It is also called relief-printing, as the image is in relief (in French, en épargne), unwanted parts of the design having been cut away. Duplicate impressions can be electrotyped or stereotyped from an original die, the resulting clichés being locked together to form the printing plate.

Wing Margins. As the vertical gutters (spaces) between the panes, into which sheets of stamps of most values were divided until the introduction of the Imperial Crown watermark, were perforated through the centre with a single row of holes, instead of each vertical row of stamps on the inner side of the panes having its own line of perforation as is now usual, a proportion of the stamps in each sheet have what is called a "wing margin" about 5 mm wide on one or other side.

The stamps with "wing margins" are the watermark Emblems and Spray of Rose series (3d., 6d., 9d., 10d., 1s. and 2s.) with letters D, E, H or I in S.E. corner, and the watermark Garter series (4d. and 8d.) with letters F or G in S.E. corner. Knowledge of this lettering will enable collectors to guard against stamps with wing margin cut down and re-perforated, but note that wing margin stamps of Nos. 62 to 73 are also to be found re-perforated.

PRINTERS. The issues of Queen Victoria, Nos. 62/214, were typo by Thomas De La Rue & Co.

PERFORATIONS. All the surface-printed issues of Queen Victoria are Perf 14, with the exception of Nos. 126/9.

1855–57. No corner letters.
(a) Wmk Small Garter, W **15**. Highly glazed, deeply blued paper (31 July 1855)

			Un	Used	★ Used on cover
62	14	4d. carmine (shades)	£2250	£140	£200
		a. Paper slightly blued	£2500	£130	
		b. White paper	£3000	£325	
		Wi. Watermark inverted	—	£200	

(b) Wmk Medium Garter, W **16**

(i) Thick, blued highly glazed paper (25 February 1856)

63	14	4d. carmine (shades)	£2750	£140	£225
		a. White paper	£2500		
		Wi. Watermark inverted	—	£250	

(ii) Ordinary thin white paper (September 1856)

64	14	4d. pale carmine	£1750	£120	£200
		a. Stamp printed double	†	—	
		Wi. Watermark inverted	—	£160	

(iii) Ordinary white paper, specially prepared ink (1 November 1856)

65	14	4d. rose or dp rose	£1800	£130	£225

(c) Wmk Large Garter, W **17**. Ordinary white paper (January 1857)

66	14	4d. rose-carmine	£700	35.00	60.00
		a. Rose	£600	35.00	
		b. Thick glazed paper	£1700	80.00	
		Wi. Watermark inverted	—	40.00	
		Wj. Watermark inverted & reversed			
★62/6b		**For well-centred, lightly used**		+**125**%	

18   19   20 Emblems wmk (normal)

20a Watermark error, three roses and shamrock

20b Watermark error, three roses and thistle

(d) Wmk Emblems, W **20**

			Un	Used	★ Used on cover
69	18	6d. dp lilac (21.10.56)	£550	50.00	
70		6d. pale lilac	£500	35.00	65.00
		a. Azure paper	£2500	£325	
		b. Thick paper	£750	80.00	
		c. Error. Watermark. W **20a**			
		Wi. Watermark inverted	—	65.00	
		Wj. Watermark reversed			
		Wk. Watermark inverted & reversed			
71	19	1s. dp green (1.11.56)	£1200	£125	
72		1s. green	£600	£100	£135

14   15 Small Garter

16 Medium Garter   17 Large Garter

73	**19**	1s. pale green		£600	£100
		a. Azure paper		—	£450
		b. Thick paper......................		—	£130
		Wi. Watermark inverted.............		—	£120
		Wj. Watermark reversed		—	£650
		Wk. Watermark inverted and reversed			
★69/73b		**For well-centred, lightly used .....**			**+125%**

KEY TO SURFACE–PRINTED ISSUES 1855–83

S.G. Nos.	Description	Watermark	Date of Issue
	NO CORNER LETTERS		
62	4d. carmine	Small Garter	31.7.55
63/5	4d. carmine	Medium Garter	25.2.56
66/a	4d. carmine	Large Garter	Jan 1857
69/70	6d. lilac	Emblems	21.10.56
71/3	1s. green	Emblems	1.11.56
	SMALL WHITE CORNER LETTERS		
75/7	3d. carmine	Emblems	1.5.62
78	3d. carmine (dots)	Emblems	Aug 1862
79/82	4d. red	Large Garter	15.1.62
83/5	6d. lilac	Emblems	1.12.62
86/8	9d. bistre	Emblems	15.1.62
89/91	1s. green	Emblems	1.12.62
	LARGE WHITE CORNER LETTERS		
92	3d. rose	Emblems	1.3.65
102/3	3d. rose	Spray	July 1867
93/5	4d. vermilion	Large Garter	4.7.65
96/7	6d. lilac	Emblems	7.3.65
104/7	6d. lilac	Spray	21.6.67
108/9	6d. lilac	Spray	8.3.69
122/4	6d. chestnut	Spray	12.4.72
125	6d. grey	Spray	24.4.73
98	9d. straw	Emblems	1.12.65
110/11	9d. straw	Spray	3.10.67
99	10d. brown	Emblems	11.11.67
112/14	10d. brown	Spray	1.7.67
101	1s. green	Emblems	Feb 1865
115/17	1s. green	Spray	13.7.67
118/20b	2s. blue	Spray	1.7.67
121	2s. brown	Spray	27.2.80
126/7	5s. rose	Cross	1.7.67
128	10s. grey	Cross	26.9.78
129	£1 brown-lilac	Cross	26.9.78
130, 134	5s. rose	Anchor	25.11.82
131, 135	10s. grey-green	Anchor	Feb 1883
132, 136	£1 brown-lilac	Anchor	Dec 1882
133, 137	£5 orange	Anchor	21.3.82
	LARGE COLOURED CORNER LETTERS		
138/9	2½d. rosy mauve	Anchor	1.7.75
141	2½d. rosy mauve	Orb	1.5.76
142	2½d. blue	Orb	5.2.80
157	2½d. blue	Crown	23.3.81
143/4	3d. rose	Spray	5.7.73
158	3d. rose	Crown	Jan 1881
159	3d. on 3d. purple	Crown	1.1.83
152	4d. vermilion	Large Garter	1.3.76
153	4d. sage-green	Large Garter	12.3.77
154	4d. brown	Large Garter	15.8.80
160	4d. brown	Crown	9.12.80
145	6d. buff	Spray	15.3.73

146/7	6d. grey	Spray	20.3.74
161	6d. grey	Crown	1.1.81
162	6d. on 6d. purple	Crown	1.1.83
156a	8d. purple-brown	Large Garter	July 1876
156	8d. orange	Large Garter	11.9.76
148/50	1s. green	Spray	1.9.73
151	1s. brown	Spray	14.10.80
163	1s. brown	Crown	29.5.81

Watermarks:	Anchor	W **40, 47**
	Cross	W **39**
	Crown	W **49**
	Emblems	W **20**
	Large Garter	W **17**
	Medium Garter	W **16**
	Orb	W **48**
	Small Garter	W **15**
	Spray	W **33**

21   22

23   24   25 Plate 2

A. White dots added

B. Hair lines

1862–64. *A small uncoloured letter in each corner, the 4d. wmk Large Garter. W **17**, the others Emblems, W **20**.*

				★ Used on		
				Un	Used	cover
75	**21**	3d. dp carmine-rose (Plate 2) (1.5.62)		£1100	£125	
76		3d. brt carmine-rose		£700	95.00	£225
		Wi. Watermark inverted............			—	£125
77		3d. pale carmine-rose		£700	95.00	
		b. Thick paper......................		—	£140	
78		3d. rose (with white dots, Type A, Plate 3) (8.62)...................		*	£2250	
		a. Imperf (Plate 3)		£1750		

Queen Victoria/Surface-printed

79	22	4d. brt red (Plate 3) (15.1.62).......	£750	45.00	
80		4d. pale red............................	£500	30.00	75.00
		Wi. Watermark inverted............	—	65.00	
81		4d. brt red (Hair lines, Type B, Plate 4) (16.10.63)	£650	35.00	
82		4d. pale red (Hair lines, Type B, Plate 4)	£550	26.00	70.00
		a. Imperf (Plate 4)	£1200		
		Wi. Watermark inverted............	—	40.00	
83	23	6d. dp lilac (Plate 3) (1.12.62)	£750	50.00	
84		6d. lilac	£650	28.00	65.00
		a. Azure paper	—	£300	
		b. Thick paper.......................	—	50.00	
		c. Error. Watermark W **20b** (stamp TF).........................			
		Wi. Watermark inverted............	—	55.00	
85		6d. lilac (Hair lines, Plate 4) (20.4.64)	£800	50.00	£120
		a. Imperf	£1100		
		c. Thick paper.......................	£1200	65.00	
		Wi. Watermark inverted............	—	75.00	
86	24	9d. bistre (Plate 2) (15.1.62)	£1100	£140	£250
		Wi. Watermark inverted............	—	£160	
		Wj. Watermark reversed	—	£170	
87		9d. straw	£1100	£130	
		a. On azure paper			
		b. Thick paper.......................	£1700	£160	
88		9d. bistre (Hair lines, Plate 3) (5.62)	£6000	£1700	
89	25	1s. dp green (Plate No. 1 = Plate 2) (1.12.62)	£800	£100	
90		1s. green (Plate No. 1 = Plate 2) .	£700	60.00	£125
		a. "K" in lower left corner in white circle (stamp KD)	£4250	£500	
		aa. "K" normal (stamp KD)	—	£700	
		b. On azure paper			
		c. Thick paper.......................	—	£120	
		ca. Thick paper, "K" in circle as No. 99a............................	—	£1000	
		Wi. Watermark inverted............	—	80.00	
91		1s. dp green (Plate No. 2 = Plate 3)	£11000	*	
		a. Imperf	£1200		
		aWi. Watermark inverted............	£1000		
★75/91		**For well-centred, lightly used**			+125%

The 3d. as Type **21**, but with network background in the spandrels which is found overprinted SPECIMEN, was never issued.

The plates of this issue may be distinguished as follows:
3d. Plate 2 No white dots
    Plate 3 White dots as Illustration A.
4d. Plate 3 No hair lines. Roman I next to lower corner letters.
    Plate 4. Hair lines in corners. (Illustration B.). Roman II.
6d. Plate 3. No hair lines.
    Plate 4. Hair lines in corners.
9d. Plate 2. No hair lines
    Plate 3. Hair lines in corners. Beware of faked lines.
1s. Plate 2. Numbered 1 on stamps.
    Plate 3. Numbered 2 on stamps & with hair lines.

The 9d. on azure paper (No. 87a) is very rare, only one specimen being known.

The variety "K" in circle, No. 90a, is believed to be due to a damaged letter having been cut out and replaced. It is probable that the punch was driven in too deeply, causing the flange to penetrate the surface, producing an indentation showing as an uncoloured circle.

The watermark variety "three roses and a shamrock" illustrated in W **20a** was evidently due to the substitution of an extra rose for the thistle in a faulty watermark bit. It is found on stamp T A of Plates 2 and 4 of the 3d., Plates 1 (No. 70c) 3, 5 and 6 of the 6d., Plate 4 of the 9d. and Plate 4 of the 1s.

A similar variety, W **20b**, but showing three roses and a thistle is found on stamp T F of the 6d. (No. 84) and 9d. (No. 98).

26	27

28 (with hyphen)	28a (without hyphen)

29	30	31

1865–67. *Large uncoloured corner letters. Wmk. Large Garter (4d.); others Emblems.*

			Un	★ Used	Used on cover
92	26	3d. rose (Plate 4) (1.3.65)...........	£375	32.00	90.00
		a. Error. Watermark W **20a**	£900	£275	
		b. Thick paper.......................	£500	40.00	
		Wi. Watermark inverted............	—	55.00	
		Wj. Watermark reversed			
93	27	4d. dull vermilion (4.7.65)	£225	15.00	35.00
94		4d. vermilion	£225	15.00	
		a. Imperf (Plates 11, 12)	£500		
		Wi. Watermark inverted............	£225	15.00	
95		4d. dp vermilion	£225	20.00	
		Plate			
		7 (1865)	£300	19.00	
		8 (1866)	£250	19.00	
		9 (1867)	£250	15.00	
		10 (1868)	£300	26.00	
		11 (1869)	£250	15.00	
		12 (1870)	£225	15.00	
		13 (1872)	£250	17.00	
		14 (1873)	£300	30.00	
96	28	6d. dp lilac (with hyphen) (7.3.65)	£400	35.00	
97		6d. lilac (with hyphen)	£350	25.00	60.00
		a. Thick paper.......................	£450	40.00	
		b. Stamp doubly printed (Plate 6)	—	£3750	
		c. Error. Watermark W **20a** (Pl 5, 6) .... *from*	—	£300	
		Wi. Watermark inverted............	—	50.00	
		Wj. Watermark reversed			
		Plate			
		5 (1865)	£350	25.00	
		6 (1867)	£1000	55.00	
98	29	9d. straw (Plate 4) (1.12.65)........	£700	£170	£275
		a. Thick paper.......................	£950	£300	
		b. Error. Watermark W **20a**	—	£350	
		c. Error. Watermark W **20b** (stamp TF).........................			
		Wi. Watermark inverted............	—	£200	
99	30	10d. red-brown (Plate 1) (11.11.67)	*	£12000	

12

			Un	Used	cover
101	31	1s. green (Plate 4) (1.2.65)..........	£650	60.00	£100
		a. Error. Watermark W **20**a	—	£350	
		b. Thick paper........................	£750	£100	
		c. Imperf between (vert pair)....	—	£3750	
		Wi. Watermark inverted............	—	80.00	
		Wj. Imperf watermark inverted ...			
★92/101c		**For well-centred, lightly used**		**+100**%	

From mid-1866 to about the end of 1871 4d. stamps of this issue appeared generally with watermark inverted.

Unused copies of No. 98 from Plate 5 exist, but this was never put to press and all evidence points to the existing copies being from a portion of the Imprimatur sheet which was perforated by De La Rue in 1887 for insertion in albums to be presented to members of the Stamp Committee (Price £10000 un).

The 10d. stamps, No. 99, were printed in error on paper watermarked "Emblems" instead of on "Spray of Rose".

32

33 Spray of Rose

34

1867–80. *Wmk Spray of Rose, W* **33**.

				★	Used on
			Un	Used	cover
102	26	3d. dp rose (12.7.67)	£225	18.00	
103		3d. rose	£200	12.00	38.00
		a. Imperf (Plates 5, 6, 8) ....from	£500		
		Wi. Watermark inverted............	£300	45.00	
		Plate			
		4 (1867)	£300	50.00	
		5 (1868)	£200	14.00	
		6 (1870)	£225	12.00	
		7 (1871)	£275	15.00	
		8 (1872)	£250	14.00	
		9 (1872)	£250	18.00	
		10 (1873)	£275	40.00	
104	28	6d. lilac (with hyphen) (Plate 6) (21.6.67)	£550	28.00	90.00
		Wi. Watermark inverted............	—	50.00	
105		6d. dp lilac (with hyphen) (Plate 6)	£550	26.00	
106		6d. purple (with hyphen) (Pl 6) ...	£550	35.00	
107		6d. brt violet (with hyphen) (Plate 6) (22.7.68)	£550	28.00	
108	28a	6d. dull violet (without hyphen) (Plate 8) (18.3.69)	£325	22.00	
		Wi. Watermark inverted............	—	45.00	
109		6d. mauve (without hyphen)	£275	22.00	55.00
		a. Imperf (Plate Nos. 8 & 9)	£700	£600	
		Wi. Watermark inverted............	—	45.00	
		Plate			
		8 (1869, mauve)	£275	25.00	
		9 (1869, mauve)	£275	22.00	
		10 (1869, mauve)	*	£1200v	
110	29	9d. straw (Plate No. 4) (3.10.67)...	£600	90.00	£200
		Wi. Watermark inverted............	—	£120	
111		9d. pale straw (Plate No. 4)	£600	90.00	
		a. Imperf (Plate 4)	£1700		
112	30	10d. red-brown (1.7.67)	£1000	£120	£325
		Wi. Watermark inverted............	—	£200	

			Un	Used	cover
113	30	10d. pale red-brown...................	£1000	£150	
114		10d. dp red-brown	£1200	£130	
		a. Imperf (Plate 1)	£1400		
		Plate			
		1 (1867)	£1000	£120	
		2 (1867)	£12000	£2500	
115	31	1s. dp green (13.7.67)	£425	10.00	
117		1s. green	£350	10.00	20.00
		a. Imperf between (pair) (Pl 7)	£800	£550	
		b. Imperf (Plate 4)	£450	30.00	
		Wi. Watermark inverted............			
		Plate			
		4 (1867)	£350	15.00	
		5 (1871)	£400	12.00	
		6 (1872)	£525	10.00	
		7 (1873)	£525	26.00	
118	32	2s. dull blue (1.7.67)	£950	50.00	£325
		Wi. Watermark inverted............	—	£130	
119		2s. dp blue	£950	50.00	
120		a. Imperf (Plate 1)	£1600		
		2s. pale blue	£1500	90.00	
		aa. Imperf (Plate 1)	£1700		
120a		2s. cobalt	£4750	£800	
120b		2s. milky blue.......................	£3000	£350	
		Plate			
		1 (1867)	£950	50.00	
		3 (1868)	*	£3000	
121		2s. brown (Plate No. 1) (27.2.80) .	£6000	£900	
		a. Imperf	£3750		
		Wi. Watermark inverted............			
★102/21		**For well-centred, lightly used**		**+75**%	

1872–73. *Uncoloured letters in corners. Wmk Spray, W* **33**.

				★	Used on
			Un	Used	cover
122	34	6d. dp chestnut (12.4.72)	£425	18.00	50.00
123		6d. chestnut (23.5.72)	£350	18.00	
		Wi. Watermark inverted............	—	60.00	
124		6d. pale buff (25.10.72)	£400	30.00	£130
		Wi. Watermark inverted............	—	90.00	
		Plate			
		11 (1872, dp chestnut)	£425	18.00	
		11 (1872, chestnut)	£350	18.00	
		11 (1872, pale buff)	£400	28.00	
		12 (1872, pale chestnut)	*	£1200	
		12 (1872, chestnut)	*	£1200	
		12 (1872, pale buff)	£750	50.00	
125		6d. grey (Plate No. 12) (24.4.73)...	£600	60.00	£100
		a. Imperf	£1200		
		Wi. Watermark inverted............	£750	75.00	
★122/5		**For well-centred, lightly used**		**+50**%	

35

36

37

41

42

43

44   45   46

38

47 Small Anchor   48 Orb

39 Maltese Cross   40 Large Anchor

1873–80. *Large coloured letters in the corners.*

1867–83. *Uncoloured letters in corners.*

(a) Wmk Anchor, W **47**

			Un	Used	★ Used on cover
138	**41**	2½d. rosy mauve *(blued paper)* (1.7.75)	£375	32.00	
		a. Imperf	£450	45.00	
		Wi. Watermark inverted			
139		2½d. rosy mauve *(white paper)*	£225	16.00	38.00
		Wi. Watermark inverted	£300	30.00	
		Plate			
		1 *(blued paper)* (1875)	£375	32.00	
		1 *(white paper)* (1875)	£225	16.00	
		2 *(blued paper)* (1875)	£3000	£375	
		2 *(white paper)* (1875)	£225	16.00	
		3 *(white paper)* (1875)	£400	28.00	
		3 *(blued paper)* (1875)	—	£1300	

(a) Wmk Maltese Cross, W **39.** *P* 15½ ×15

			Un	Used ★
126	**35**	5s. rose (1.7.67)	£2500	£200
127		5s. pale rose	£2750	£200
		a. Imperf (Plate 1)	£3250	
		Plate		
		1 (1867)	£2500	£200
		2 (1874)	£3500	£275
128	**36**	10s. greenish grey (Plate 1) (26.9.78)	£18000	£800
129	**37**	£1 brown-lilac (Plate 1) (26.9.78)	£22000	£1100

Error of Lettering L H—F L *for* L H—H L *(Plate 2)*

140	**41**	2½d. rosy mauve	£7000	£600

(b) Wmk Anchor, W **40.** *P* 14. *(i) Blued paper*

130	**35**	5s. rose (Plate 4) (25.11.82)	£4750	£800
		Wi. Watermark inverted	—	£1500
131	**36**	10s. grey-green (Plate 1) (2.83)	£20000	£1000
132	**37**	£1 brown-lilac (Plate 1) (12.82)	£27000	£1800
133	**38**	£5 orange (Plate 1) (21.3.82)	£15000	£3000

(b) Wmk Orb, W **48**

141	**41**	2½d. rosy mauve (1.5.76)	£200	12.00	35.00
		Wi. Watermark inverted	£300	22.00	
		Plate			
		3 (1876)	£500	30.00	
		4 (1876)	£200	12.00	
		5 (1876)	£200	16.00	
		6 (1876)	£200	12.00	
		7 (1877)	£200	12.00	
		8 (1877)	£200	16.00	
		9 (1877)	£200	12.00	
		10 (1878)	£225	17.00	
		11 (1878)	£200	12.00	
		12 (1878)	£200	16.00	
		13 (1878)	£200	16.00	

(ii) White paper

134	**35**	5s. rose (Plate 4)	£4500	£800
135	**36**	10s. greenish grey (Plate 1)	£22000	£1000
136	**37**	£1 brown-lilac (Plate 1)	£32000	£1800
137	**38**	£5 orange (Plate 1)	£3750	£1200
★126/37		**For well-centred, lightly used**		+75%

For full information on all future British issues, collectors should write to the British Post Office Philatelic Bureau, 20 Brandon Street, Edinburgh EH3 5TT

		Plate			
(141)		14 (1879)	£200	12.00	
		15 (1879)	£200	12.00	
		16 (1879)	£200	12.00	
		17 (1880)	£500	80.00	
142	**41**	2½d. blue (5.2.80)	£150	8.00	15.00
		Wi. Watermark inverted	£225	18.00	
		Plate			
		17 (1880)	£150	18.00	
		18 (1880)	£175	10.00	
		19 (1880)	£150	8.00	
		20 (1880)	£150	8.00	

*(c) Wmk Spray, W **33***

143	**42**	3d. rose (5.7.73)	£200	11.00	35.00
		Wi. Watermark inverted	£300	35.00	
144		3d. pale rose	£200	11.00	
		Plate			
		11 (1873)	£200	11.00	
		12 (1873)	£225	13.00	
		14 (1874)	£250	14.00	
		15 (1874)	£200	13.00	
		16 (1875)	£200	13.00	
		17 (1875)	£225	13.00	
		18 (1875)	£225	13.00	
		19 (1876)	£200	13.00	
		20 (1879)	£200	28.00	
145	**43**	6d. pale buff (Plate 13) (15.3.73) ..	*	£4500	
146		6d. dp grey (20.3.74)	£225	16.00	38.00
147		6d. grey	£225	16.00	
		Wi. Watermark inverted	£325	35.00	
		Plate			
		13 (1874)	£225	18.00	
		14 (1875)	£225	18.00	
		15 (1876)	£225	16.00	
		16 (1878)	£225	16.00	
		17 (1880)	£300	35.00	
148	**44**	1s. dp green (1.9.73)	£325	24.00	
150		1s. pale green	£250	24.00	40.00
		Wi. Watermark inverted	£300	32.00	
		Plate			
		8 (1873)	£325	30.00	
		9 (1874)	£325	30.00	
		10 (1874)	£300	30.00	
		11 (1875)	£300	30.00	
		12 (1875)	£250	24.00	
		13 (1876)	£250	24.00	
		14 (—)	*	£10000	
151		1s. orange-brown (Plate 13)			
		(14.10.80)	£1100	£130	£250
		Wi. Watermark inverted	£1400	£175	

*(d) Wmk Large Garter, W **17***

152	**45**	4d. vermilion (1.3.76)	£600	£130	£275
		Wi. Watermark inverted	—	£175	
		Plate			
		15 (1876)	£600	£130	
		16 (1877)	*	£10000	
153		4d. sage-green (12.3.77)	£400	85.00	£175
		Wi. Watermark inverted	—	£100	
		Plate			
		15 (1877)	£450	90.00	
		16 (1877)	£400	85.00	
		17 (1877)	*	£6000	
154		4d. grey-brown (Plate 17)			
		(15.8.80)	£600	90.00	£170
		a. Imperf			
		Wi. Watermark inverted	—	£120	
156	**46**	8d. orange (Plate 1) (11.9.76)	£550	£100	£200
		Wi. Watermark inverted	—	£110	
★138/56		**For well-centred, lightly used**		**+100%**	

1876 (July). *Prepared for use but not issued.*

156a	**46**	8d. purple-brown (Plate 1)	£3000

49 Imperial Crown   (50)

1880–83. *Wmk Imperial Crown, W **49**.*

			Un	Used	★ Used on cover
157	**41**	2½d. blue (23.3.81)	£150	7.00	15.00
		Wi. Watermark inverted	£225	16.00	
		Plate			
		21 (1881)	£225	8.00	
		22 (1881)	£150	7.00	
		23 (1881)	£150	7.00	
158	**42**	3d. rose (1.81)	£180	16.00	28.00
		Wi. Watermark inverted	£500	40.00	
		Plate			
		20 (1881)	£225	35.00	
		21 (1881)	£180	16.00	
159		3d. on 3d. lilac (T **50**) (C.) (Plate 21) (1.1.83)	£225	55.00	£200
		Wi. Watermark inverted			
160	**45**	4d. grey-brown (8.12.80)	£175	22.00	60.00
		Wi. Watermark inverted	—	70.00	
		Plate			
		17 (1880)	£175	22.00	
		18 (1882)	£175	22.00	
161	**43**	6d. grey (1.1.81)	£150	18.00	40.00
		Wi. Watermark inverted	—	40.00	
		Plate			
		17 (1881)	£180	18.00	
		18 (1882)	£150	18.00	
162		6d. on 6d. lilac (as T **50**) (C.) (Plate 18) (1.1.83)	£200	55.00	£130
		a. Slanting dots (various) ..*from*	£250	75.00	
		b. Opt double	—	£3500	
		Wi. Watermark inverted	£325	80.00	
163	**44**	1s. orange-brown (29.5.81)	£225	40.00	90.00
		Wi. Watermark inverted	£300	55.00	
		Plate			
		13 (1881)	£275	40.00	
		14 (1881)	£225	40.00	
★157/63		**For well-centred, lightly used**		**+75%**	

The 1s. plate 14 (line perf 14) exists in purple but was not issued in this shade (*Price* £2500 *unused*). Examples were included in a few of the Souvenir Albums prepared for members of the "Stamp Committee of 1884".

52   53

| 54 | 55 | 56 |

The variety "frame broken at bottom" (No. 173b) shows a white space just inside the bottom frame-line from between the "N" and "E" of "ONE" to below the first "N" of "PENNY", breaking the pearls and cutting into the lower part of the oval below "PEN".

1880–81. *Wmk Imperial Crown*, W **49**.

					★ Used on
			Un	Used	cover
164	52	½d. dp green (14.10.80)	15.00	2.50	5.00
		a. Imperf	£350		
		Wi. Watermark inverted	—	18.00	
165		½d. pale green	17.00	4.00	
166	53	1d. Venetian red (1.1.80)	4.00	1.25	2.00
		a. Imperf	£350		
		Wi. Watermark inverted	—	17.00	
167	54	1½d. Venetian red (14.10.80)	60.00	14.00	60.00
168	55	2d. pale rose (8.12.80)	75.00	22.00	50.00
		Wi. Watermark inverted	£130	30.00	
168a		2d. dp rose	75.00	22.00	
169	56	5d. indigo (15.3.81)	£350	30.00	£120
		a. Imperf	£800		
		Wi. Watermark inverted	—	£700	
★164/9		**For well-centred, lightly used**	+75%		

| 57 | Die I | Die II |

1881. *Wmk Imperial Crown*, W **49**. (a) 14 *dots in each corner, Die I* (12 July).

				★ Used on
		Un	Used	cover
170	57	1d. lilac	75.00	12.00	20.00
		Wi. Watermark inverted			
171		1d. pale lilac	75.00	12.00	

(b) 16 *dots in each corner, Die II (12 December)*

172	57	1d. lilac	80	40	1.10
		Wi. Watermark inverted	9.00	4.50	
172a		1d. bluish lilac	£180	35.00	
173		1d. dp purple	80	30	
		a. Printed both sides	£400	†	
		b. Frame broken at bottom	£475	£175	
		c. Printed on gummed side	£375	†	
		d. Imperf three sides (pair)	£1500	†	
		e. Printed both sides but impression on back inverted	£400	†	
		f. No watermark	£250	†	
174		1d. mauve	80	30	
		a. Imperf (pair)	£800		
★170/4		**For well-centred, lightly used**	+50%		

1d. stamps with the words "PEARS SOAP" printed on back in *orange, blue* or *mauve* price *from* £300, *unused*.

KEY TO SURFACE–PRINTED ISSUES 1880–1900

S.G. Nos.	Description	Date of Issue
164/5	½d. green	14.10.80
187	½d. slate-blue	1.4.84
197/d	½d. vermilion	1.1.87
213	½d. blue-green	17.4.1900
166	1d. Venetian red	1.1.80
170/1	1d. lilac, Die I	12.7.81
172/4	1d. lilac, Die II	12.12.81
167	1½d. Venetian red	14.10.80
188	1½d. lilac	1.4.84
198	1½d. purple & green	1.1.87
168/a	2d. rose	8.12.80
189	2d. lilac	1.4.84
199/200	2d. green & red	1.1.87
190	2½d. lilac	1.4.84
201	2½d. purple on blue paper	1.1.87
191	3d. lilac	1.4.84
202/4	3d. purple on yellow paper	1.1.87
192	4d. dull green	1.4.84
205/a	4d. green & brown	1.1.87
206	4½d. green & carmine	15.9.92
169	5d. indigo	15.3.81
193	5d. dull green	1.4.84
207	5d. purple & blue, Die I	1.1.87
207a	5d. purple & blue, Die II	—
194	6d. dull green	1.4.84
208/a	6d. purple on rose-red paper	1.1.87
195	9d. dull green	1.8.83
209	9d. purple & blue	1.1.87
210	10d. purple & carmine	24.2.90
196	1s. dull green	1.4.84
211	1s. green	1.1.87
214	1s. green & carmine	11.7.1900
175	2s. 6d. lilac on blued paper	2.7.83
178/9	2s. 6d. lilac	1884
176	5s. rose on blued paper	1.4.84
180/1	5s. rose	1884
177/a	10s. ultramarine on blued paper	1.4.84
182/3a	10s. ultramarine	1884
185	£1 brown-lilac, wmk Crowns	1.4.84
186	£1 brown-lilac, wmk Orbs	1.2.88
212	£1 green	27.1.91

Note that the £5 value used with the above series is listed as Nos. 133 and 137.

| 58 | 59 |

60

62

63

64

65   66

1883–84. *Coloured letters in the corners. Wmk Anchor, W* **40.**

(a) Blued paper

			Un	★ Used
175	58	2s. 6d. lilac (2.7.83)	£1700	£400
176	59	5s. rose (1.4.84)	£3250	£900
177	60	10s. ultramarine (1.4.84)	£11000	£1900
177a		10s. cobalt (5.84)	£12000	£3500

(b) White paper

			Un	★ Used
178	58	2s. 6d. lilac	£200	50.00
		Wi. Watermark inverted		
179		2s. 6d. dp lilac	£200	50.00
		a. Deep lilac, blued paper	£1600	£475
180	59	5s. rose	£400	60.00
		Wi. Watermark inverted	†	—
181		5s. crimson	£400	60.00
182	60	10s. cobalt	£13000	£3250
183		10s. ultramarine	£700	£200
183a		10s. pale ultramarine	£700	£200
★175/83a		**For well-centred, lightly used**		+50%

For No. 180 perf 12 see second note below No. 196.

61

Broken frames, Plate 2

1884 (1 April). *Wmk Three Imperial Crowns, W* **49.**

			Un	★ Used
185	61	£1 brown-lilac	£8000	£800
		a. Frame broken	£15000	£1300
		Wi. Watermark inverted	—	£1400

1888 (1 Feb). *Watermark Three Orbs, W* **48.**

			Un	Used
186	61	£1 brown-lilac	£16000	£1200
		a. Frame broken	—	£2250
★185/6a		**For well-centred, lightly used**		+50%

The broken-frame varieties, Nos. 185a and 186a, are on Plate 2 stamps JC and TA, as illustrated. *See also* No. 212a.

1883 (1 Aug) (9d.) *or* **1884** (1 April) *(others). Wmk Imperial Crown, W* **49** *(sideways on horiz designs).*

			Un	★ Used	Used on cover
187	52	½d. slate-blue	8.00	1.00	2.00
		a. Imperf	£350		
		Wi. Watermark inverted............	—	32.00	
188	62	1½d. lilac	55.00	18.00	55.00
		a. Imperf	£350		
		Wi. Watermark inverted............	—	60.00	
189	63	2d. lilac	70.00	22.00	50.00
		a. Imperf	£400		
		Wi. Watermark sideways-inverted			
190	64	2½d. lilac	40.00	5.00	12.00
		a. Imperf	£400		
		Wi. Watermark sideways-inverted			
191	65	3d. lilac	90.00	35.00	55.00
		a. Imperf	£400		
		Wi. Watermark inverted............	†	—	
192	66	4d. dull green	£175	65.00	£130
		a. Imperf	£450		
193	62	5d. dull green	£175	65.00	£120
		a. Imperf	£450		
194	63	6d. dull green	£225	75.00	£140
		a. Imperf	£450		
		Wi. Watermark sideways-inverted			
195	64	9d. dull green (1.8.83)	£475	£200	£500
		Wi. Watermark sideways-inverted	£500	£225	
196	65	1s. dull green	£350	£120	£250
		a. Imperf	£850		
		Wi. Watermark-inverted			
★187/96		**For well-centred, lightly used**		+100%	

The above prices are for stamps in the true dull green colour. Stamps which have been soaked, causing the colour to run, are virtually worthless.

Stamps of the above set and No. 180 are also found perf 12; these are official perforations, but were never issued. A second variety of the 5d. is known with a line instead of a stop under the "d" in the value; this was never issued and is therefore only known *unused* (Price £4500).

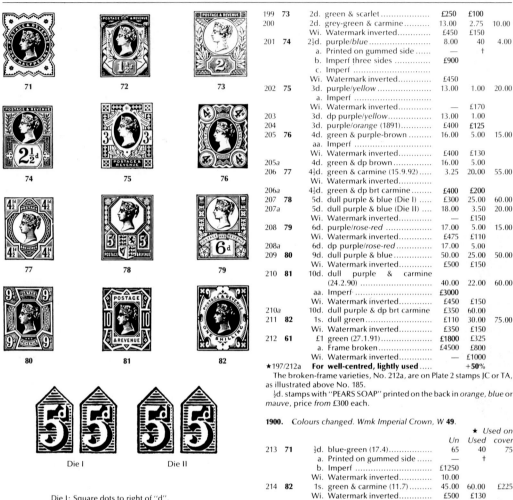

71 72 73

74 75 76

77 78 79

80 81 82

Die I   Die II

Die I: Square dots to right of "d".
Die II: Thin vertical lines to right of "d".

1887 (1 Jan)–**1892**. *"Jubilee" issue. New types. The bicoloured stamps have the value tablets, or the frames including the value tablets, in the second colour. Wmk Imperial Crown, W* **49** *(Three Crowns on £1).*

			Un	★ Used	Used on cover
197	71	½d. vermilion	75	30	75
		a. Printed on gummed side	£650	†	
		b. Printed both sides			
		c. Doubly printed	£1300		
		d. Imperf	£400		
		Wi. Watermark inverted	12.00		
197e		½d. orange-vermilion	75	30	
198	72	1½d. dull purple & pale green	8.00	1.50	15.00
		a. Purple part of design double	—	£2500	
		Wi. Watermark inverted	£350	£140	

199	73	2d. green & scarlet	£250	£100	
200		2d. grey-green & carmine	13.00	2.75	10.00
		Wi. Watermark inverted	£450	£150	
201	74	2½d. purple/*blue*	8.00	40	4.00
		a. Printed on gummed side	—	†	
		b. Imperf three sides	£900		
		c. Imperf			
		Wi. Watermark inverted	£450		
202	75	3d. purple/*yellow*	13.00	1.00	20.00
		a. Imperf			
		Wi. Watermark inverted	—	£170	
203		3d. dp purple/*yellow*	13.00	1.00	
204		3d. purple/*orange* (1891)	£400	£125	
205	76	4d. green & purple-brown	16.00	5.00	15.00
		aa. Imperf			
		Wi. Watermark inverted	£400	£130	
205a		4d. green & dp brown	16.00	5.00	
206	77	4½d. green & carmine (15.9.92)	3.25	20.00	55.00
		Wi. Watermark inverted			
206a		4½d. green & dp brt carmine	£400	£200	
207	78	5d. dull purple & blue (Die I)	£300	25.00	60.00
207a		5d. dull purple & blue (Die II)	18.00	3.50	20.00
		Wi. Watermark inverted	—	£150	
208	79	6d. purple/*rose-red*	17.00	5.00	15.00
		Wi. Watermark inverted	£475	£110	
208a		6d. dp purple/*rose-red*	17.00	5.00	
209	80	9d. dull purple & blue	50.00	25.00	50.00
		Wi. Watermark inverted	£500	£150	
210	81	10d. dull purple & carmine (24.2.90)	40.00	22.00	60.00
		aa. Imperf	£3000		
		Wi. Watermark inverted	£450	£150	
210a		10d. dull purple & dp brt carmine	£350	60.00	
211	82	1s. dull green	£110	30.00	75.00
		Wi. Watermark inverted	£350	£150	
212	61	£1 green (27.1.91)	£1800	£325	
		a. Frame broken	£4500	£800	
		Wi. Watermark inverted	—	£1000	
★197/212a		For well-centred, lightly used	+50%		

The broken-frame varieties, No. 212a, are on Plate 2 stamps JC or TA, as illustrated above No. 185.

½d. stamps with "PEARS SOAP" printed on the back in *orange, blue* or *mauve,* price *from* £300 each.

1900. *Colours changed. Wmk Imperial Crown, W* **49**.

			Un	★ Used	Used on cover
213	71	½d. blue-green (17.4)	65	40	75
		a. Printed on gummed side	—	†	
		b. Imperf	£1250		
		Wi. Watermark inverted	10.00		
214	82	1s. green & carmine (11.7)	45.00	60.00	£225
		Wi. Watermark inverted	£500	£130	
		Set of 14	£300	£160	
★213/14		For well-centred, lightly used	+50%		

The ½d. No. 213, in bright blue, is a colour changeling.

KING EDWARD VII

22 January 1901–6 May 1910

PRINTINGS. Distinguishing De La Rue printings from the provisional printings of the same values made by Harrison & Sons Ltd. or at Somerset House may prove difficult in some cases. For very full guidance Volume 2 of the Stanley Gibbons *Great Britain Specialised Catalogue* should prove helpful.

Note that stamps perforated 15 × 14 must be Harrison; the 2½d., 3d. and 4d. in this perforation are useful reference material, their shades and appearance in most cases matching the Harrison perf 14 printings.

Except for the 6d. value, all stamps on chalk-surfaced paper were printed by De La Rue.

Of the stamps on ordinary paper, the De La Rue impressions are usually clearer and of a higher finish than those of the other printers. The shades are markedly different except in some printings of the 4d., 6d. and 7d. and in the 5s., 10s. and £1.

Used stamps in good, clean, unrubbed condition and with dated postmarks can form the basis of a useful reference collection, the dates often assisting in the assignment to the printers.

> **USED STAMPS.** For well-centred, lightly used examples of King Edward VII stamps, add the following percentages to the used prices quoted below:
>
> De La Rue printings (Nos. 215/66)—3d. values + 35%, 4d. orange +100%, 6d. +75%, 7d. & 1s. + 25%, all other values + 50%.
> Harrison printings (Nos. 267/86)—all values and perforations +75%.
> Somerset House printings (Nos. 287/320)—1s. values + 25%, all other values + 50%.

97

(Des E. Fuchs)

1902 (1 Jan)–**10.** *Printed by De La Rue & Co. Wmk Imperial Crown (½d. to 1s.); Anchor (2s. to 10s.); Three Crowns (£1). P 14.*

O = "Ordinary" paper.   C = Chalk-surfaced paper

			Un	Used	Used on cover
215	**83**	½d. dull blue-green. **O** (1.1.02)....	60	30	60
		Wi. Watermark inverted............	£550		
216		½d. blue-green, **O**	60	30	
217		½d. pale yellowish green, **O** (26.11.04)	50	20	30
218		½d. yellowish green, **O**..............	50	20	
		a. Booklet pane. Five stamps plus St. Andrew's Cross label (6.06)	£180		
		b. Doubly printed (bottom row on one pane) (Control H9)....	£4750		
		Wi. Watermark inverted............	1.75	1.25	
219		1d. scarlet, **O** (1.1.02)...............	50	15	1.50
220		1d. brt scarlet, **O**.....................	50	15	
		a. Imperf (pair)......................	£6500		
		Wi. Watermark inverted............	2.00	1.25	
221	**84**	1½d. dull purple & green, **O** (21.3.02)...............................	15.00	6.00	
222		1½d. slate-purple and green, **O**	12.00	4.75	12.00
		Wi. Watermark inverted............	—	£400	
223		1½d. pale dull purple & green, **C** (8.05)...............................	25.00	5.50	
224		1½d. slate-purple & bluish green, **C**	20.00	4.25	
225	**85**	2d. yellowish green & carmine-red, **O** (25.3.02)..................	18.00	4.00	12.00
226		2d. grey-green & carmine-red, **O** (1904)................................	18.00	4.00	
227		2d. pale grey-green & carmine-red, **C** (4.06)	22.00	6.00	
		Wi. Watermark inverted............			
228		2d. pale grey-green & scarlet, **C** (1909)	25.00	6.00	
229		2d. dull blue-green & carmine, **C** (1907)	40.00	20.00	
230	**86**	2½d. ultramarine, **O** (1.1.02)........	5.50	2.50	10.00
231		2½d. pale ultramarine, **O**	4.50	2.50	
		Wi. Watermark inverted............	£550		
232	**87**	3d. dull purple/orange-yellow, **O** (20.3.02)	18.00	2.50	20.00
		Wi. Watermark inverted............			
232a		3d. dp purple/orange-yellow, **O** .	20.00	2.50	
232b		3d. pale reddish purple/orange-yellow, **C** (3.06)..................	70.00	15.00	
233		3d. dull purple/orange-yellow, **C**	80.00	18.00	
233a		3d. dull reddish purple/yellow (lemon back), **C**	60.00	22.00	
233b		3d. pale purple/lemon, **C**..........	16.00	6.00	
234		3d. purple/lemon, **C**	13.00	6.00	
235	**88**	4d. green & grey-brown, **O** (27.3.02)	30.00	11.00	
		Wi. Watermark inverted............			
236		4d. green & chocolate-brown, **O**	30.00	12.00	

83   84   85

86   87   88

89   90   91

92   93   94

95   96

237	**88**	4d. green & chocolate-brown, **C** (1.06)	22.00	7.00	25.00	
238		4d. dp green & chocolate-brown, **C**	25.00	8.50		
239		4d. brown-orange, **O** (1.11.09)	£140	80.00		
240		4d. pale orange, **O** (12.09)	7.50	6.50	20.00	
241		4d. orange-red (12.09)	9.00	7.00		
242	**89**	5d. dull purple & ultramarine, **O** (14.5.02)	20.00	6.00	30.00	
243		5d. dull purple & ultramarine, **C** (5.06)	25.00	8.00		
244		5d. slate-purple & ultramarine, **C**	20.00	8.00		
		Wi. Watermark inverted	£500			
245	**83**	6d. pale dull purple, **O** (1.1.02)	15.00	4.00	30.00	
246		6d. slate-purple, **O**	15.00	4.00		
247		6d. pale dull purple, **C** (1.06)	22.00	4.00		
248		6d. dull purple, **C**	18.00	4.00		
		Wi. Watermark inverted				
249	**90**	7d. grey-black, **O** (4.5.10)	3.50	6.00	£120	
249a		7d. dp grey-black, **O**	80.00	60.00		
250	**91**	9d. dull purple & ultramarine, **O** (7.4.02)	40.00	24.00	£120	
251		9d. slate-purple & ultramarine, **O**	40.00	24.00		
252		9d. dull purple & ultramarine, **C** (6.05)	45.00	30.00		
		Wi. Watermark inverted	—	£750		
253		9d. slate-purple & ultramarine, **C**	45.00	30.00		
254	**92**	10d. dull purple & carmine, **O** (3.7.02)	40.00	18.00	£120	
		a. No cross on crown	£225	90.00		
255		10d. slate-purple & carmine, **C** (9.06)	40.00	28.00		
		a. No cross on crown	£200	80.00		
256	**92**	10d. dull purple & scarlet, **C** (9.10)	45.00	35.00		
		a. No cross on crown	£190	75.00		
257	**93**	1s. dull green & carmine, **O** (24.3.02)	35.00	8.50	80.00	
258		1s. dull green & carmine, **C** (9.05)	40.00	12.00		
259		1s. dull green & scarlet, **C** (9.10)	40.00	20.00		
260	**94**	2s. 6d. lilac, **O** (5.4.02)	£150	40.00	£500	
		Wi. Watermark inverted	£800	£500		
261		2s. 6d. pale dull purple, **C** (7.10.05)	£140	80.00		
		Wi. Watermark inverted	£800	£500		
262		2s. 6d. dull purple, **C**	£160	55.00		
263	**95**	5s. brt carmine, **O** (5.4.02)	£200	50.00	£500	
		Wi. Watermark inverted	—	£750		
264		5s. dp brt carmine, **O**	£200	50.00		
265	**96**	10s. ultramarine, **O** (5.4.02)	£475	£200		
266	**97**	£1 dull blue-green, **O** (16.6.02)	£1100	£250		

97a

1910 (May). *Prepared for use, but not issued.*

266a	**97a**	2d. Tyrian plum	£12000	

One example of this stamp is known used, but it was never issued to the public.

For full information on all future British issues, collectors should write to the British Post Office Philatelic Bureau, 20 Brandon Street, Edinburgh EH3 5TT

1911. *Printed by Harrison & Sons. "Ordinary" paper. Wmk Imperial Crown. (a). P 14.*

			Un	Used	Used on cover
267	**83**	½d. dull yellow-green (3.5.11)	1.10	40	3.00
		Wi. Watermark inverted	3.75	2.75	
268		½d. dull green	1.75	40	
269		½d. dp dull green	8.00	2.00	
270		½d. pale bluish green	22.00	22.00	
		a. Booklet pane. Five stamps plus St. Andrew's Cross label	£250		
		b. Watermark sideways	†	—	
		c. Imperf (pair)	£3750		
271		½d. brt green (fine impression) (6.11)	£200	£110	
272		1d. rose-red (3.5.11)	1.75	4.00	6.00
		Wi. Watermark inverted	5.50	4.50	
		a. No wmk	40.00	35.00	
273		1d. dp rose-red	2.75	4.00	
274		1d. rose-carmine	35.00	9.00	
275		1d. aniline pink (5.11)	£325	£110	
275a		1d. aniline rose	£110	75.00	
276	**86**	2½d. brt blue (10.7.11)	22.00	10.00	18.00
		Wi. Watermark inverted	£400		
277	**87**	3d. purple/*lemon* (12.9.11)	40.00	90.00	£140
277a		3d. grey/*lemon*	£3500		
278	**88**	4d. brt orange (13.7.11)	45.00	40.00	£100

		(b) P 15 × 14			
279	**83**	½d. dull green (30.10.11)	20.00	22.00	65.00
279a		½d. dp dull green	24.00	20.00	
280		1d. rose-red (5.10.11)	18.00	10.00	
281		1d. rose-carmine	5.00	3.00	15.00
282		1d. pale rose-carmine	5.00	3.00	
283	**86**	2½d. brt blue (14.10.11)	11.00	5.00	12.00
284		2½d. dull blue	12.00	5.00	
		Wi. Watermark inverted	—	£200	
285	**87**	3d. purple/*lemon* (22.9.11)	18.00	3.50	15.00
285a		3d. grey/*lemon*	£3000		
286	**88**	4d. brt orange (11.11.11)	13.00	6.00	40.00
		Set of 5	60.00	32.00	

1911–13. *Printed at Somerset House. Ordinary paper, unless marked C (= chalk-surfaced paper). Wmk as 1902–10. P 14.*

287	**84**	1½d. reddish purple & brt green (13.7.11)	25.00	9.50	
288		1½d. dull purple & green	13.00	6.00	30.00
289		1½d. slate-purple & green (9.12)	18.00	10.00	
290	**85**	2d. dp dull green & red (8.8.11)	12.00	4.50	30.00
291		2d. dp dull green & carmine	10.00	4.50	
292		2d. grey-green & brt carmine (carmine shows clearly on back) (11.3.12)	10.00	6.00	
293	**89**	5d. dull reddish purple & brt blue (7.8.11)	15.00	4.75	50.00
294		5d. dp dull reddish purple & brt bl	11.00	4.75	
295	**83**	6d. royal purple, **O** (31.10.11)	35.00	40.00	
296		6d. brt magenta, **C** (31.10.11)	£2000		
297		6d. dull purple, **O**	18.00	6.00	60.00
298		6d. reddish purple, **O** (11.11)	18.00	8.00	
		a. No cross on crown (various shades)	£130		
299		6d. very dp reddish purple, **O** (11.11)	38.00	18.00	
300		6d. dark purple, **O** (3.12)	18.00	15.00	
301		6d. dull purple "Dickinson" coated paper* (3.13)	£110	80.00	
303		6d. dp plum, **C** (7.13)	14.00	35.00	
		a. No cross on crown	£180		
305	**90**	7d. slate-grey (1.8.12)	5.00	8.50	85.00

306	91	9d. reddish purple & lt blue (24.7.11)	50.00	30.00	
306a		9d. dp dull reddish purple & dp brt blue (9.11)	60.00	32.00	
307		9d. dull reddish purple & blue (10.11)	40.00	22.00	85.00
307a		9d. dp plum & blue (7.13)	40.00	30.00	
308		9d. slate-purple & cobalt-blue (3.12)	60.00	35.00	
309	92	10d. dull purple & scarlet (9.10.11)	45.00	25.00	
310		10d. dull reddish purple & aniline pink	£160	£110	
311		10d. dull reddish purple & carmine (5.12)	35.00	20.00	85.00
		a. No cross on crown	£250		
312	93	1s. dark green & scarlet (17.7.11)	60.00	25.00	
313		1s. dp green & scarlet (9.10.11)	45.00	9.00	85.00
314		1s. green & carmine (15.4.12)	28.00	8.00	
		Wi. Watermark inverted	90.00		
315	94	2s. 6d. dull greyish purple (27.9.11)	£350	£150	
316		2s. 6d. dull reddish purple (10.11)	£125	45.00	
317		2s. 6d. dark purple	£125	50.00	
318	95	5s. carmine (29.2.12)	£200	50.00	
319	96	10s. blue (14.1.12)	£450	£200	
320	97	£1 dp green (3.9.11)	£1000	£250	
		Set of 14 (to 1s incl. 4d (2))	£190	85.00	

*No. 301 was on an experimental coated paper which does not respond to the silver test.

KING GEORGE V

6 May 1910–20 January 1936

Further detailed information on the issues of King George V will be found in Volume 2 of the Stanley Gibbons *Great Britain Specialised Catalogue.*

PRINTERS. Types **98** to **102** were typographed by Harrison & Sons Ltd, with the exception of certain preliminary printings made at Somerset House and distinguishable by the controls "A.11", "B.11" or "B.12" (the Harrison printings do not have a full stop after the letter). The booklet stamps, Nos. 334/7, and 344/5 were printed by Harrison only.

WATERMARK VARIETIES. Many British stamps to 1967 exist without watermark owing to misplacement of the paper, with either inverted, reversed, or inverted and reversed watermarks. A proportion of the low-value stamps issued in booklets have the watermark inverted in the normal course of printing.

Low values with *watermark sideways* are normally from stamp rolls used in machines with sideways delivery or, from June 1940, certain booklets.

STAMPS WITHOUT WATERMARK. Stamps found without watermark, due to misplacement of the sheet in relation to the dandy roll, are not listed here but will be found in the *Great Britain Specialised Catalogue.*

The 1½d. and 5d. 1912–22, and 2d. and 2½d., 1924–26, listed here, are from *whole* sheets completely without watermark.

98	**99**

For type differences with T **101/2** see notes below the latter.

Die A   Die B

Dies of Halfpenny

Die A. The three upper scales on the body of the right hand dolphin form a triangle; the centre jewel of the cross inside the crown is suggested by a comma.

Die B. The three upper scales are incomplete; the centre jewel is suggested by a crescent.

Die A   Die B

Dies of One Penny

Die A. The second line of shading on the ribbon to the right of the crown extends right across the wreath; the line nearest to the crown on the right hand ribbon shows as a short line at the bottom of the ribbon.

Die B. The second line of shading is broken in the middle; the first line is little more than a dot.

(Des Bertram Mackennal and G. W. Eve. Head from photograph by W. and D. Downey. Die eng J. A. C. Harrison)

1911–12. *Wmk Imperial Crown,* W **49.** P 15 ×14.

			Un	Used
321	98	½d. pale green (Die A) (22.6.11)	3.25	85
322		½d. green (Die A) (22.6.11)	1.75	60
		a. Error. Perf 14	£4000	£250
		Wi. Watermark inverted		
323		½d. bluish green (Die A)	£375	£125
324		½d. yellow-green (Die B)	4.00	50
325		½d. brt green (Die B)	3.75	50
		a. Watermark sideways	—	£1700
		Wi. Watermark inverted	4.50	1.50
326		½d. bluish green (Die B)	£200	70.00

327	**99**	1d. carmine-red (Die A) (22.6.11)		2.00	60
		a. Error. Perf 14...............................			
		b. Experimental ptg on chalk-surfaced			
		paper (Control A.11)		£225	
		c. Watermark sideways		†	
		Wi. Watermark inverted		£225	
328		1d. pale carmine (Die A) (22.6.11)		10.00	1.00
		a. No cross on crown........................		£350	£150
329		1d. carmine (Die B)		2.50	75
		Wi. Watermark inverted		6.00	2.25
330		1d. pale carmine (Die B)		2.75	75
		a. No cross on crown........................		£300	£100
331		1d. rose-pink (Die B)		70.00	18.00
332		1d. scarlet (Die B) (6.12)		13.00	9.00
		Wi. Watermark inverted		14.00	6.00
333		1d. aniline scarlet (Die B)		£120	55.00

For note on the aniline scarlet No. 333 *see* below No. 343.

100 Simple Cypher

1912 (Aug). *Booklet stamps. Wmk Royal Cypher ("Simple"), W* **100**. *P* 15 × 14.

334	**98**	½d. pale green (Die B)		25.00	19.00
335		½d. green (Die B)		25.00	19.00
		Wi. Watermark inverted		25.00	19.00
		Wj. Watermark reversed......................		£180	
		Wk. Watermark inverted & reversed		£250	
336	**99**	1d. scarlet (Die B)		12.00	10.00
		Wi. Watermark inverted		12.00	10.00
		Wj. Watermark reversed......................		£150	
		Wk. Watermark inverted & reversed		—	75.00
337		1d. brt scarlet (Die B).........................		12.00	12.00

101	**102**	**103** Multiple Cypher

Type differences

½d. In T **98** the ornament above "P" of "HALFPENNY" has two thin lines of colour and the beard is undefined. In T **101** the ornament has one thick line and the beard is well defined.

1d. In T **99** the body of the lion is unshaded and in T **102** it is shaded.

1912 (1 Jan). *Wmk Imperial Crown, W* **49**. *P* 15 × 14.

338	**101**	½d. dp green		7.00	3.00
339		½d. green		2.50	40
340		½d. yellow-green		2.50	40
		a. No cross on crown........................		60.00	12.00
		Wi. Watermark inverted		£150	
341	**102**	1d. brt scarlet		1.00	35
		a. No cross on crown........................		45.00	12.00
		b. Printed double, one albino		£125	
		Wi. Watermark inverted		£140	90.00
342		1d. scarlet		1.00	35

343	**102**	1d. aniline scarlet*		£120	55.00
		a. No cross on crown........................		£750	

* Our prices for the aniline scarlet 1d. stamps, Nos. 333 and 343, are for the specimens in which the colour is suffused on the surface of the stamp and shows through clearly on the back. Specimens without these characteristics but which show "aniline" reactions under the quartz lamp are relatively common.

1912 (Aug). *Wmk Royal Cypher ("Simple"), W* **100**. *P* 15 × 14.

344	**101**	½d. green		2.00	50
		a. No cross on crown........................		65.00	15.00
		Wi. Watermark inverted		40.00	15.00
		Wj. Watermark reversed......................		28.00	15.00
		Wk. Watermark inverted & reversed		3.75	2.00
345	**102**	1d. scarlet		1.10	35
		a. No cross on crown on crown...........		55.00	13.00
		Wi. Watermark inverted		9.00	4.50
		Wj. Watermark reversed......................		17.00	6.00
		Wk. Watermark inverted & reversed		8.00	4.00

1912 (Oct). *Wmk Royal Cypher ("Multiple"), W* **103**. *P* 15 × 14.

346	**101**	½d. green		4.00	1.75
		a. No cross on crown........................		65.00	20.00
		b. Imperf		£110	
		c. Watermark sideways		†	£800
		Wi. Watermark inverted		3.50	2.50
		Wj. Watermark reversed......................		4.00	2.75
		Wk. Watermark inverted & reversed		18.00	
347		½d. yellow-green		4.00	3.75
348		½d. pale green		4.00	3.50
349	**102**	1d. brt scarlet.................................		5.00	2.50
350		1d. scarlet		6.00	3.00
		a. No cross on crown........................		70.00	16.00
		b. Imperf		85.00	
		c. Watermark sideways		£110	55.00
		d. Watermark sideways. No cross on			
		crown		£550	
		Wi. Watermark inverted		8.00	
		Wj. Watermark reversed......................		8.00	
		Wk. Watermark inverted & reversed		£250	£100

104	**105**	**106**

107	**108**

No. 357a

No. 357ab

No. 357ac

Die I

Die II

Two Dies of the 2d.

Die I.—Inner frame-line at top and sides close to solid of background. *Four* complete lines of shading between top of head and oval frame-line. These four lines do *not* extend to the oval itself. White line round "TWOPENCE" thin.

Die II.—Inner frame-line farther from solid of background. *Three* lines between top of head and extending to the oval. White line round "TWOPENCE" thicker.

(Des Bertram Mackennal (heads) and G. W. Eve (frames). Coinage head (½, 1½, 2, 3 and 4d.); large medal head (1d., 2½d.); intermediate medal head (5d. to 1s.); small medal head used for fiscal stamps. Dies eng J. A. C. Harrison)

(Typo by Harrison & Sons Ltd., except the 6d. printed by the Stamping Department of the Board of Inland Revenue, Somerset House. The latter also made printings of the following which can only be distinguished by the controls: ½d. B.13; 1½d. A.12; 2d. C.13; 2½d. A.12; 3d. A.12, B.13, C.13; 4d. B.13; 5d. B.13; 7d. C.13; 8d. C.13; 9d. agate B.13; 10d. C.13; 1s. C.13)

1912–24. *Wmk Royal Cypher, W* **100.** *P* 15 × 14.

351	**105**	½d. green (1.13)		40	10
		a. Doubly printed		£5000	
		Wi. Watermark inverted		75	25
		Wj. Watermark reversed		9.00	5.00
		Wk. Watermark inverted & reversed		2.25	1.50
352		½d. brt green		40	15
353		½d. dp green		2.25	90
354		½d. yellow-green		5.00	1.25
355		½d. very yellow (Cyprus) green (1914)		£2400	
356		½d. blue-green		32.00	12.00
357	**104**	1d. brt scarlet (10.12)		25	12
		a. "Q" for "O" (R.1/4) (Control↓ E14)		£200	
		ab. "Q" for "O" (R.4/11) (Control T22)		£350	
		ac. Reversed "Q" for "O" (R.15/9) (Control T22)		£400	
		ad. Inverted "Q" for "O" (R.20/3)		£450	
		b. *Tête-bêche* (pair)			
		Wi. Watermark inverted		75	25
		Wj. Watermark reversed		9.00	5.00
		Wk. Watermark inverted & reversed		1.75	50
358		1d. vermilion		1.50	60
359		1d. pale rose-red		6.00	40
360		1d. carmine-red		7.00	2.25
361		1d. scarlet-vermilion		70.00	20.00
		a. Printed on back†		£200	†
362	**105**	1½d. red-brown (10.12)		80	12
		a. "PENCF" (R.15/12)		£225	90.00
		b. Booklet pane. Four stamps plus two printed labels (2.24)		£200	
		Wi. Watermark inverted		1.50	65
		Wj. Watermark reversed		7.50	3.00
		Wk. Watermark inverted & reversed		4.50	2.25
363		1½d. chocolate-brown		1.00	35
		a. No watermark		£120	
364		1½d. chestnut		1.25	25
		a. "PENCF" (R.15/12)		£110	50.00
365		1½d. yellow-brown		15.00	9.00
366	**106**	2d. orange-yellow (Die I) (8.12)		3.00	1.50
367		2d. reddish orange (Die I) (11.13)		1.00	35
368		2d. orange (Die I)		90	35
		Wi. Watermark inverted		6.50	3.00
		Wj. Watermark reversed		9.00	4.50
		Wk. Watermark inverted & reversed		7.00	2.50
369		2d. brt orange (Die I)		1.10	55
370		2d. orange (Die II) (9.21)		2.50	1.75
		Wi. Watermark inverted		12.00	4.50
		Wj. Watermark inverted & reversed		12.00	4.50
371	**104**	2½d. cobalt-blue (10.12)		4.50	1.00
371a		2½d. brt blue (1914)		4.00	1.00
372		2½d. blue		4.00	1.00
		Wi. Watermark inverted		18.00	5.00
		Wj. Watermark reversed		10.00	3.50
		Wk. Watermark inverted & reversed		9.00	4.00
373		2½d. indigo-blue* (1920)		£850	
373a		2½d. dull Prussian blue* (1921)		£550	
374	**106**	3d. dull reddish violet (10.12)		7.00	1.00
375		3d. violet		2.00	55
		Wi. Watermark inverted		18.00	7.00
		Wj. Watermark reversed		32.00	15.00
		Wk. Watermark inverted & reversed		10.00	6.00
376		3d. bluish violet (11.13)		2.50	90
377		3d. pale violet		4.00	90
378		4d. dp grey-green (1.13)		18.00	3.50
379		4d. grey-green		4.50	60
		Wi. Watermark inverted		15.00	4.50
		Wj. Watermark reversed		20.00	6.00
		Wk. Watermark inverted & reversed		18.00	4.50
380		4d. pale grey-green		9.00	1.75
381	**107**	5d. brown (6.13)		4.50	2.25
		Wi. Watermark inverted		£200	50.00
		Wj. Watermark inverted & reversed		£110	40.00
382		5d. yellow-brown		4.50	2.25
		a. No watermark		£450	
383		5d. bistre-brown		65.00	25.00
384		6d. dull purple, C (8.13)		14.00	3.00
385		6d. reddish purple, C		7.00	1.00
		a. Perf 14 (10.20)		60.00	75.00
		Wi. Watermark inverted		14.00	4.75
		Wj. Watermark reversed		£300	
		Wk. Watermark inverted & reversed		18.00	6.00
386		6d. dp reddish purple, C		9.00	1.50
387		7d. olive (8.13)		9.00	3.75
		Wi. Watermark inverted		20.00	6.00
		Wj. Watermark inverted & reversed			
388		7d. bronze-green (1915)		50.00	12.00
389		7d. sage-green (1917)		25.00	6.00
390		8d. black/yellow (8.13)		20.00	6.50
		Wi. Watermark inverted		50.00	22.00
		Wj. Watermark reversed		55.00	
		Wk. Watermark inverted & reversed		£1100	
391		8d. black/yellow-buff (granite) (5.17)		20.00	8.00
392	**108**	9d. agate (6.13)		7.00	2.00
		Wi. Watermark inverted		30.00	15.00
		Wj. Watermark inverted & reversed		28.00	14.00
393		9d. dp agate		12.00	2.75

393a **108**	9d.	olive-green (9.22)............................	65.00	14.00
	aWi.	Watermark inverted	£400	£170
	aWj.	Watermark inverted & reversed	£350	£170
393b	9d.	pale olive-green	70.00	14.00
394	10d.	turquoise-blue (8.13).....................	13.00	11.00
	Wi.	Watermark inverted	£450	65.00
	Wj.	Watermark inverted & reversed	85.00	28.00
394a	10d.	dp turquoise-blue...........................	30.00	15.00
395	1s.	bistre-brown (8.13)	7.50	75
	Wi.	Watermark inverted	65.00	15.00
	Wj.	Watermark inverted & reversed	30.00	10.00
396	1s.	olive-bistre	20.00	5.00
		Set of 15......................................	£130	38.00

Imperf stamps of this issue exist but may be war-time colour trials.

† The impression of No. 361a is set sideways and is very pale.

* No. 373 comes from Control O 20 and also exists on toned paper.
No. 373a comes from Control R 21 and also exists on toned paper, but both are unlike the rare Prussian blue shade of the 1935 2½d. Jubilee issue.

See also Nos. 418/29.

Examples of the 2d., T106 which are in the hands of philatelists, are known bisected in Guernsey from 27 December 1940 to February 1941.

1913 (Aug).   *Wmk Royal Cypher ("Multiple"), W* **103**. *P* 15 ×14.

397 **105**	½d.	brt green......................................	75.00	90.00
	Wi.	Watermark inverted	£275	
398 **104**	1d.	dull scarlet	£150	£130
	Wi.	Watermark inverted	£300	

Both these stamps were originally issued in rolls only. Subsequently sheets were found, so that horizontal pairs and blocks are known but are of considerable rarity.

109

A

110 Single Cypher

Major Re-entries on 2s. 6d.

Nos. 400a and 408a

No. 415b

(Des Bertram Mackennal. Dies eng J. A. C. Harrison. Recess)

High values, so-called "Sea Horses" design: T **109**. Background around portrait consists of horizontal lines, Type A. Wmk Single Cypher, W **110**. P 11 × 12.

1913 (30 June–Aug).   *Printed by Waterlow Bros & Layton.*

399	2s. 6d.	dp sepia-brown.....................	£175	65.00
400	2s. 6d.	sepia-brown	£175	60.00
	a.	Re-entry (R.2/1)	£900	£400
401	5s.	rose-carmine (4 July)	£300	£130
402	10s.	indigo-blue (1 Aug)	£400	£200
403	£1	green (1 Aug)	£1250	£500
404	£1	dull blue-green (1 Aug)..........	£1250	£500
★399/404		**For well-centred, lightly used**		+25%

1915 (Dec)–**18**.   *Printed by De La Rue & Co.*

405	2s. 6d.	dp yellow-brown	£200	70.00
	Wi.	Watermark inverted	£350	
406	2s. 6d.	yellow-brown	£200	65.00
	Wi.	Watermark inverted	£300	
	Wj.	Watermark reversed.................	£300	
	Wk.	Watermark inverted & reversed	£900	
407	2s. 6d.	pale brown (worn plate)	£175	65.00
	Wi.	Watermark inverted	£300	
	Wj.	Watermark reversed.................	£350	
408	2s. 6d.	sepia (seal-brown)...................	£200	70.00
	a.	Re-entry (R.2/1)	£700	£400
	Wi.	Watermark inverted	£300	
	Wj.	Watermark reversed.................	£300	
409	5s.	brt carmine...........................	£300	£130
	Wi.	Watermark inverted	£950	
	Wj.	Watermark reversed.................	£850	
	Wk.	Watermark inverted & reversed		
410	5s.	pale carmine (worn plate)	£300	£130
411	10s.	dp blue	£1100	£250
412	10s.	blue	£900	£200
	Wi.	Watermark inverted & reversed		
413	10s.	pale blue	£900	£200
★405/13		**For well-centred, lightly used**		+25%

1918 (Dec)–**19**.   *Printed by Bradbury, Wilkinson & Co, Ltd.*

413a	2s. 6d.	olive-brown............................	70.00	24.00
414	2s. 6d.	chocolate-brown.....................	90.00	26.00
415	2s. 6d.	reddish-brown........................	95.00	26.00
415a	2s. 6d.	pale brown............................	80.00	24.00
	b.	Major re-entry (R.1/2)	£600	£250
416	5s.	rose-red (1.19).......................	£175	30.00
417	10s.	dull grey-blue (1.19)	£300	75.00
		Set of 4	£1600	£575
★413a/17		**For well-centred, lightly used**		+25%

DISTINGUISHING PRINTINGS.   Note that the £1 value was only printed by Waterlow.

Waterlow and De La Rue stamps measure exactly 22 mm vertically. In the De La Rue printings the gum is usually patchy and yellowish, and the colour of the stamp, particularly in the 5s., tends to show through the back. The holes of the perforation are smaller than those of the other two printers.

In the Bradbury Wilkinson printings the height of the stamp is 22¾ or 23 mm. On most of the 22¾ mm high stamps a minute coloured guide dot appears in the margin just above the middle of the upper frame-line.

For (1934) re-engraved Waterlow printings see Nos. 450/2.

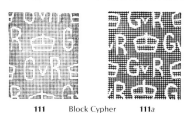

| 111 | Block Cypher | 111a |

The watermark Type **111**a, as compared with Type **111**, differs as follows: Closer spacing of horizontal rows (12½ mm instead of 14½ mm). Letters shorter and rounder. Watermark thicker.

(Typo by Waterlow & Sons, Ltd (all values except 6d.) and later, 1934–35, by Harrison & Sons, Ltd (all values). Until 1934 the 6d. was printed at Somerset House where a printing of the 1½d. was also made in 1926 (identifiable only by control E.26). Printings by Harrisons in 1934–35 can be identified, when in mint condition, by the fact that the gum shows a streaky appearance vertically, the Waterlow gum being uniformly applied, but Harrisons also used up the balance of the Waterlow "smooth gum" paper)

1924 (Feb)–**26.** *Wmk Block Cypher, W* **111**. *P* 15 × 14.

418	**105**	½d. green	12	10
		a. Watermark sideways (5.24)	7.00	2.50
		b. Doubly printed	£3250	
		Wi. Watermark inverted	75	30
		Wj. Watermark sideways-inverted		
419	**104**	1d. scarlet	25	20
		a. Watermark sideways	16.00	8.00
		b. Experimental paper, W **111**a (10.24)	30.00	
		c. Inverted "Q" for "O" (R.20/3)	£325	
		Wi. Watermark inverted	75	45
420	**105**	1½d. red-brown	20	15
		a. *Tête-bêche* (pair)	£375	£300
		b. Watermark sideways (8.24)	4.25	1.75
		c. Printed on the gummed side	£425	†
		d. Booklet pane. Four stamps plus two printed labels (6.24)	55.00	
		e. Ditto. Watermark sideways	£1250	
		f. Experimental paper, W **111**a (10.24)	40.00	
		g. Double impression		
		Wi. Watermark inverted	60	30
		Wj. Watermark sideways-inverted		
421	**106**	2d. orange (Die II) (9.24)	60	45
		a. No watermark	£350	
		b. Watermark sideways (7.26)	70.00	50.00
		c. Doubly printed	£5000	
		Wi. Watermark inverted	10.00	4.50
422	**104**	2½d. blue (10.24)	3.25	70
		a. No watermark	£475	
		b. Watermark sideways	†	—
		Wi. Watermark inverted	19.00	9.00
423	**106**	3d. violet (10.24)	4.00	60
		Wi. Watermark inverted	16.00	8.00
424		4d. grey-green (11.24)	6.00	90
		a. Printed on the gummed side	£800	†
		Wi. Watermark inverted	18.00	8.00
425	**107**	5d. brown (11.24)	14.00	1.40
		Wi. Watermark inverted	19.00	7.00

426	**107**	6d. reddish purple, C (9.24)	5.00	1.50
		Wi. Watermark inverted	16.00	9.00
		Wj. Watermark inverted & reversed	23.00	
426a		6d. purple, O (6.26)	2.00	35
		aWi. Watermark inverted	21.00	9.00
427	**108**	9d. olive-green (12.24)	8.00	1.75
		Wi. Watermark inverted	25.00	7.00
428		10d. turquoise-blue (11.24)	24.00	14.00
		Wi. Watermark inverted	£600	
429		1s. bistre-brown (10.24)	16.00	75
		Wi. Watermark inverted	£200	
		Set of 12	75.00	17.00

There are numerous shades in this issue.

The 6d. on both chalky and ordinary papers was printed by both Somerset House and Harrisons. The Harrison printings have streaky gum, differ slightly in shade, and that on chalky paper is printed in a highly fugitive ink. The prices quoted are for the commonest (Harrison) printing in each case.

112

(Des H. Nelson. Eng J. A. C. Harrison. Recess Waterlow)

1924–25. British Empire Exhibition. *W* **111**. *P* 14.

(a) Dated "1924" (23.4.24)

430	**112**	1d. scarlet	2.25	4.50
431		1½d. brown	4.00	11.00
		Set of 2	6.50	14.00
		Set of 2 unmounted	25.00	
		First Day Cover		£350

(b) Dated "1925" (9.5.25)

432	**112**	1d. scarlet	7.50	12.00
433		1½d. brown	23.00	50.00
		Set of 2	30.00	60.00
		Set of 2 unmounted	65.00	
		First Day Cover		£1200

| 113 | 114 | 115 |

116 St. George and the Dragon

117

(Des J. Farleigh (T **113** and **115**), E. Linzell (T **114**) and H. Nelson (T **116**). Eng C. G. Lewis (T **113**), T. E. Storey (T **115**), both at the Royal Mint; J. A. C. Harrison, of Waterlow (T **114** & **116**). Typo by Waterlow from plates made at the Royal Mint, except T **116**, recess by Bradbury, Wilkinson from die and plate of their own manufacture)

1929 (10 May). **Ninth U.P.U. Congress, London.**

(a) W **111**. P 15 × 14

434	**113**	½d. green	50	90
		a. Watermark sideways	45.00	32.00
		Wi. Watermark inverted	10.00	7.50
435	**114**	1d. scarlet	60	90
		a. Watermark sideways	45.00	38.00
		Wi. Watermark inverted	10.00	7.50
436		1½d. purple-brown	60	90
		a. Watermark sideways	22.00	21.00
		b. Booklet pane. Four stamps plus two printed labels..............................	£120	
		Wi. Watermark inverted	8.00	5.50
437	**115**	2½d. blue	5.00	9.00
		Wi. Watermark inverted	£600	£350

(b) W **117**. P 12

438	**116**	£1 black	£650	£450
		Set of 4 (to 2½d.)	6.00	11.00
		Set of 4 (to 2½d.) unmounted	23.00	
		£1 unmounted	£725	
		First Day Cover (4 vals.)		£500
		First Day Cover (5 vals.)		£2500

PRINTERS. All subsequent issues were printed in photogravure by Harrison & Sons, Ltd, *except where otherwise stated.*

118

119

120

121

122

1934–36. W **111**. P 15 × 14.

439	**118**	½d. green (19.11.34)..............................	10	15
		a. Watermark sideways	10.00	2.75
		b. Imperf three sides	£650	
		Wi. Watermark inverted	6.00	1.00
		Wj. Watermark sideways-inverted..........	£150	30.00
440	**119**	1d. scarlet (24.9.34)	15	15
		a. Imperf (pair)	£850	
		b. Printed on the gummed side	£400	
		c. Watermark sideways	10.00	2.75
		d. Double impression	£900	
		Wi. Watermark inverted	6.00	2.50
		Wj. Watermark sideways-inverted..........	30.00	
441	**118**	1½d. red-brown (20.8.34)	10	15
		a. Imperf (pair)	£225	
		b. Imperf (three sides) (pair)	£400	
		c. Watermark sideways	6.00	2.00
		d. Booklet pane. Four stamps plus two printed labels (1.35)	60.00	
		Wi. Watermark inverted	1.50	30
442	**120**	2d. orange (21.1.35).............................	30	30
		a. Imperf (pair)	£900	
		b. Watermark sideways	60.00	35.00
443	**119**	2½d. ultramarine (18.3.35)	1.00	50
444	**120**	3d. violet (18.3.35).............................	1.00	50
		Wi. Watermark inverted	—	£300
445		4d. dp grey-green (2.12.35)	1.50	55
		Wi. Watermark inverted	†	
446	**121**	5d. yellow-brown (17.2.36)	5.00	1.50
447	**122**	9d. dp olive-green (2.12.35)	9.00	1.60
448		10d. turquoise-blue (24.2.36)	12.00	8.00
449		1s. bistre-brown (24.2.36)	12.00	40
		Set of 11	35.00	11.00

Owing to the need for wider space for the perforations the size of the designs of the ½d. and 2d. were once, and the 1d. and 1½d. twice reduced from that of the first printings.

The format description, size in millimetres and S.G. catalogue number are given but further details will be found in the *Great Britain Specialised Catalogue, Volume 2.*

Description	Size	S.G. Nos.	Date of Issue
½d. intermediate format	18.4 × 22.2	—	19.11.34
½d. small format	17.9 × 21.7	439	1935
1d. large format	18.7 × 22.5	—	24.9.34
1d. intermediate format	18.4 × 22.2	—	1934
1d. small format	17.9 × 21.7	440	1935
1½d. large format	18.7 × 22.5	—	20.8.34
1½d. intermediate format	18.4 × 22.2	—	1934
1½d. small format	17.9 × 21.7	441	1935
2d. intermediate format	18.4 × 22.2	—	21.1.35
2d. small format	18.15 × 21.7	442	1935

There are also numerous minor variations, due to the photographic element in the process.

The ½d. imperf three sides, No. 439b, is known in a block of four, from a sheet, in which the bottom pair is imperf at top and sides.

Examples of the 2d., T **120** which are in the hands of philatelists are known bisected in Guernsey from 2 December 1940 to February 1941.

B

123

(Eng J. A. C. Harrison. Recess Waterlow)

1934 (Oct). *T* **109** (re-engraved). *Background around portrait consists of horizontal and diagonal lines, Type B, W* **110**. *P* 11 × 12.

450	**109**	2s. 6d. chocolate-brown	65.00	12.00
451		5s. brt rose-red	£130	28.00
452		10s. indigo	£275	35.00
		Set of 3	£425	65.00

There are numerous other minor differences in the design of this issue.

(Des B. Freedman)

1935 (7 May). **Silver Jubilee.** *W* **111**. *P* 15 × 14.

453	**123**	½d. green	25	20
		Wi. Watermark inverted	4.50	7.00
454		1d. scarlet	45	90
		Wi. Watermark inverted	4.50	7.00
455	**123**	1½d. red-brown	25	20
		Wi. Watermark inverted	2.50	1.00
456		2½d. blue	5.00	5.00
456a		2½d. Prussian blue	£3750	£3500
		Set of 4	5.00	5.00
		Set of 4 unmounted	8.00	
		First Day Cover		£400

The 1d., 1½d. and 2½d. values differ from T **123** in the emblem in the panel at right.

No. 456*a*, from three sheets printed with the wrong ink, was issued at a P.O. in Edmonton, North London.

KING EDWARD VIII

20 January–10 December 1936

Further detailed information on the stamps of King Edward VIII will be found in Volume 2 of the Stanley Gibbons *Great Britain Specialised Catalogue*.

> **PRICES.** From S.G.457 prices quoted in the first column are for stamps in unmounted mint condition.

124	125

(Des from photo by Hugh Cecil)

1936. *W* **125**. *P* 15 × 14.

457	**124**	½d. green	20	10
		a. Double impression		
		Wi. Watermark inverted	5.00	1.60
458		1d. scarlet (14.9.36)	20	20
		Wi. Watermark inverted	4.75	1.10
459		1½d. red-brown (1.9.36)	30	10
		a. Booklet pane. Four stamps plus two printed labels..............................	24.00	
		Wi. Watermark inverted	80	60
460		2½d. brt blue (1.9.36)	20	50
		Set of 4	80	80

KING GEORGE VI

11 December 1936–6 February 1952

Further detailed information on the stamps of King George VI will be found in Volume 2 of the Stanley Gibbons *Great Britain Specialised Catalogue*.

126 King George VI and Queen Elizabeth

(Des E. Dulac)

1937 (13 May). **Coronation.** *W* **127**. *P* 15 × 14.

461	**126**	1½d. maroon	35	20
		First Day Cover		28.00

127	128

129	130

King George VI and National Emblems

(Des T **128/9**, E. Dulac (head) and E. Gill (frames). T **130**, E. Dulac (whole stamp))

1937–47. *W* **127**. *P* 15 × 14.

462	**128**	½d. green (10.5.37)	10	10
		a. Watermark sideways (1.38)	20	20
		ab. Booklet pane of 4	6.00	
		Wi. Watermark inverted	6.00	40
463		1d. scarlet (10.5.37)	10	10
		a. Watermark sideways (2.38)	8.00	4.00
		ab. Booklet pane of 4	35.00	
		Wi. Watermark inverted	25.00	1.00
464		1½d. red-brown (30.7.37)	20	10
		a. Watermark sideways (2.38)	90	65
		b. Booklet pane. Four stamps plus two printed labels.............................	35.00	
		c. Imperf three sides (pair)		
		Wi. Watermark inverted	8.00	40
465		2d. orange (31.1.38)	1.00	30
		a. Watermark sideways (2.38)	65.00	25.00
		b. Bisected (on cover)	†	20.00
		Wi. Watermark inverted	50.00	2.00

466	128	2½d. ultramarine (10.5.37)		20	10
		a. Watermark sideways (6.40)		75.00	12.00
		b. *Tête-bêche* (horiz pair)			
		Wi. Watermark inverted		25.00	1.60
467		3d. violet (31.1.38).............................		4.00	60
468	129	4d. grey-green (21.11.38)		30	30
		a. Imperf (pair)		£750	
		b. Imperf three sides (pair)			
469		5d. brown (21.11.38)		2.50	35
		a. Imperf (pair)		£800	
		b. Imperf three sides (pair)		£600	
470		6d. purple (30.1.39)		1.00	20
471	130	7d. emerald-green (27.2.39)		4.50	30
		a. Imperf three sides (pair)		£600	
472		8d. brt carmine (27.2.39)		4.75	40
473		9d. dp olive-green (1.5.39)...................		5.00	40
474		10d. turquoise-blue (1.5.39)		4.00	40
		aa. Imperf (pair)			
474a		11d. plum (29.12.47)...........................		3.50	1.10
475		1s. bistre-brown (1.5.39)		5.00	20
		Set of 15......................................		32.00	4.25

For later printings of the lower values in apparently lighter shades and different colours, see Nos. 485/90 and 503/8.

No. 465b was authorised for use in Guernsey from 27 December 1940 until February 1941.

131	132

133

(Des E. Dulac (T **131**) and Hon. G. R. Bellew (T **132**). Eng J. A. C. Harrison. Recess Waterlow)

1939–48. W **133**. P 14.

476	131	2s. 6d. brown (4.9.39)........................		40.00	8.00
476a		2s. 6d. yellow-green (9.3.42)................		11.00	75
477		5s. red (21.8.39)		22.00	1.40
478	132	10s. dark blue (30.10.39)......................		£190	18.00
478a		10s. ultramarine (30.11.42)...................		38.00	4.00
478b		£1 brown (1.10.48)		16.00	18.00
		Set of 6		£290	45.00

134 Queen Victoria and King George VI

(Des H. L. Palmer)

1940 (6 May). **Centenary of First Adhesive Postage Stamps.** W **127**. P 14½ × 14.

479	134	½d. green		30	20
480		1d. scarlet		40	30
481		1½d. red-brown		30	30
482		2d. orange		50	40
		a. Bisected (on cover)		†	15.00
483		2½d. ultramarine		1.90	60
484		3d. violet		4.50	3.75
		Set of 6		7.00	5.00
		First Day Cover			27.00

No. 482a was authorised for use in Guernsey from 27 December 1940 until February 1941.

1941–42. *Head as Nos. 462/7, but lighter background.* W **127**. P 15 × 14.

485	128	½d. pale green (1.9.41)		10	8
		a. *Tête-bêche* (horiz pair)		£1250	
		b. Imperf (pair)		£1000	
		Wi. Watermark inverted		4.00	60
486		1d. pale scarlet (11.8.41)		10	8
		a. Watermark sideways (10.42)		4.00	6.00
		b. Imperf (pair)		£850	
		c. Imperf three sides (pair)		£600	
		d. Imperf between (vert pair)			
487		1½d. pale red-brown (28.9.42)		60	35
488		2d. pale orange (6.10.41)		50	25
		a. Watermark sideways (6.42)		10.00	10.00
		b. *Tête-bêche* (horiz pair)			
		c. Imperf (pair)		£1250	
		d. Imperf pane*			
		Wi. Watermark inverted		3.00	60
489		2½d. light ultramarine (21.7.41)		10	8
		a. Watermark sideways (8.42)		14.00	10.00
		b. *Tête-bêche* (horiz pair)		£1000	
		c. Imperf (pair)		£750	
		d. Imperf pane*		£1300	
		Wi. Watermark inverted		1.00	60
490		3d. pale violet (3.11.41)		1.50	30
		Set of 6		2.75	1.00

The *tête-bêche* varieties are from defectively made-up stamp booklets.

* BOOKLET ERRORS. Those listed as "imperf panes" show one row of perforations either at the top or at the bottom of the pane of 6.

135	136

Symbols of Peace and Reconstruction

(Des H. L. Palmer (T **135**) and R. Stone (T **136**))

1946 (11 June). **Victory.** W **127**. P 15 × 14.

491	135	2½d. ultramarine		10	10
492	136	3d. violet.......................................		8	8
		Set of 2		15	15
		First Day Cover			38.00

137   138

King George VI and Queen Elizabeth

(Des G. Knipe and Joan Hassall from photographs by Dorothy Wilding)

1948 (26 Apr).   **Royal Silver Wedding.** W **127**. P 15 × 14 (2½d.) *or* 14 × 15 (£1).

493	**137**	2½d. ultramarine	20	20
494	**138**	£1 blue	50.00	40.00
		Set of 2	50.00	40.00
		First Day Cover		£300

1948 (10 May).   Stamps of 1d. and 2½d. showing seaweed-gathering were on sale at eight Head Post Offices in Great Britain, but were primarily for use in the Channel Islands and are listed there (see Nos. C1/2, after Royal Mail Postage Labels).

139 Globe and Laurel Wreath

140 "Speed"

141 Olympic Symbol

142 Winged Victory

(Des P. Metcalfe, A. Games, S. D. Scott and E. Dulac)

1948 (29 July).   **Olympic Games.** W **127**. P 15 × 14.

495	**139**	2½d. ultramarine	8	8
496	**140**	3d. violet	20	20
497	**141**	6d. brt purple	25	20
498	**142**	1s. brown	1.10	1.00
		Set of 4	1.50	1.25
		First Day Cover		28.00

143 Two Hemispheres

144 U.P.U. Monument, Berne

145 Goddess Concordia, Globe and Points of Compass

146 Posthorn & Globe

(Des Mary Adshead (T **143**), P. Metcalfe (T **144**), H. Fleury (T **145**) and Hon. G. R. Bellew (T **146**))

1949 (10 Oct). **75th Anniv of Universal Postal Union.** W **127**. P 15 × 14.

499	**143**	2½d. ultramarine	10	8
500	**144**	3d. violet	30	30
501	**145**	6d. brt purple	45	40
502	**146**	1s. brown	1.25	1.25
		Set of 4	1.75	1.75
		First Day Cover		55.00

1950–52. 4d. *as Nos.* 468 *and others as Nos.* 485/9, *but colours changed.*

503	**128**	½d. pale orange (3.5.51)	10	8
		a. Imperf (pair)		
		b. *Tête-bêche* (horiz pair)	£1500	
		c. Imperf pane*		
		Wi. Watermark inverted	12	35
504		1d. lt ultramarine (3.5.51)	10	8
		a. Watermark sideways (5.51)	20	45
		b. Imperf (pair)	£750	
		c. Imperf three sides (pair)	£500	
		d. Booklet pane. Three stamps plus three printed labels (3.52)	15.00	
		e. Ditto. Partial *tête-bêche* pane	£1500	
		Wi. Watermark inverted	3.00	1.00
505		1½d. pale green (3.5.51)	20	30
		a. Watermark sideways (9.51)	2.00	2.50
		Wi. Watermark inverted	2.00	80
506		2d. pale red-brown (3.5.51)	20	20
		a. Watermark sideways (5.51)	90	1.10
		b. *Tête-bêche* (horiz pair)	£1500	
		c. Imperf three sides (pair)	£500	
		Wi. Watermark inverted	2.75	3.25
507		2½d. pale scarlet (3.5.51)	12	12
		a. Watermark sideways (5.51)	90	90
		b. *Tête-bêche* (horiz pair)		
		Wi. Watermark inverted	80	60
508	**129**	4d. lt ultramarine (2.10.50)	1.10	1.00
		Set of 6	1.60	1.50

* BOOKLET ERRORS. Those listed as "imperf panes" show one row of perforations either at the top or at the bottom of the pane of 6.

147 H.M.S. *Victory*

148 White Cliffs of Dover

149 St. George and the Dragon

150 Royal Coat of Arms

(Des Mary Adshead (T **147/8**), P. Metcalfe (T **149/50**). Recess Waterlow)

1951 (3 May). W **133**. P 11 × 12.
509	**147**	2s. 6d. yellow-green	12.00	75
510	**148**	5s. red..	30.00	1.50
511	**149**	10s. ultramarine	18.00	6.00
512	**150**	£1 brown	42.00	20.00
		Set of 4	85.00	25.00

151 "Commerce and Prosperity"

152 Festival Symbol

(Des E. Dulac (T **151**), A. Games (T **152**))

1951 (3 May). **Festival of Britain**. W **127**. P 15 × 14.
513	**151**	2½d. scarlet	10	8
514	**152**	4d. ultramarine	35	35
		Set of 2	40	40
		First Day Cover		16.00

QUEEN ELIZABETH II
6 February 1952

Further detailed information on the stamps of Queen Elizabeth II will be found in Volumes 3 and 4 of the Stanley Gibbons *Great Britain Specialised Catalogue*.

153 Tudor Crown

154

155   **156**   **157**

158   **159**   **160**

Queen Elizabeth II and National Emblems

I   II

Two types of the 2½d.

Type I:—In the frontal cross of the diadem, the top line is only half the width of the cross.

Type II:—The top line extends to the full width of the cross and there are signs of strengthening in other parts of the diadem.

(Des Enid Marx (T **154**), M. Farrar-Bell (T **155/6**), G. Knipe (T **157**), Mary Adshead (T **158**), E. Dulac (T **159/60**). Portrait by Dorothy Wilding)

1952–54. W **153**. P 15 × 14.
515	**154**	½d. orange-red (31.8.53)	10	10
		Wi. Watermark inverted (3.54)	30	30
516		1d. ultramarine (31.8.53)	20	20
		a. Booklet pane. Three stamps plus three printed labels	20.00	
		Wi. Watermark inverted (3.54)	3.50	1.50
517		1½d. green (5.12.52)	10	12
		a. Watermark sideways (15.10.54)	30	60
		b. Imperf pane*	£1000	
		Wi. Watermark inverted (5.53)	20	40
518		2d. red-brown (31.8.53)	20	15
		a. Watermark sideways (8.10.54)	80	1.25
		Wi. Watermark inverted (3.54)	16.00	14.00
519	**155**	2½d. carmine-red (Type I) (5.12.52)	10	10
		a. Watermark sideways (15.11.54)	10.00	7.50
		b. Type II (Booklets) (5.53)	75	60
		bWi. Watermark inverted (5.53)	15	45
520		3d. dp lilac (18.1.54)	1.40	30
521	**156**	4d. ultramarine (2.11.53)	3.50	80
522	**157**	5d. brown (6.7.53)	1.00	1.25
523		6d. reddish purple (18.1.54)	4.50	60
		a. Imperf three sides (pair)		
524		7d. brt green (18.1.54)	12.00	2.10
525	**158**	8d. magenta (6.7.53)	1.25	60
526		9d. bronze-green (8.2.54)	18.00	3.00
527		10d. Prussian blue (8.2.54)	14.00	3.00
528		11d. brown-purple (8.2.54)	35.00	11.00
529	**159**	1s. bistre-brown (6.7.53)	1.00	40
530	**160**	1s. 3d. green (2.11.53)	7.00	2.00
531	**159**	1s. 6d. grey-blue (2.11.53)	14.00	2.00
		Set of 17	90.00	24.00

See also Nos. 540/56, 561/6, 570/94 and 599/618a.

* BOOKLET ERRORS.—This pane of 6 stamps is *completely* imperf (see No. 540a, etc.).

Stamps with *sideways watermark* come from left-side delivery coils and stamps with *inverted watermark* are from booklets.

First Day Covers		
5.12.52	1½d., 2½d. (517, 519)	5.50
6.7.53	5d., 8d., 1s. (522, 525, 529)	25.00
31.8.53	½d., 1d., 2d. (515/16, 518)	20.00
2.11.53	4d., 1s. 3d., 1s. 6d. (521, 530/1)	50.00
18.1.54	3d., 6d., 7d. (520, 523/4)	30.00
8.2.54	9d., 10d., 11d. (526/28)	60.00

161   **162**

163   **164**

(Des E. Fuller (2½d.), M. Goaman (4d.), E. Dulac (1s. 3d.), M. Farrar-Bell (1s. 6d.), Portrait (except 1s. 3d.) by Dorothy Wilding)

1953 (3 June). **Coronation.** W **153**. *P* 15 × 14.

532	**161**	2½d. carmine-red	10	8
533	**162**	4d. ultramarine	30	20
534	**163**	1s. 3d. dp yellow-green	5.50	3.75
535	**164**	1s. 6d. dp grey-blue...........................	10.00	7.00
		Set of 4	14.00	10.00
		First Day Cover		32.00

165 St. Edward's Crown

166 Carrickfergus Castle   **167** Caernarvon Castle

168 Edinburgh Castle   **169** Windsor Castle

(Des L. Lamb. Portrait by Dorothy Wilding. Recess Waterlow (until 31.12.57) and De La Rue (subsequently))

1955–58. W **165**. *P* 11 × 12.

536	**166**	2s. 6d. black-brown (23.9.55)	10.00	1.50
		a. De La Rue printing (17.7.58).............	25.00	2.25
537	**167**	5s. rose-carmine (23.9.55)	42.00	3.00
		a. De La Rue printing (30.4.58).............	70.00	6.00
538	**168**	10s. ultramarine (1.9.55)....................	90.00	10.00
		a. De La Rue printing. *Dull ultramarine* (25.4.58)	£150	12.00
539	**169**	£1 black (1.9.55)	£110	25.00
		a. De La Rue printing (28.4.58).............	£275	40.00
		Set of 4 (Nos. 536/9)	£240	35.00
		Set of 4 (Nos. 536a/9a)	£475	50.00
		First Day Cover (538/9)		£400
		First Day Cover (536/7)		£175

See also Nos. 595/8a & 759/62.

On 1 January 1958, the contract for printing the high values, T **166** to **169** was transferred to De La Rue & Co, Ltd.

The work of the two printers is very similar, but the following notes will be helpful to those attempting to identify Waterlow and De La Rue stamps of the W **165** issue.

The De La Rue sheets are printed in pairs and have a ⊣ or ⊢ shaped guide-mark at the centre of one side-margin, opposite the middle row of perforations, indicating left- and right-hand sheets respectively.

The Waterlow sheets have a small circle (sometimes crossed) instead of a "⊢" and this is present in both side-margins opposite the 6th row of stamps, though one is sometimes trimmed off. Short dashes are also present in the perforation gutter between the marginal stamps marking the middle of the four sides and a cross is at the centre of the sheet. The four corners of the sheet have two lines forming a right-angle as trimming marks, but some are usually trimmed off. All these gutter marks and sheet-trimming marks are absent in the De La Rue printings.

De La Rue used the Waterlow die and no alterations were made to it, so that no difference exists in the design or its size, but the making of new plates at first resulted in slight but measurable variations in the width of the gutters between stamps, particularly the horizontal, as follows:

	Waterlow	De La Rue
Horiz gutters, mm	3.8 to 4.0	3.4 to 3.8

Later D.L.R. plates were however less distinguishable in this respect.

For a short time in 1959 the D.L.R. 2s. 6d. appeared with one dot in the bottom margin below the first stamp.

It is possible to sort singles with reasonable certainty by general characteristics. The individual lines of the D.L.R. impression are cleaner and devoid of the whiskers of colour of Waterlow's, and the whole impression lighter and softer.

Owing to the closer setting of the horizontal rows the strokes of the perforating comb are closer; this results in the topmost tooth on each side of De La Rue stamps being narrower than the corresponding teeth in Waterlow's which were more than normally broad.

Shades also help. The 2s. 6d. D.L.R. is a warmer, more chocolate shade than the blackish brown of Waterlow; the 5s. a lighter red with less carmine than Waterlow's; the 10s. more blue and less ultramarine; the £1 less intense black.

The paper of D.L.R. printings is uniformly white, identical with that of Waterlow printings from February 1957 onwards, but earlier Waterlow printings are on paper which is creamy by comparison.

In this and later issues of T **166/9** the dates of issue given for changes of watermark or paper are those on which supplies were first sent by the Supplies Department to Postmasters.

1955–58. W **165**. *P* 15 × 14.

540	**154**	½d. orange-red (booklets 8.55, sheets 12.12.55)	10	10
		a. Part perf pane*	£800	
		Wi. Watermark inverted (9.55)...............	10	20
541		1d. ultramarine (19.9.55)	20	10
		a. Booklet pane. Three stamps plus three printed labels	15.00	
		b. *Tête-bêche* (horiz pair)	£500	
		Wi. Watermark inverted (9.55)...............	30	30
542		1½d. green (booklets 8.55, sheets 11.10.55)	10	10
		a. Watermark sideways (7.3.56)	10	75
		b. *Tête-bêche* (horiz pair)	£900	
		Wi. Watermark inverted (8.55)...............	20	20
543		2d. red-brown (6.9.55)	20	20
		aa. Imperf between (vert pair)	£1500	
		a. Watermark sideways (31.7.56)	20	60
		ab. Imperf between (wmk sideways) (horiz pair)	£1500	
		Wi. Watermark inverted (9.55)...............	9.00	5.50
543*b*		2d. light red-brown (17.10.56)	20	12
		ba. *Tête-bêche* (horiz pair)	£600	
		bb. Imperf pane*	£800	
		bc. Part perf pane*	£850	
		*b*Wi. Watermark inverted (1.57)............	3.00	2.00
		d. Watermark sideways (5.3.57)	10.00	5.50

544	155	2½d. carmine-red (Type I) (28.9.55)	10	10
		a. Watermark sideways (Type I) (23.3.56)	80	1.25
		b. Type II (booklets 9.55, sheets 1957)...	20	40
		ba. *Tête-bêche* (horiz pair)	£750	
		bb. Imperf pane*	£800	
		bc. Part perf pane*	£750	
		bWi. Watermark inverted (9.55)...............	20	40
545		3d. dp lilac (17.7.56)	20	15
		aa. *Tête-bêche* (horiz pair)	£700	
		a. Imperf three sides (pair)	£450	
		b. Watermark sideways (22.11.57)	8.00	11.00
		Wi. Watermark inverted (1.10.57)..........	60	1.00
546	156	4d. ultramarine (14.11.55)	1.40	40
547	157	5d. brown (21.9.55)	6.50	2.00
548		6d. reddish purple (20.12.55)	5.00	80
		aa. Imperf three sides (pair)	£350	
		a. *Deep claret* (8.5.58)	2.40	80
		ab. Imperf three sides (pair)	£400	
549		7d. brt green (23.4.56)	30.00	6.00
550	158	8d. magenta (21.12.55)	5.00	1.00
551		9d. bronze-green (15.12.55)	13.00	1.50
552		10d. Prussian blue (22.9.55)	9.00	1.50
553		11d. brown-purple (28.10.55).................	40	1.00
554	159	1s. bistre-brown (3.11.55)	7.50	40
555	160	1s. 3d. green (27.3.56)	14.00	1.25
556	159	1s. 6d. grey-blue (27.3.56)	24.00	1.00
		Set of 18....................................	95.00	16.00

The dates given for Nos. 540/556 are those on which they were first issued by the Supplies Dept to postmasters.

In December 1956 a completely imperforate sheet of No. 543b was noticed by clerks in a Kent post office, one of whom purchased it against P.O. regulations. In view of this irregularity we do not consider it properly issued.

Types of 2½d. In this issue, in 1957, Type II formerly only found in stamps from booklets, began to replace Type I on sheet stamps.

*BOOKLET ERRORS. Those listed as "imperf panes" show one row of perforations either at top or bottom of the booklet pane; those as "part perf panes" have one row of 3 stamps imperf on three sides.

For Nos. 542 and 553 in Presentation Pack, see after No. 586.

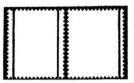

173 ½d. to 1½d., 2½d., 3d. 2d.
Graphite-line arrangements
(Stamps viewed from back)

1957 (12 Sept). **46th Inter-Parliamentary Union Conference.** W **165**. P 15 × 14.

560	**173**	4d. ultramarine	90	1.00
		First Day Cover		80.00

GRAPHITE–LINED ISSUES. These were used in connection with automatic sorting machinery, first introduced experimentally at Southampton.

The graphite lines were printed in black on the back, beneath the gum; two lines per stamp, except for the 2d.

In November 1959 phosphor bands were introduced (see notes after No. 598).

1957 (19 Nov). *Graphite-lined issue. Two graphite lines on the back, except 2d. value, which has one line.* W **165**. P 15 × 14.

561	**154**	½d. orange-red	15	25
562		1d. ultramarine	15	35
563		1½d. green	40	1.25
		a. Both lines at left	£750	£350
564		2d. light red-brown	3.00	1.60
		a. Line at left	£500	£175
565	**155**	2½d. carmine-red (Type II)	7.00	7.50
566		3d. dp lilac	70	50
		Set of 6	10.00	10.00
		First Day Cover		60.00

No. 564a results from a misplacement of the line and horizontal pairs exist showing one stamp without line. No. 563a results from a similar misplacement.

See also Nos. 587/94.

170 Scout Badge and "Rolling Hitch"

171 "Scouts coming to Britain"

176 Welsh Dragon

177 Flag and Games Emblem

172 Globe within a Compass

178 Welsh Dragon

(Des Mary Adshead (2½d.), P. Keely (4d.), W. H. Brown (1s. 3d.))

1957 (1 Aug). **World Scout Jubilee Jamboree.** W **165**. P 15 × 14.

557	**170**	2½d. carmine-red	15	10
558	**171**	4d. ultramarine	50	50
559	**172**	1s. 3d. green	6.50	5.00
		Set of 3	6.75	5.00
		First Day Cover		11.00

(Des R. Stone (3d.), W. H. Brown (6d.), P. Keely (1s. 3d.))

1958 (18 July). **Sixth British Empire and Commonwealth Games, Cardiff.** W **165**. P 15 × 14.

567	**176**	3d. dp lilac.....................................	15	10
568	**177**	6d. reddish purple	25	20
569	**178**	1s. 3d. green	2.50	2.00
		Set of 3	2.75	2.10
		First Day Cover		50.00

179 Multiple Crowns

1958–65. *W* 179. *P* 15 × 14.

570	**154**	½d. orange-red (25.11.58)	5	8
		a. Watermark sideways (26.5.61)	5	15
		c. Part perf pane*	£800	
		Wi. Watermark inverted (11.58)	30	25
		k. Chalky paper (15.7.63)	2.00	2.25
		kWi. Watermark inverted	2.00	2.25
		l. Booklet pane. No. 570k ×3 *se-tenant*		
		with 574k....................................	8.00	
		m. Booklet pane. No. 570a × 2 *se-tenant*		
		with 574l × 2 (1.7.64)	1.50	
571		1d. ultramarine (booklets 11.58, sheets		
		24.3.59)	5	5
		aa. Imperf (vert pair from coil)..............	£900	
		a. Watermark sideways (26.5.61)	60	40
		b. Part perf pane*	£300	
		c. Imperf pane.................................	£900	
		Wi. Watermark inverted (11.58)	12	20
		l. Booklet pane No 571a × 2 *se-tenant*		
		with 575a ×2† (16.8.65)	3.50	
572		1½d. green (booklets 12.58, sheets 30.8.60)	5	10
		a. Imperf three sides (horiz strip of 3)...	£1200	
		b. Watermark sideways (26.5.61)	7.00	3.00
		Wi. Watermark inverted (12.58)	80	40
573		2d. light red-brown (4.12.58)...............	5	8
		a. Watermark sideways (3.4.59)	20	60
		Wi. Watermark inverted (10.4.61)..........	80.00	30.00
574	**155**	2½d. carmine-red (Type II) (booklets 11.58,		
		sheets 15.9.59)	5	10
		aa. Imperf strip of 3	£200	
		ab. *Tête-bêche* (horiz pair)	£600	
		ac. Imperf pane................................	£800	
		Wi. Watermark inverted (II) (11.58).........	3.50	1.00
		a. Watermark sideways (Type I)		
		(10.11.60)	20	30
		b. Type I (wmk upright) (4.10.61)	12	40
		ba. Imperf strip of 6		
		k. Type II. Chalky paper (15.7.63).........	20	45
		kWi. Do. Watermark inverted (15.7.63)	20	45
		l. Watermark sideways (Type II) Ord		
		paper (1.7.64)	40	70
575		3d. dp lilac (booklets 11.58, sheets		
		8.12.58)	10	8
		a. Watermark sideways (24.10.58)	12	25
		b. Imperf pane*	£850	
		c. Part perf pane*	£750	
		d. Phantom "?" (Cyl 41 no dot)	£250	
		Eda. Do. First retouch	10.00	
		Edb. Do. Second retouch	10.00	
		e. Phantom "R" (Cyl 37 no dot)	25.00	
		Eea. Do. Retouch	8.00	
		Wi. Watermark inverted (11.58)	10	20
576	**156**	4d. ultramarine (29.10.58)....................	50	20
		a. *Dp ultramarine*†† (28.4.65)	10	8
		ab. Watermark sideways (31.5.65)	40	30
		ac. Imperf pane*	£800	
		ad. Part perf pane*	£650	
		aWi. Watermark inverted (21.6.65)...........	30	30

577	**156**	4½d. chestnut (9.2.59)............................	10	12
		Ea. Phantom frame	5.00	
578	**157**	5d. brown (10.11.58)...........................	20	20
579		6d. dp claret (23.12.58)........................	20	12
		a. Imperf three sides (pair)	£450	
		b. Imperf (pair)	£550	
580		7d. brt green (26.11.58)	30	20
581	**158**	8d. magenta (24.2.60)	40	12
582		9d. bronze-green (24.3.59)	35	12
583		10d. Prussian blue (18.11.58)	80	12
584	**159**	1s. bistre-brown (30.10.58)	25	10
585	**160**	1s. 3d. green (17.6.59)	25	12
586	**159**	1s. 6d. grey-blue (16.12.58)	4.00	40
		Set of 17 (one of each value)............	6.00	1.60
		First Day Cover (577)		45.00
		*Presentation Pack***......................	80.00	

*BOOKLET ERRORS. See note after No. 556.

**This was issued in 1960 and comprises Nos. 542, 553, 570/1 and 573/86. It exists in two forms: (a) inscribed "10s 8d" for sale in the U.K.; and (b) inscribed "$1.80" for sale in the U.S.A.

†Booklet pane No. 571l comes in two forms, with the 1d. stamps on the left or on the right.

††This "shade" was brought about by making more deeply etched cylinders, resulting in apparent depth of colour in parts of the design. There is no difference in the colour of the ink.

Sideways watermark. The 2d., 2½d., 3d. and 4d. come from coils and the ½d., 1d., 1½d., 2½d., 3d. and 4d. come from booklets. In *coil* stamps the sideways watermark shows the top of the watermark to the left. In the *booklet* stamps it comes equally to the left or right.

Nos. 570k and 574k only come from 2s. "Holiday Resort" Experimental undated booklets issued in 1963, in which one page contained 1 × 2½d. *se-tenant* with 3 × ½d. (See No. 570l.)

No. 574l comes from coils, and the "Holiday Resort" Experimental booklets dated "1964" comprising four panes each containing two of these 2½d. stamps *se-tenant* vertically with two ½d. No. 570a. (See No. 570m.)

2½d. imperf. No. 574aa comes from a booklet with watermark upright. No. 574ba is from a coil with sideways watermark.

No. 574b comes from *sheets* bearing cylinder number 42 and is also known on vertical delivery coils.

In 1964 No. 575 was printed from cylinder number 70 no dot and dot on an experimental paper which is distinguished by an additional watermark letter "T" lying on its side, which occurs about four times in the sheet, usually in the side margins. 48,000 sheets were issued.

Phantom "R" varieties

Nos. 575d and 615a (Cyl 41 no dot)   No. 575Eda

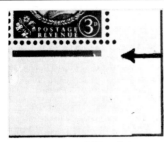

No. 575e (Cyl 37 no dot)

3d. An incomplete marginal rule revealed an ''R'' on cyls 37 and 41 no dot below R.20/12. It is more noticeable on cyl 41 because of the wider marginal rule. The ''R'' on cyl 41 was twice retouched, the first being as illustrated here (No. 575Eda) and traces of the ''R'' can still be seen in the second retouch.

The rare variety, No. 575d, is best collected in a block of 4 or 6 with full margins in order to be sure that it is not 615a with phosphor lines removed.

The retouch on cyl 37 is not easily identified: there is no trace of the ''R'' but the general appearance of that part of the marginal rule is uneven.

Phantom Frame variety

Nos. 577Ea and 616Eba

4½d. An incomplete marginal rule revealed a right-angled shaped frame-line on cyl 8 no dot below R.20/12. It occurs on ordinary and phosphor.

WHITER PAPER. On 18 May 1962 the Post Office announced that a whiter paper was being used for the current issue (including Nos. 595/8). This is beyond the scope of this catalogue, but the whiter papers are listed in Vol. 3 of the Stanley Gibbons *Great Britain Specialised Catalogue.*

1958 (24 Nov)–**61**. *Graphite-lined issue. Two graphite lines on the back, except 2d. value, which has one line.* W **179**. P 15 × 14.

587	**154**	½d. orange-red (15.6.59)	1.75	2.50
		Wi. Watermark inverted (4.8.59)	1.25	2.10
588		1d. ultramarine (18.12.58)	80	1.25
		a. Misplaced graphite lines (7.61)*	60	75
		Wi. Watermark inverted (4.8.59)	1.00	2.00
589		1½d. green (4.8.59)	80.00	55.00
		Wi. Watermark inverted (4.8.59)	30.00	22.00
590		2d. lt red-brown (24.11.58)	7.00	4.00
591	**155**	2½d. carmine-red (Type II) (9.6.59)...........	10.00	9.00
		Wi. Watermark inverted (21.8.59)...........	45.00	45.00

592	**155**	3d. dp lilac (24.11.58)	40	35
		a. Misplaced graphite lines (5.61)*	£400	£350
		Wi. Watermark inverted (4.8.59)	20	50
593	**156**	4d. ultramarine (29.4.59)	4.00	4.00
		a. Misplaced graphite lines (1961)*.......	£1200	
594		4½d. chestnut (3.6.59)...........................	4.50	3.50
		Set of 8 (cheapest)	55.00	42.00

Nos. 587/9 were only issued in booklets or coils (587/8).

*No. 588a (in coils), and Nos. 592a and 593a (both in sheets) result from the use of a residual stock of graphite-lined paper. As the use of graphite lines had ceased, the register of the lines in relation to the stamps was of no importance and numerous misplacements occurred —two lines close together, one line only, etc. No. 588a refers to two lines at left or at right; No. 592a refers to stamps with two lines only at left and both clear of the perforations and No. 593a to stamps with two lines at left (with left line down perforations) and traces of a third line down the opposite perforations.

(Recess D.L.R. (until 31.12.62), then B.W.)

1959–68. W **179**. P 11 × 12.

595	**166**	2s. 6d. black-brown (22.7.59)................	18.00	75
		Wi. Watermark inverted		
		a. B.W. printing (1.7.63)	30	30
		aWi. Watermark inverted	£800	† 75.00
		k. Chalk-surfaced paper (30.5.68)........	30	1.10
596	**167**	5s. scarlet-vermilion (15.6.59)	60.00	1.10
		Wi. Watermark inverted		
		a. B.W. ptg. *Red (shades)* (3.9.63)	1.00	60
		ab. Printed on the gummed side	£750	
		aWi. Watermark inverted	£225	50.00
597	**168**	10s. blue (21.7.59)	45.00	5.00
		a. B.W. ptg. *Bright ultramarine* (16.10.63)...................................	3.00	2.50
		aWi. Watermark inverted	—	£650
598	**169**	£1 black (23.6.59)	£125	12.00
		Wi. Watermark inverted	—	£1500
		a. B.W. printing (14.11.63)	11.00	4.50
		aWi. Watermark inverted	£225	17.00
		Set of 4 (Nos. 595/8)	14.00	7.00
		Set of 4 (Nos. 595a/8a)	£550	
		*Presentation Pack (1960)**		

The B.W. printings have a marginal Plate Number. They are generally more deeply engraved than the D.L.R., showing more of the Diadem detail and heavier lines on Her Majesty's face. The vertical perf is 11.9 to 12 as against D.L.R. 11.8.

*This exists in two forms: (a) inscribed ''$6.50'' for sale in the U.S.A.; and (b) without price for sale in the U.K.

See also Nos. 759/62.

PHOSPHOR BAND ISSUES. These are printed on the front and are wider than graphite lines. They are not easy to see but show as broad vertical bands at certain angles to the light.

Values representing the rate for printed papers (and when this was abolished in 1968 for second class mail) have one band and others two, three or four bands as stated, according to the size and format.

In the small size stamps the bands are on each side with the single band at left (*except where otherwise stated*). In the large-size commemorative stamps the single band may be at left, centre or right, varying in different designs. The bands are vertical on both horizontal and vertical designs *except where otherwise stated*.

The phosphor was originally applied typographically but later usually by photogravure and sometimes using flexography, a typographical process using rubber cylinders.

Three different types of phosphor have been used, distinguishable by the colour emitted under an ultra-violet lamp, the first being green, then blue and now violet. Different sized bands are also known. All these are fully listed in Vol. 3 of the Stanley Gibbons *Great Britain Specialised Catalogue.*

Varieties. Misplaced and missing phosphor bands are known but such varieties are beyond the scope of this Catalogue.

1959 (18 Nov). *Phosphor-Graphite issue. Two phosphor bands on front and two graphite lines on back, except 2d. value, which has one band on front and one line on back.* P 15 × 14. (a) W **165**.

599	**154**	½d. orange-red	5.00	5.00
600		1d. ultramarine	6.00	5.00
601		1½d. green	3.00	5.00

*(b) W **179***

605	**154**	2d. lt red-brown (1 band)	5.00	5.00
		a. Error. W **165**	£190	£160
606	**155**	2½d. carmine-red (Type II)	12.00	14.00
607		3d. dp lilac	14.00	9.00
608	**156**	4d. ultramarine	7.50	25.00
609		4½d. chestnut	32.00	22.00
		Set of 8	60.00	70.00
		Presentation Pack*	£250	

*This was issued in 1960 and comprises two each of Nos. 599/609. It exists in two forms: (a) inscribed "3s 8d" for sale in the U.K. and (b) inscribed "50 c" for sale in the U.S.A.

1960 (22 June)–**67**. *Phosphor issue. Two phosphor bands on front, except where otherwise stated.* W **179**. P 15 × 14.

610	**154**	½d. orange-red	8	10
		a. Watermark sideways (26.5.61)	8.00	9.00
		Wi. Watermark inverted (14.8.60)	90	90
611		1d. ultramarine	8	10
		a. Watermark sideways (14.7.61)	25	40
		Wi. Watermark inverted (14.8.60)	20	20
		l. Booklet pane. No. 611a ×2 se-tenant with 615d × 2† (16.8.65)	10.00	
		m. Booklet pane. No. 611a × 2 se-tenant with 615b× 2†† (11.67)	3.00	
612		1½d. green	10	20
		a. Watermark sideways (14.7.61)	8.00	8.00
		Wi. Watermark inverted (14.8.60)	8.00	8.00
613		2d. lt red-brown (1 band)	22.00	16.00
613a		2d. lt red-brown (2 bands) (4.10.61)	8	10
		aa. Imperf three sides***		
		ab. Watermark sideways (6.4.67)	10	50
614	**155**	2½d. carmine-red (Type II) (2 bands)*	10	20
		Wi. Watermark inverted (14.8.60)	£150	90.00
614a		2½d. carmine-red (Type II) (1 band) (4.10.61)	35	60
		aWi. Watermark inverted (3.62)	17.00	18.00
614b		2½d. carmine-red (Type I) (1 band) (7.11.61)	32.00	27.00
615		3d. dp lilac (2 bands)	45	40
		a. Phantom "R" (Cyl 41 no dot)	18.00	
		Wi. Watermark inverted (14.8.60)	45	70
		b. Watermark sideways (14.7.61)	80	70
615c		3d. dp lilac (1 side band) (29.4.65)	35	45
		cWi. Watermark inverted (band at right) (2.67)	60	60
		cWia. Watermark inverted (band at left) (2.67)	11.00	11.00
		d. Watermark sideways (16.8.65)	2.50	3.50
		e. One centre band (8.12.66)	20	35
		eWi. Watermark inverted (8.67)	80	90
		ea. Wmk sideways (19.6.67)	25	55
616	**156**	4d. ultramarine	3.00	2.50
		a. Dp ultramarine (28.4.65)	12	10
		aa. Part perf pane**	£650	
		ab. Watermark sideways (16.8.65)	20	20
		aWi. Watermark inverted (21.6.65)	20	20
616b		4½d. chestnut (13.9.61)	12	25
		Eba. Phantom frame	5.00	
616c	**157**	5d. brown (9.6.67)	20	20
617		6d. dp claret (27.6.60)	25	20
617a		7d. brt green (15.2.67)	40	25
617b	**158**	8d. magenta (28.6.67)	20	20
617c		9d. bronze-green (29.12.66)	45	20
617d		10d. Prussian blue (30.12.66)	70	30

617e	**159**	1s. bistre-brown (28.6.67)	30	20
618	**160**	1s. 3d. green	2.00	2.00
618a	**159**	1s. 6d. grey-blue (12.12.66)	1.25	1.00
		Set of 17 (one of each value)	6.50	5.50

The automatic facing equipment was brought into use on 6 July 1960 but the phosphor stamps may have been released a few days earlier.

The stamps with watermark sideways are from booklets except Nos. 613ab and 615ea which are from coils. No. 616ab comes from both booklets and coils.

No. 615a. See footnote after No. 586.

*No. 614 with two bands on the creamy paper was originally from cylinder 50 dot and no dot. When the change in postal rates took place in 1965 it was reissued from cylinder 57 dot and no dot on the whiter paper. Some of these latter were also released in error in districts of S.E. London in September 1964. The shade of the reissue is slightly more carmine.

**Booklet error. Two stamps at bottom left imperf on three sides and the third imperf on two sides.

***This comes from the bottom row of a sheet which is imperf at bottom and both sides.

†Booklet pane No. 611l comes in two forms, with the 1d. stamps on the left or on the right. This was printed in this manner to provide for 3d. stamps with only one band.

††Booklet pane No. 611m comes from 2s. booklets of January and March 1968. The two bands on the 3d. stamp thus created are intentional because of the technical difficulty of producing a single band on one stamp se-tenant with a two-banded stamp, as this requires perfect registration of the bands.

The Phosphor-Graphite stamps had the phosphor applied by typography but the Phosphor issue can be divided into those with the phosphor applied typographically and others where it was applied by photogravure. Moreover the photogravure form can be further divided into those which phosphoresce green and others which phosphoresce blue under ultra-violet light. From 1965 violet phosphorescence was introduced in place of the blue. All these are fully listed in Vol. 3 of the Stanley Gibbons *Great Britain Specialised Catalogue*.

The Stanley Gibbons Uvitec Micro ultra-violet lamp will reveal these differences. See also Philatelic Information at the beginning of this Catalogue.

Unlike previous one-banded phosphor stamps, No. 615c has a broad band extending over two stamps so that alternate stamps have the band at left or right (same prices either way). No. 615cWi comes from the 10s. phosphor booklet of February 1967 and No. 615eWi comes from the 10s. phosphor booklets of August 1967 and February 1968.

Varieties:

Nos. 615a (Phantom "R") and 616Eba (Phantom frame), see illustrations following No. 586.

180 Postboy of 1660   **181** Posthorn of 1660

(Des R. Stone (3d.), Faith Jaques (1s. 3d.))

1960 (7 July). **Tercentenary of Establishment of General Letter Office.** W **179** (sideways on 1s. 3d.). P 15 × 14 (3d.) or 14 × 15 (1s. 3d.).

619	**180**	3d. dp lilac	10	10
620	**181**	1s. 3d. green	5.00	4.00
		Set of 2	5.00	4.00
		First Day Cover		45.00

182 Conference Emblem

(Des R. Stone (emblem, P. Rahikainen))

1960 (19 Sept). **First Anniv of European Postal and Telecommunications Conference.** *Chalk-surfaced paper.* W **179**. *P* 15 × 14.

621	**182**	6d. bronze-green and purple	40	55
622		1s. 6d. brown and blue	5.75	5.50
		Set of 2	6.00	5.50
		First Day Cover		28.00

SCREENS. Up to this point all photogravure stamps were printed in a 200 screen (200 dots per linear inch), but all later commemorative stamps are a finer 250 screen. Exceptionally No. 622 has a 200 screen for the portrait and a 250 screen for the background.

183 Thrift Plant   **184** "Growth of Savings"

185 Thrift Plant

(Des P. Gauld (2½d.), M. Goaman (others))

1961 (28 Aug). **Centenary of Post Office Savings Bank.** *Chalk-surfaced paper.* W **179** (*sideways on* 2½d.) *P* 14 × 15 (2½d.) or 15 × 14 (*others*).
I. "TIMSON" Machine
II. "THRISSELL" Machine

			I		II	
623	**183**	2½d. black and red	10	10	2.00	1.75
		a. Black omitted	£6000	—	†	
624	**184**	3d. orange-brown & violet	10	10	25	25
		a. Orange-brown omitted	£125	—	£200	—
		x. Perf through side sheet margin	20.00	—	†	
		xa. Orange-brown omitted	—	—	†	
625	**185**	1s. 6d. red and blue	2.60	2.00	†	
		Set of 3	2.60	2.00		
		First Day Cover	60.00			

2½d. TIMSON. Cyls 1E–1F. Deeply shaded portrait (brownish black).
2½d. THRISSELL. Cyls 1D–1B or 1D (dot)–1B (dot). Lighter portrait (grey-black).

3d. TIMSON. Cyls 3D–3E. Clear, well-defined portrait with deep shadows and bright highlights.
3d. THRISSELL. Cyls 3C–3B or 3C (dot)–3B (dot). Dull portrait, lacking in contrast.

Sheet marginal examples *without* single extension perf hole on the short side of the stamp are always "Timson", as are those with large punch-hole *not* coincident with printed three-sided box guide mark.
The 3d. "Timson" perforated completely through the right-hand side margin comes from a relatively small part of the printing perforated on a sheet-fed machine.
Normally the "Timsons" were perforated in the reel, with three large punch-holes in both long margins and the perforations complete through both short margins. Only one punch-hole coincides with the guide-mark.
The "Thrissells" have one large punch-hole in one long margin, coinciding with guide-mark and one short margin imperf (except sometimes for encroachments).

186 C.E.P.T. Emblem   **187** Doves and Emblem

188 Doves and Emblem

(Des M. Goaman (doves T. Kurpershoek))

1961 (18 Sept). **European Postal and Telecommunications (C.E.P.T.) Conference, Torquay.** *Chalk-surfaced paper.* W **179**. *P* 15 × 14.

626	**186**	2d. orange, pink and brown	10	10
627	**187**	4d. buff, mauve and ultramarine	10	10
628	**188**	10d. turquoise, pale green & Prussian blue	25	25
		a. Pale green omitted	£2750	
		b. Turquoise omitted	£2750	
		Set of 3	35	35
		First Day Cover		2.00

189 Hammer Beam Roof,   **190** Palace of
Westminster Hall   Westminster

(Des Faith Jaques)

1961 (25 Sept). **Seventh Commonwealth Parliamentary Conference.** *Chalk-surfaced paper.* W **179** (*sideways on* 1s. 3d.). P 15 × 14 (6d.) *or* 14 × 15 (1s. 3d.).

629	**189**	6d. purple and gold	20	25
		a. Gold omitted	£500	
630	**190**	1s. 3d. green and blue........................	2.40	1.90
		a. Blue (Queen's head) omitted..........	£3000	
		Set of 2	2.50	2.00
		First Day Cover		25.00

191 "Units of Productivity"

192 "National Productivity"

193 "Unified Productivity"

(Des D. Gentleman)

1962 (14 Nov). **National Productivity Year.** *Chalk-surfaced paper.* W **179** (*inverted on* 2½d. *and* 3d.). P 15 × 14.

631	**191**	2½d. myrtle-green & carmine-red (*shades*)	15	10
		Ea. Blackish olive & carmine-red	25	15
		p. One phosphor band. *Blackish olive &*		
		carmine-red	60	40
632	**192**	3d. light blue and violet (*shades*)..........	15	10
		a. Lt blue (Queen's head) omitted	£1000	
		p. Three phosphor bands	60	60
633	**193**	1s. 3d. carmine, lt blue & dp green........	2.10	1.50
		a. Lt blue (Queen's head) omitted	£2000	
		p. Three phosphor bands	29.00	20.00
		Set of 3 (*Ordinary*)	2.25	1.60
		Set of 3 (*Phosphor*)	29.00	20.00
		First Day Cover (*Ordinary*)		24.00
		First Day Cover (*Phosphor*)		90.00

194 Campaign Emblem and Family

195 Children of Three Races

(Des M. Goaman)

1963 (21 Mar). **Freedom from Hunger.** *Chalk-surfaced paper.* W **179** (*inverted*). P 15 × 14.

634	**194**	2½d. crimson and pink	10	10
		p. One phosphor band	1.00	1.00

635	**195**	1s. 3d. bistre-brown and yellow		2.40	2.50
		p. Three phosphor bands		28.00	21.00
		Set of 2 (*Ordinary*)		2.50	2.50
		Set of 2 (*Phosphor*)		29.00	22.00
		First Day Cover (*Ordinary*)			24.00
		First Day Cover (*Phosphor*)			25.00

196 "Paris Conference"

(Des R. Stone)

1963 (7 May). **Paris Postal Conference Centenary.** *Chalk-surfaced paper.* W **179** (*inverted*). P 15 × 14.

636	**196**	6d. green & mauve..........................	40	40
		a. Green omitted	£1800	
		p. Three phosphor bands	8.00	6.00
		First Day Cover (*Ordinary*)		12.00
		First Day Cover (*Phosphor*)		20.00

197 Posy of Flowers

198 Woodland Life

(Des S. Scott (3d.), M. Goaman (4½d.))

1963 (16 May). **National Nature Week.** *Chalk-surfaced paper.* W **179.** P 15 × 14.

637	**197**	3d. yellow, green, brown and black	8	8
		p. Three phosphor bands	50	50
638	**198**	4½d. black, blue, yellow, magenta &		
		brown-red..................................	25	25
		p. Three phosphor bands	3.50	3.00
		Set of 2 (*Ordinary*)	30	30
		Set of 2 (*Phosphor*)	3.75	3.50
		First Day Cover (*Ordinary*)		10.00
		First Day Cover (*Phosphor*)		25.00

Special First Day of Issue Postmark

	Ordin-ary	Phos-phor
London E.C. (Type A)	12.00	30.00

This postmark was used on first day covers serviced by the Philatelic Bureau.

199 Rescue at Sea

200 19th-century Lifeboat

201 Lifeboatmen

(Des D. Gentleman)

1963 (31 May). **Ninth International Lifeboat Conference, Edinburgh.** *Chalk-surfaced paper. W* **179**. *P* 15 × 14.

639	**199**	2½d. blue, black and red	10	10
		p. One phosphor band	40	50
640	**200**	4d. red, yellow, brown, black and blue ..	40	30
		p. Three phosphor bands	20	30
641	**201**	1s. 6d. sepia, yellow and grey-blue........	4.25	3.75
		p. Three phosphor bands	35.00	28.00
		Set of 3 (Ordinary)	4.25	4.00
		Set of 3 (Phosphor)	35.00	28.00
		First Day Cover (Ordinary)		24.00
		First Day Cover (Phosphor)		30.00

Special First Day of Issue Postmark

	Ordin-	Phos-
	ary	phor
London	32.00	40.00

This postmark was used on first day covers serviced by the Philatelic Bureau.

202 Red Cross

203

204

(Des H. Bartram)

1963 (15 Aug). **Red Cross Centenary Congress.** *Chalk-surfaced paper. W* **179**. *P* 15 × 14.

642	**202**	3d. red & dp lilac	10	10
		a. Red omitted................................	£2000	
		p. Three phosphor bands	60	60
		pa. Red omitted................................	£2500	
643	**203**	1s. 3d. red, blue and grey	3.25	3.25
		p. Three phosphor bands	50.00	40.00

644	**204**	1s. 6d. red, blue & bistre	3.25	3.25
		p. Three phosphor bands	30.00	25.00
		Set of 3 (Ordinary)	6.00	6.00
		Set of 3 (Phosphor)	80.00	65.00
		First Day Cover (Ordinary)		26.00
		First Day Cover (Phosphor)		65.00

Special First Day of Issue Postmark

	Ordin-	Phos-
	ary	phor
London E.C.	45.00	80.00

This postmark was used on first day covers serviced by the Philatelic Bureau.

205 Commonwealth Cable

(Des P. Gauld)

1963 (3 Dec). **Opening of COMPAC (Trans-Pacific Telephone Cable).** *Chalk-surfaced paper. W* **179**. *P* 15 × 14.

645	**205**	1s. 6d. blue and black	4.00	3.25
		a. Black omitted..............................	£2000	
		p. Three phosphor bands	26.00	20.00
		First Day Cover (Ordinary)		18.00
		First Day Cover (Phosphor)		22.00

Special First Day of Issue Postmark

	Ordin-	Phos-
	ary	phor
Philatelic Bureau, London E.C.1 (Type A)	26.00	28.00

PRESENTATION PACKS. Special Packs comprising slip-in cards with printed commemorative inscriptions and descriptive notes on the back and with protective covering, were introduced in 1964 with the Shakespeare issue. These are listed and priced.

Issues of 1968–69 (British Paintings to the Prince of Wales Investiture) were also issued in packs with text in German for sale through the Post Office's German Agency and these are also quoted. Subsequently, however, the packs sold in Germany were identical with the normal English version with the addition of a separate printed insert card with German text. These, as also English packs with Japanese and Dutch printed cards for sale in Japan and the Netherlands respectively, are listed in Vols. 3 and 4 of the Stanley Gibbons *Great Britain Specialised Catalogue.*

206 Puck and Bottom
(*A Midsummer Night's Dream*)

207 Feste (*Twelfth Night*)

208 Balcony Scene
(*Romeo and Juliet*)

209 "Eve of Agincourt" (*Henry V*)

211 Flats near Richmond Park
("Urban Development")

212 Shipbuilding Yards, Belfast
("Industrial Activity")

210 Hamlet contemplating Yorick's
Skull (*Hamlet*) and Queen Elizabeth II

213 Beddgelert Forest Park,
Snowdonia ("Forestry")

214 Nuclear Reactor, Dounreay
("Technological Development")

(Des D. Bailey)

(Des D. Gentleman. Photo Harrison & Sons (3d., 6d., 1s. 3d., 1s. 6d.).
Des C. and R. Ironside. Recess B.W. (2s. 6d.))

1964 (23 April). **Shakespeare Festival.** *Chalk-surfaced paper.* W 179.
P 11 × 12 (2s. 6d.) or 15 × 14 (*others*).

646	**206**	3d. yellow-bistre, black & dp violet blue (*shades*)	10	10
		p. Three phosphor bands	20	20
647	**207**	6d. yellow, orange, black & yellow-olive (*shades*)	20	20
		p. Three phosphor bands	60	40
648	**208**	1s. 3d. cerise, blue-green, black & sepia (*shades*)	1.00	1.25
		Wi. Watermark inverted		
		p. Three phosphor bands	10.00	8.00
		pWi. Watermark inverted	£110	
649	**209**	1s. 6d. violet, turquoise, black & blue (*shades*)	1.25	1.25
		Wi. Watermark inverted		
		p. Three phosphor bands	10.00	8.00
650	**210**	2s. 6d. dp slate-purple (*shades*)	2.00	2.00
		Wi. Watermark inverted	£225	
		Set of 5 (*Ordinary*)	4.00	4.00
		Set of 4 (*Phosphor*)	20.00	14.00
		First Day Cover (*Ordinary*)		10.00
		First Day Cover (*Phosphor*)		15.00
		Presentation Pack (*Ordinary*)	7.50	

The 3d. is known with yellow-bistre missing in the top two-thirds of the
figures of Puck and Bottom. This occurred in the top row only of a
sheet.

Special First Day of Issue Postmark

	Ordinary	Phosphor
Stratford-upon-Avon, Warwicks	12.00	16.00

This postmark was used on first day covers serviced by the
Philatelic Bureau, as well as on covers posted at Stratford P.O.

1964 (1 July). **20th International Geographical Congress, London.**
Chalk-surfaced paper. W 179. P 15 × 14.

651	**211**	2½d. black, olive-yellow, olive-grey & turquoise-blue	8	8
		p. One phosphor band	50	40
652	**212**	4d. orange-brown, red-brown, rose, black & violet	20	20
		a. Violet omitted	£225	
		b. Red-brown omitted	£400	
		c. Violet and red-brown omitted	£250	
		Wi. Watermark inverted	£600	
		p. Three phosphor bands	1.10	75
653	**213**	8d. yellow-brown, emerald, green & black	40	40
		a. Green (lawn) omitted	£1500	
		Wi. Watermark inverted	£200	
		p. Three phosphor bands	2.50	1.50
654	**214**	1s. 6d. yellow-brown, pale pink, black & brown	4.00	3.75
		Wi. Watermark inverted	22.00	
		p. Three phosphor bands	30.00	24.00
		Set of 4 (*Ordinary*)	4.25	4.00
		Set of 4 (*Phosphor*)	32.00	25.00
		First Day Cover (*Ordinary*)		18.00
		First Day Cover (*Phosphor*)		26.00
		Presentation Pack (*Ordinary*)	80.00	

Special First Day of Issue Postmark

	Ordinary	Phosphor
G.P.O. Philatelic Bureau, London E.C.1 (Type B)	22.00	32.00

215 Spring Gentian

216 Dog Rose

217 Honeysuckle

218 Fringed Water Lily

(Des M. and Sylvia Goaman)

1964 (5 Aug). **Tenth International Botanical Congress, Edinburgh.** *Chalk-surfaced paper.* W **179**. *P* 15 × 14.

655	215	3d. violet, blue and sage-green	8	8
		a. Blue omitted................................	£3500	
		p. Three phosphor bands	20	20
656	216	6d. apple-green, rose, scarlet and green.	20	20
		Wi. Watermark inverted		
		p. Three phosphor bands	1.60	1.40
657	217	9d. lemon, green, lake and rose-red	2.40	2.25
		a. Green (leaves) omitted	£3500	
		Wi. Watermark inverted	40.00	
		p. Three phosphor bands	5.00	5.00
658	218	1s. 3d. yellow, emerald, reddish violet & grey-green	2.60	2.00
		a. Yellow (flowers) omitted................	£200	
		Wi. Watermark inverted		
		p. Three phosphor bands	28.00	28.00
		Set of 4 (Ordinary)	4.50	4.00
		Set of 4 (Phosphor)	32.00	32.00
		First Day Cover (Ordinary)		18.00
		First Day Cover (Phosphor)		32.00
		Presentation Pack (Ordinary)	65.00	

Special First Day of Issue Postmark

	Ordin-ary	Phos-phor
G.P.O. Philatelic Bureau, London E.C.1 (Type B)	25.00	38.00

219 Forth Road Bridge   **220** Forth Road and Railway Bridges

(Des A. Restall)

1964 (4 Sept). **Opening of Forth Road Bridge.** *Chalk-surfaced paper.* W **179**. *P* 15 × 14.

659	219	3d. black, blue & reddish violet.............	8	8
		p. Three phosphor bands	40	50
660	220	6d. black, lt blue & carmine-red	30	30
		a. Lt blue omitted	£1750	£900
		Wi. Watermark inverted	2.00	
		p. Three phosphor bands	5.75	5.25
		pWi. Watermark inverted	55.00	
		Set of 2 (Ordinary)	35	35
		Set of 2 (Phosphor)	6.00	5.50
		First Day Cover (Ordinary)		4.50
		First Day Cover (Phosphor)		7.00
		Presentation Pack (Ordinary)	£175	

Special First Day of Issue Postmarks

	Ordin-ary	Phos-phor
G.P.O. Philatelic Bureau, London E.C.1 (Type B)	7.50	10.00
North Queensferry, Fife	20.00	80.00
South Queensferry, West Lothian	15.00	55.00

The Queensferry postmarks were applied to first day covers sent to a temporary Philatelic Bureau at Edinburgh.

221 Sir Winston Churchill

(Des D. Gentleman and Rosalind Dease, from photograph by Karsh)

1965 (8 July). **Churchill Commemoration.** *Chalk-surfaced paper.* W **179**. *P* 15 × 14.

I. "REMBRANDT" Machine

661	221	4d. black and olive-brown...................	8	8
		Wi. Watermark inverted	1.75	
		p. Three phosphor bands	30	30

II "TIMSON" Machine

661a	221	4d. black and olive-brown...................	25	25

III. "L. & M. 4" Machine

662	—	1s. 3d. black and grey	30	30
		Wi. Watermark inverted	55.00	
		p. Three phosphor bands	3.75	3.50
		Set of 2 (Ordinary)	35	35
		Set of 2 (Phosphor)	4.00	3.75
		First Day Cover (Ordinary)		2.10
		First Day Cover (Phosphor)		4.50
		Presentation Pack (Ordinary)	9.00	

The 1s. 3d. shows a closer view of Churchill's head.

4d. REMBRANDT, Cyls 1A-1B dot and no dot. Lack of shading detail on Churchill's portrait. Queen's portrait appears dull and coarse. This is a rotary machine which is sheet-fed.

4d. TIMSON. Cyls 5A-6B no dot. More detail on Churchill's portrait —furrow on forehead, his left eyebrow fully drawn and more shading on cheek. Queen's portrait lighter and sharper. This is a reel-fed, two-colour 12-in. wide rotary machine and the differences in impression are due to the greater pressure applied by this machine.

1s. 3d. Cyls 1A-1B no dot. The "Linotype and Machinery No. 4" machine is an ordinary sheet-fed rotary press machine. Besides being used for printing the 1s. 3d. stamps it was als employed for overprinting the phosphor bands on both values.

Two examples of the 4d. value exist with the Queen's head omitted, one due to something adhering to the cylinder and the other due to a paper fold. The stamp also exists with Churchill's head omitted, also due to a paper fold.

Special First Day of Issue Postmark

	Ordin-ary	Phos-phor
G.P.O. Philatelic Bureau, London E.C.1 (Type B)	3.00	5.50

A First Day of Issue handstamp was provided at Bladon, Oxford, for this issue.

222 Simon de Montfort's Seal

226 Lister's Carbolic Spray

227 Lister and Chemical Symbols

223 Parliament Buildings (after engraving by Hollar, 1647)

(Des S. Black (6d.), R. Guyatt (2s. 6d.))

1965 (19 July). **700th Anniv of Simon de Montfort's Parliament.** *Chalk-surfaced paper.* W **179**. P 15 × 14.

663	222	6d.	olive-green	10	10
		p.	Three phosphor bands	40	40
664	223	2s.	6d. black, grey and pale drab	90	95
		Wi.	Watermark inverted	14.00	
			Set of 2 (Ordinary)	1.00	1.00
			First Day Cover (Ordinary)		9.00
			First Day Cover (Phosphor)		11.00
			Presentation Pack (Ordinary)	27.00	

Special First Day of Issue Postmark

	Ordinary
G.P.O. Philatelic Bureau, London E.C.1 (Type B) ..	12.00

A First Day of Issue handstamp was provided at Evesham, Worcs, for this issue.

224 Bandsmen and Banner

225 Three Salvationists

(Des M. Farrar-Bell (3d.), G. Trenaman (1s. 6d))

1965 (9 Aug). **Salvation Army Centenary.** *Chalk-surfaced paper.* W **179**. P 15 × 14.

665	224	3d.	indigo, grey-blue, cerise, yellow & brown	10	10
		p.	One phosphor band	40	40
666	225	1s.	6d. red, blue, yellow and brown	1.00	1.00
		p.	Three phosphor bands	3.75	4.00
			Set of 2 (Ordinary)	1.10	1.10
			Set of 2 (Phosphor)	4.00	4.25
			First Day Cover (Ordinary)		17.00
			First Day Cover (Phosphor)		18.00

The Philatelic Bureau did not provide first day cover services for Nos. 665/70.

(Des P. Gauld (4d.), F. Ariss (1s.))

1965 (1 Sept). **Centenary of Joseph Lister's Discovery of Antiseptic Surgery.** *Chalk-surfaced paper.* W **179**. P 15 × 14.

667	226	4d.	indigo, brown-red and grey-black	10	10
		a.	Brown-red (tube) omitted	£175	75.00
		b.	Indigo omitted	£1200	
		p.	Three phosphor bands	15	15
		pa.	Brown-red (tube) omitted	£425	
668	227	1s.	black, purple and new blue	90	1.25
		Wi.	Watermark inverted	£140	
		p.	Three phosphor bands	1.25	1.60
		pWi.	Watermark inverted	£140	
			Set of 2 (Ordinary)	1.00	1.25
			Set of 2 (Phosphor)	1.40	1.75
			First Day Cover (Ordinary)		8.00
			First Day Cover (Phosphor)		7.00

228 Trinidad Carnival Dancers

229 Canadian Folk-dancers

(Des D. Gentleman and Rosalind Dease)

1965 (1 Sept). **Commonwealth Arts Festival.** *Chalk-surfaced paper.* W **179**. P 15 × 14.

669	228	6d.	black and orange	15	15
		p.	Three phosphor bands	20	20
670	229	1s.	6d. black & lt reddish violet	1.25	1.25
		p.	Three phosphor bands	1.10	1.25
			Set of 2 (Ordinary)	1.40	1.40
			Set of 2 (Phosphor)	1.25	1.40
			First Day Cover (Ordinary)		8.50
			First Day Cover (Phosphor)		9.00

SE–TENANT COMBINATIONS. When these occur they are listed, and priced. Such items can occasionally be supplied in used condition at a premium over the used prices for the single stamps concerned.

230 Flight of Spitfires

231 Pilot in Hurricane

232 Wing-tips of Spitfire and Messerschmitt "ME-109"

233 Spitfires attacking Heinkel "HE-111" Bomber

234 Spitfire attacking Stuka Dive-bomber

235 Hurricanes over Wreck of Dornier "DO-17z2" Bomber

236 Anti-aircraft Artillery in Action

237 Air-battle over St. Paul's Cathedral

(Des D. Gentleman and Rosalind Dease (4d. × 6 and 1s. 3d.), A. Restall (9d.))

1965 (13 Sept). **25th Anniv of Battle of Britain.** *Chalk-surfaced paper.* W **179**. P 15 ×14.

671	**230**	4d. yellow-olive and black	30	35
		a. Block of 6. Nos. 671/6	4.50	5.00
		p. Three phosphor bands	40	50
		pa. Block of 6. Nos. 671p/6p	8.00	7.50
672	**231**	4d. yellow-olive, olive-grey and black	30	35
		p. Three phosphor bands	40	50
673	**232**	4d. red, new blue, yellow-olive, olive-grey & black	30	35
		p. Three phosphor bands	40	50
674	**233**	4d. olive-grey, yellow-olive and black	30	35
		p. Three phosphor bands	40	50
675	**234**	4d. olive-grey, yellow-olive and black	30	35
		p. Three phosphor bands	40	50
676	**235**	4d. olive-grey, yellow-olive, new blue & black	30	35
		a. New blue omitted	—	£3000
		p. Three phosphor bands	40	50
677	**236**	9d. bluish violet, orange & slate-purple	1.25	1.25
		Wi. Watermark inverted	25.00	
		p. Three phosphor bands	80	80
678	**237**	1s. 3d. lt grey, dp grey, black, lt blue and brt blue	1.25	1.25
		Wi. Watermark inverted	18.00	
		p. Three phosphor bands	80	80
		pWi. Watermark inverted	3.50	
		Set of 8 (Ordinary)	6.00	4.25
		Set of 8 (Phosphor)	9.00	4.25
		First Day Cover (Ordinary)		14.00
		First Day Cover (Phosphor)		14.00
		Presentation Pack (Ordinary)	42.00	

Nos. 671/6 were issued together *se-tenant* in blocks of 6 (3 ×2) within the sheet.

Special First Day of Issue Postmark

	Ordin-ary	Phos-phor
G.P.O. Philatelic Bureau, London E.C.1 (Type C)	16.00	18.00

238 Tower and Georgian Buildings

239 Tower and "Nash" Terrace, Regent's Park

(Des C. Abbott)

1965 (8 Oct). **Opening of Post Office Tower.** *Chalk-surfaced paper.* W **179** (*sideways on 3d.*). P 14 × 15 (3d.) or 15 × 14 (1s. 3d.).

679	**238**	3d. olive-yellow, new blue & bronze-green	10	10
		a. Olive-yellow (Tower) omitted	£950	
		p. One phosphor band	5	8
680	**239**	1s. 3d. bronze-green, yellow-green & blue	35	40
		Wi. Watermark inverted	38.00	
		p. Three phosphor bands	30	35
		pWi. Watermark inverted	35.00	
		Set of 2 (Ordinary)	45	50
		Set of 2 (Phosphor)	35	40
		First Day Cover (Ordinary)		5.00
		First Day Cover (Phosphor)		5.00
		Presentation Pack (Ordinary)	1.25	
		Presentation Pack (Phosphor)	1.25	

The one phosphor band on No. 679p was produced by printing broad phosphor bands across alternate vertical perforations. Individual stamps show the band at right or left (same prices either way).

Special First Day of Issue Postmark

	Ordin-ary	Phos-phor
G.P.O. Philatelic Bureau, London E.C.1 (Type C)	6.50	7.00

240 U.N. Emblem

241 I.C.Y. Emblem

(Des J. Matthews)

1965 (25 Oct). **20th Anniv of U.N.O. and International Co-operation Year.** *Chalk-surfaced paper.* W **179**. P 15 ×14.

681	**240**	3d. black, yellow-orange & lt blue	10	10
		p. One phosphor band	10	10

682 **241** 1s. 6d. black, brt purple & lt blue 75 75
  Wi. Watermark inverted ....
  p. Three phosphor bands 80 80
   Set of 2 (Ordinary) 80 80
   Set of 2 (Phosphor) 90 90
   First Day Cover (Ordinary) 7.50
   First Day Cover (Phosphor) 7.00

The Philatelic Bureau did not provide first day cover services for Nos. 681/4.

242 Telecommunications
Network

243 Radio Waves and
Switchboard

(Des A. Restall)

1965 (15 Nov). **I.T.U. Centenary.** *Chalk-surfaced paper.* W **179**.
P 15 × 14.
683 **242** 9d. red, ultramarine, dp slate, violet,
   black & pink 20 20
  Wi. Watermark inverted 14.00
  p. Three phosphor bands 60 50
  pWi. Watermark inverted 60.00
684 **243** 1s. 6d. red, greenish blue, indigo, black
   & pink 90 90
  a. Lt pink omitted £750
  Wi. Watermark inverted 45.00
  p. Three phosphor bands 6.00 6.00
   Set of 2 (Ordinary) 1.10 1.10
   Set of 2 (Phosphor) 6.00 6.00
   First Day Cover (Ordinary) 6.00
   First Day Cover (Phosphor) 9.00

Originally scheduled for issue on 17 May 1965, supplies from the Philatelic Bureau were sent in error to reach a dealer on that date and another dealer received his supply on 27 May.

244 Robert Burns (after Skirving
chalk drawing)

245 Robert Burns (after Nasmyth
portrait)

(Des G. Huntly)

1966 (25 Jan). **Burns Commemoration.** *Chalk-surfaced paper.* W **179**.
P 15 × 14.
685 **244** 4d. black, dp violet-blue & new blue...... 8 10
  p. Three phosphor bands 10 10
686 **245** 1s. 3d. black, slate-blue & yellow-orange 50 55
  p. Three phosphor bands 65 70
   Set of 2 (Ordinary) 55 60
   Set of 2 (Phosphor) 70 80
   First Day Cover (Ordinary) 2.00
   First Day Cover (Phosphor) 2.50
   Presentation Pack (Ordinary) 14.00

Special First Day of Issue Postmarks

(35 mm diameter)

	Ordin-ary	Phos-phor
Alloway, Ayrshire	5.00	5.50
Ayr...	9.00	9.00
Dumfries	6.50	8.00
Edinburgh	7.00	8.00
Glasgow	7.00	8.00
Kilmarnock, Ayrshire........................	9.00	9.00

A special Philatelic Bureau was set up in Edinburgh to deal with first day covers of this issue. The Bureau serviced covers to receive the above postmarks, and other versions were applied locally. The locally applied handstamps were 38–39mm in diameter, the Bureau postmarks, applied by machine, 33mm. The Ayr, Edinburgh, Glasgow and Kilmarnock postmarks are similar in design to that for Alloway. Similar handstamps were also provided at Greenock and Mauchline, but the Bureau did not provide a service for these.

246 Westminster Abbey

247 Fan Vaulting, Henry VII
Chapel

(Des Sheila Robinson. Photo Harrison (3d.). Des and eng Bradbury, Wilkinson. Recess (2s. 6d.))

1966 (28 Feb). **900th Anniv of Westminster Abbey.** *Chalk-surfaced paper* (3d.). W **179**. P 15 × 14 (3d.) *or* 11 ×12 (2s. 6d.).
687 **246** 3d. black, red-brown & new blue 5 5
  p. One phosphor band 15 20
688 **247** 2s. 6d. black 55 65
   Set of 2 .... 60 70
   First Day Cover (Ordinary) 4.00
   First Day Cover (Phosphor) 6.00
   Presentation Pack (Ordinary) 12.00

Special First Day of Issue Postmark

             Ordin-
              ary
G.P.O. Philatelic Bureau, London E.C.1 (Type B) .. 7.00
 The Bureau did not provide a first day cover service for the 3d. phosphor stamp.

248 View near Hassocks, Sussex

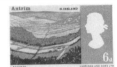

249 Antrim, Northern Ireland

254 Goalkeeper saving Goal

250 Harlech Castle, Wales

251 Cairngorm Mountains, Scotland

(Des L. Rosoman. Queen's portrait, adapted by D. Gentleman from coinage)

1966 (2 May). **Landscapes.** *Chalk-surfaced paper. W* **179**. *P* 15 ×14.

689	**248**	4d. black, yellow-green & new blue	8	8
		p. Three phosphor bands	8	8
690	**249**	6d. black, emerald & new blue.............	10	10
		Wi. Watermark inverted	4.00	
		p. Three phosphor bands	15	15
		pWi. Watermark inverted	25.00	
691	**250**	1s. 3d. black, greenish yellow & greenish blue	25	30
		p. Three phosphor bands	25	30
692	**251**	1s. 6d. black, orange and Prussian blue ..	40	45
		Wi. Watermark inverted	7.00	
		p. Three phosphor bands	30	35
		Set of 4 (Ordinary)	70	80
		Set of 4 (Phosphor)	65	70
		First Day Cover (Ordinary)		4.50
		First Day Cover (Phosphor)		6.00

Special First Day of Issue Postmark

	Ordin-ary	Phos-phor
G.P.O. Philatelic Bureau, London E.C.1 (Type B)	6.50	8.50

First Day of Issue handstamps were provided at Lewes, Sussex; Coleraine, Co. Londonderry; Harlech, Merioneth and Grantown-on-Spey, Morayshire, for this issue.

(Des D. Gentleman (4d.), W. Kempster (6d.), D. Caplan (1s. 3d.). Queen'sportrait adapted by D. Gentleman from coinage)

1966 (1 June). **World Cup Football Competition.** *Chalk-surfaced paper. W* **179** (*sideways on 4d.*). *P* 14 ×15 (4d.) *or* 15 ×14 (*others*).

693	**252**	4d. red, reddish purple, brt blue, flesh & black	8	8
		p. Two phosphor bands	8	8
694	**253**	6d. black, sepia, red, apple-green & blue	12	15
		a. Black omitted.................................	75.00	
		b. Apple-green omitted......................	£900	
		c. Red omitted...................................	£1100	
		Wi. Watermark inverted	1.75	
		p. Three phosphor bands	8	10
		pa. Black omitted................................	£350	
695	**254**	1s. 3d. black, blue, yellow, red & lt yel-low-olive.................................	30	35
		a. Blue omitted.................................	£200	
		Wi. Watermark inverted	60.00	
		p. Three phosphor bands	25	30
		pWi. Watermark inverted	1.75	
		Set of 3 (Ordinary)	45	50
		Set of 3 (Phosphor)	40	40
		First Day Cover (Ordinary)		5.00
		First Day Cover (Phosphor)		5.00
		Presentation Pack (Ordinary)	6.00	

Special First Day of Issue Postmark

	Ordin-ary	Phos-phor
G.P.O. Philatelic Bureau, London E.C.1 (Type C)	6.00	6.00

A First Day of Issue handstamp was provided at Wembley, Middx, for this issue.

255 Black-headed Gull

256 Blue Tit

252 Players with Ball

253 Goalmouth Mêlée

257 Robin

258 Blackbird

(Des J. Norris Wood)

1966 (8 Aug). **British Birds.** *Chalk-surfaced paper.* W **179**. *P* 15 ×14.

696	**255**	4d.	grey, black, red, emerald-green, brt blue, greenish yellow & bistre	10	15
		a.	Block of 4. Nos. 696/9	50	80
		aWi.	Block of 4. Watermark inverted	14.00	
		ab.	Black (value), etc. omitted* *(block of four)*	£5000	
		ac.	Black only omitted*		
		Wi.	Watermark inverted	3.00	
		p.	Three phosphor bands	10	15
		pa.	Block of 4. Nos. 696p/9p	50	80
		paWi.	Block of 4. Watermark inverted	60.00	
		pWi.	Watermark inverted	14.00	
697	**256**	4d.	black, greenish yellow, grey, emerald-green, brt blue & bistre	10	15
		Wi.	Watermark inverted	3.00	
		p.	Three phosphor bands	10	15
		pWi.	Watermark inverted	14.00	
698	**257**	4d.	red, greenish yellow, black, grey, bistre, reddish brown & emerald-green	10	15
		Wi.	Watermark inverted	3.00	
		p.	Three phosphor bands	10	15
		pWi.	Watermark inverted	14.00	
699	**258**	4d.	black, reddish brown, greenish yellow, grey & bistre**	10	15
		Wi.	Watermark inverted	3.00	
		p.	Three phosphor bands	10	15
		pWi.	Watermark inverted	14.00	
			Set of 4 (Ordinary)	50	50
			Set of 4 (Phosphor)	50	50
			First Day Cover (Ordinary)		6.00
			First Day Cover (Phosphor)		5.00
			Presentation Pack (Ordinary)	2.50	

Nos. 696/9 were issued together *se-tenant* in blocks of four within the sheet.

*In No. 696ab the blue, bistre and reddish brown are also omitted but in No. 696ac only the black is omitted.

**In No. 699 the black was printed over the bistre.

Other colours omitted, and the stamps affected:

d.	Greenish yellow (Nos. 696/9)	£150
e.	Red (Nos. 696 and 698)	£275
f.	Emerald-green (Nos. 696/8)	40.00
pf.	Emerald-green (Nos. 696p/8p)	40.00
g.	Brt blue (Nos. 696/7)	£110
pg.	Brt blue (Nos. 696p and 697p)	£125
h.	Bistre (Nos. 696/9)	50.00
ph.	Bistre (Nos. 696p/9p)	50.00
j.	Reddish brown (Nos. 698/9)	50.00
pj.	Reddish brown (Nos. 698p and 699p)	75.00

The prices quoted are for each stamp.

Special First Day of Issue Postmark

	Ordin-ary	Phos-phor
G.P.O. Philatelic Bureau, London E.C.1 (Type C)	8.00	7.50

STAMP MONTHLY

Finest and most informative magazine for all collectors. Obtainable from your newsagent or by postal subscription – details on request

259 Cup Winners

1966 (18 Aug). **England's World Cup Football Victory.** *Chalk-surfaced paper.* W **179** *(sideways).* P 14 ×15.

700	**259**	4d.	red, reddish purple, brt blue, flesh & black	10	10
			First Day Cover		1.00

These stamps were only put on sale at post offices in England, the Channel Islands and the Isle of Man, and at the Philatelic Bureau in London and also, on 22 August, in Edinburgh on the occasion of the opening of the Edinburgh Festival as well as at Army post offices at home and abroad.

The Philatelic Bureau did not service first day covers for this stamp, but a First Day of Issue handstamp was provided inscribed 'Harrow & Wembley, Middx' to replace the 'Harrow, Middlesex' postmark of the initial issue.

260 Jodrell Bank Radio Telescope

261 British Motor-cars

262 "SRN 6" Hovercraft

263 Windscale Reactor

(Des D. and A. Gillespie (4d., 6d.), A. Restall (others))

1966 (19 Sept). **British Technology.** *Chalk-surfaced paper.* W **179**. P 15 × 14.

701	**260**	4d.	black & lemon..............................	8	8
		p.	Three phosphor bands	8	8
702	**261**	6d.	red, dp blue & orange	10	10
		a.	Red (Mini-cars) omitted	£2250	
		b.	Dp blue (Jaguar & inscr) omitted	£2500	
		p.	Three phosphor bands	12	15
703	**262**	1s. 3d.	black, orange-red, slate & lt greenish blue..............................	25	25
		p.	Three phosphor bands	25	30
704	**263**	1s. 6d.	black, yellow-green, bronze-green, lilac & dp blue	30	30
		p.	Three phosphor bands	40	40
			Set of 4 (Ordinary)	55	60
			Set of 4 (Phosphor)	80	80
			First Day Cover (Ordinary)		2.50
			First Day Cover (Phosphor)		2.50
			Presentation Pack (Ordinary)	4.00	

Special First Day of Issue Postmark

	Ordin- ary	Phos- phor
G.P.O. Philatelic Bureau, Edinburgh 1 (Type C)	3.50	3.50

264

265

266

267

268

269

All the above show battle scenes and they were issued together *se-tenant* in horizontal strips of six within the sheet.

270 Norman Ship

271 Norman Horsemen attacking Harold's Troops

(All the above are scenes from the Bayeaux Tapestry)

(Des D. Gentleman. Photo. Queen's head die-stamped (6d., 1s. 3d.))

1966 (14 Oct). **900th Anniv of Battle of Hastings.** *Chalk-surfaced paper.* W **179** *(sideways on* 1s. 3d.*).* P 15 ×14.

705	264	4d. black, olive-green, bistre, dp blue, orange, magenta, green, blue and grey	10	15
		a. Strip of 6. Nos. 705/10	1.40	2.00
		aWi. Strip of 6. Watermark inverted	35.00	
		Wi. Watermark inverted	5.00	
		p. Three phosphor bands	10	25
		pa. Strip of 6. Nos. 705p/10p	1.40	2.00
		paWi. Strip of 6. Watermark inverted	14.00	
		pWi. Watermark inverted	2.00	

706	265	4d. black, olive-green, bistre, dp blue, orange, magenta, green, blue and grey	10	15
		Wi. Watermark inverted	5.00	
		p. Three phosphor bands	10	25
		pWi. Watermark inverted	2.00	
707	266	4d. black, olive-green, bistre, dp blue, orange, magenta, green, blue and grey	10	15
		Wi. Watermark inverted	5.00	
		p. Three phosphor bands	10	25
		pWi. Watermark inverted	2.00	
708	267	4d. black, olive-green, bistre, dp blue, magenta, green, blue & grey	10	15
		Wi. Watermark inverted	5.00	
		p. Three phosphor bands	10	25
		pWi. Watermark inverted	2.00	
709	268	4d. black, olive-green, bistre, dp blue, orange, magenta, green, blue and grey	10	15
		Wi. Watermark inverted	5.00	
		p. Three phosphor bands	10	25
		pWi. Watermark inverted	2.00	
710	269	4d. black, olive-green, bistre, dp blue, orange, magenta, green, blue & grey	10	15
		Wi. Watermark inverted	5.00	
		p. Three phosphor bands	10	25
		pWi. Watermark inverted	2.00	
711	270	6d. black, olive-green, violet, blue, green & gold	10	10
		Wi. Watermark inverted	35.00	
		p. Three phosphor bands	10	10
		pWi. Watermark inverted	45.00	
712	271	1s. 3d. black, lilac, bronze-green, rosine, bistre-brown & gold	20	20
		a. Lilac omitted	£450	
		Wi. Watermark sideways inverted (top of crown pointing to right)*	30.00	
		p. Four phosphor bands	20	20
		pa. Lilac omitted	£650	
		pWi. Watermark sideways inverted (top of crown pointing to right)*	10.00	
		Set of 8 (Ordinary)	1.50	1.10
		Set of 8 (Phosphor)	1.50	1.60
		First Day Cover (Ordinary)		2.40
		First Day Cover (Phosphor)		2.50
		Presentation Pack (Ordinary)	3.00	

*The normal sideways watermark shows the tops of the Crowns pointing to the left, *as seen from the back of the stamp.*

Other colours omitted in the 4d. values and the stamps affected:

b.	Olive-green (Nos. 705/10)	25.00
pb.	Olive-green (Nos. 705p/10p)	25.00
c.	Bistre (Nos. 705/10)	25.00
pc.	Bistre (Nos. 705p/10p)	30.00
d.	Dp blue (Nos. 705/40)	35.00
pd.	Dp blue (Nos. 705p/10p)	35.00
e.	Orange (Nos. 705/7 and 709/10)	25.00
pe.	Orange (Nos. 705p/7p and 709p/10p)	20.00
f.	Magenta (Nos. 705/10)	30.00
pf.	Magenta (Nos. 705p/10p)	30.00
g.	Green (Nos. 705/10)	25.00
pg.	Green (Nos. 705p/10p)	25.00
h.	Blue (Nos. 705/10)	20.00
ph.	Blue (Nos. 705p/10p)	35.00
j.	Grey (Nos. 705/10)	20.00
pj.	Grey (Nos. 705p/10p)	20.00
pk.	Magenta and green (Nos. 705p/10p)	55.00

The prices quoted are for each stamp.

Nos. 705 and 709, with grey and blue omitted, have been seen commercially used, posted from Middleton-in-Teesdale.

The 6d. phosphor is known in a yellowish gold as well as the reddish gold as used in the 1s. 3d.

Three examples of No. 712 in a right-hand top corner block of 10 (2 × 5) are known with the Queen's head omitted as a result of a double paper fold prior to die-stamping. The perforation is normal. Of the other seven stamps, four have the Queen's head misplaced and three are normal.

MISSING GOLD HEADS. The 6d. and 1s. 3d. were also issued with the die-stamped gold head omitted but as these can also be removed by chemical means we are not prepared to list them unless a way is found of distinguishing the genuine stamps from the fakes which will satisfy the Expert Committees.

The same remarks apply to Nos. 713/14.

Special First Day of Issue Postmark

	Ordin-ary	Phos-phor
G.P.O. Philatelic Bureau, Edinburgh 1 (Type C)	4.00	5.00

A First Day of Issue handstamp was provided at Battle, Sussex, for this issue.

272 King of the Orient   273 Snowman

(Des Tasveer Shemza (3d.), J. Berry (1s. 6d.) (winners of children's design competition). Photo, Queen's head die-stamped)

1966 (1 Dec). **Christmas.** *Chalk-surfaced paper.* W **179** (*sideways on* 3d.). P 14 × 15.

713	**272**	3d.	black, blue, green, yellow, red & gold	5	5
		a.	Queen's head double		
		b.	Green omitted	—	£150
		p.	One phosphor band	5	5
714	**273**	1s.	6d. blue, red, pink, black & gold	15	25
		a.	Pink (hat) omitted	£550	
		Wi.	Waterwark inverted	9.00	
		p.	Two phosphor bands	15	25
		pWi.	Watermark inverted	38.00	
			Set of 2 (Ordinary)	20	30
			Set of 2 (Phosphor)	20	30
			First Day Cover (Ordinary)		75
			First Day Cover (Phosphor)		75
			Presentation Pack (Ordinary)	2.25	

See note below Nos. 679/80 which also applies to No. 713p.

Special First Day of Issue Postmarks

	Ordin-ary	Phos-phor
G.P.O. Philatelic Bureau, Edinburgh 1 (Type C)	1.10	1.10
Bethlehem, Llandeilo, Carms (Type C)	1.25	1.25

274 Sea Freight   275 Air Freight

(Des C. Abbot)

1967 (20 Feb). **European Free Trade Association (EFTA).** *Chalk-surfaced paper.* W **179**. P 15 × 14.

715	**274**	9d.	dp blue, red, lilac, green, brown, new blue, yellow & black	8	10
		a.	Black (Queen's head, etc.), brown, new blue & yellow omitted	£1000	
		b.	Lilac omitted	60.00	
		c.	Green omitted	40.00	
		d.	Brown omitted	45.00	
		e.	New blue omitted	40.00	
		f.	Yellow omitted	40.00	
		Wi.	Watermark inverted	18.00	
		p.	Three phosphor bands	8	10
		pb.	Lilac omitted	75.00	
		pc.	Green omitted	45.00	
		pd.	Brown omitted	45.00	
		pe.	New blue omitted	45.00	
		pf.	Yellow omitted	75.00	
		pWi.	Watermark inverted	10.00	
716	**275**	1s.	6d. violet, red, dp blue, brown, green, blue-grey, new blue, yellow & black	15	20
		a.	Red omitted		
		b.	Dp blue omitted	£225	
		c.	Brown omitted	42.00	
		d.	Blue-grey omitted	45.00	
		e.	New blue omitted	45.00	
		f.	Yellow omitted	45.00	
		p.	Three phosphor bands	15	20
		pa.	Red omitted		
		pb.	Dp blue omitted	£275	
		pc.	Brown omitted	42.00	
		pd.	Blue-grey omitted	40.00	
		pf.	New blue omitted	40.00	
		pWi.	Watermark inverted	22.00	
			Set of 2 (Ordinary)	20	30
			Set of 2 (Phosphor)	20	30
			First Day Cover (Ordinary)		70
			First Day Cover (Phosphor)		70
			Presentation Pack (Ordinary)	1.00	

Special First Day of Issue Postmark

	Ordin-ary	Phos-phor
G.P.O. Philatelic Bureau, Edinburgh 1 (Type C)	1.50	1.50

276 Hawthorn and Bramble   277 Larger Bindweed and Viper's Bugloss

278 Ox-eye Daisy, Coltsfoot
and Buttercup

279 Bluebell, Red Campion
and Wood Anemone

T **276/9** were issued together *se*-tenant in blocks of four within the
sheet.

280 Dog Violet

281 Primroses

(Des Rev. W. Keble Martin (T **276/9**), Mary Grierson (others))

1967 (24 Apr). **British Wild Flowers.** *Chalk-surfaced paper.* W **179**.
P 15 × 14.

717	**276**	4d.	grey, lemon, myrtle-green, red, agate & slate-purple	15	10
		a.	Block of 4 Nos. 717/20	75	95
		aWi.	Block of 4. Watermark inverted	7.00	
		b.	Grey double*		
		c.	Red omitted	£100	
		Wi.	Watermark inverted	1.50	
		p.	Three phosphor bands	10	10
		pa.	Block of 4. Nos. 717p/20p	45	55
		paWi.	Block of 4. Watermark inverted	7.00	
		pd.	Agate omitted	£450	
		pf.	Slate-purple omitted	£150	
		pWi.	Watermark inverted	1.50	
718	**277**	4d.	grey, lemon, myrtle-green, red, agate & violet	15	10
		b.	Grey double*		
		Wi.	Watermark inverted	1.50	
		p.	Three phosphor bands	10	10
		pd.	Agate omitted	£450	
		pe.	Violet omitted		
		pWi.	Watermark inverted	1.50	
719	**278**	4d.	grey, lemon, myrtle-green, red & agate	15	10
		b.	Grey double*		
		Wi.	Watermark inverted	1.50	
		p.	Three phosphor bands	10	10
		pd.	Agate omitted	£450	
		pWi.	Watermark inverted	1.50	
720	**279**	4d.	grey, lemon, myrtle-green, reddish purple, agate & violet	15	10
		b.	Grey double*		
		c.	Reddish purple omitted	£400	
		Wi.	Watermark inverted	1.50	
		p.	Three phosphor bands	10	10
		pd.	Agate omitted	£450	
		pe.	Violet omitted		
		pWi.	Watermark inverted	1.50	
721	**280**	9d.	lavender-grey, green, reddish violet & orange-yellow	8	10
		Wi.	Watermark inverted	75	
		p.	Three phosphor bands	10	10

722	**281**	1s.	9d. lavender-grey, green, greenish yellow & orange	20	20
		p.	Three phosphor bands	20	20
			Set of 6 (Ordinary)	80	65
			Set of 6 (Phosphor)	60	65
			First Day Cover (Ordinary)		2.00
			First Day Cover (Phosphor)		1.75
			Presentation Pack (Ordinary)	2.00	

*The double impression of the grey printing affects the Queen's
head, value and inscription.

Special First Day of Issue Postmark

	Ordin-ary	Phos-phor
G.P.O. Philatelic Bureau, Edinburgh 1 (Type C)	2.50	2.75

PHOSPHOR BANDS. Issues from No. 723 are normally with phosphor bands only, except for the high values but most stamps have
appeared with the phosphor bands omitted in error. Such varieties are
listed under "Ey" numbers and are priced unused only. See also further
notes after No. X980.

PHOSPHORISED PAPER. Following the adoption of phosphor bands
the Post Office started a series of experiments involving the
addition of the phosphor to the paper coating before the stamps were
printed. No. 743b was the first of these experiments to be issued for
normal postal use. See also notes after No. X980.

PVA GUM. Polyvinyl alcohol was introduced by Harrisons in place
of gum arabic in 1968. It is almost invisible except that a small
amount of pale yellowish colouring matter was introduced to make it
possible to see that the stamps had been gummed. Although this can
be distinguished from gum arabic in unused stamps there is, of course,
no means of detecting it in used examples. Where the two forms of gum
exist on the same stamp, the PVA type are listed under "Ev" numbers,
except in the case of the 1d. and 4d. (vermilion), both one centre band,
which later appeared with gum arabic and these have "Eg" numbers.
"Ev" and "Eg" numbers are priced unused only. All stamps printed
from No. 763 onwards were issued with PVA gum only *except where
otherwise stated.*

It should be further noted that gum arabic is shiny in appearance, and
that, normally, PVA gum has a matt appearance. However, depending
upon the qualities of the paper ingredients and the resultant absorp-
tion of the gum, occasionally, PVA gum has a shiny appearance. In such
cases, especially in stamps from booklets, it is sometimes impossible to
be absolutely sure which gum has been used except by testing the
stamps chemically which destroys them. Therefore, whilst all gum
arabic is shiny it does not follow that all shiny gum is gum arabic.

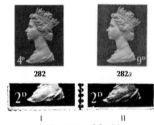

282   **282a**

I   II

Two types of the 2d.

I. Value spaced away from left side of stamp (cylinders 1 no dot and
dot).

II. Value close to left side from new multipositive used for cylinders 5
no dot and dot onwards. The portrait appears in the centre, thus
conforming to the other values.

Three types of the Machin head, known as Head A, B or C, are
distinguished by specialists. These are illustrated in Vol. 3 of the
Great Britain Specialised Catalogue.

(Des after plaster cast by Arnold Machin)

1967 (5 June)–**70.** *Chalk-surfaced paper. Two phosphor bands except where otherwise stated. No wmk. PVA gum except Nos. 725m, 728, 729, 731, 731Ea, 740, 742/Ea, 743/a and 744/Ea.*

723	**282**	½d. orange-brown (5.2.68)	5	15
		Ey. Phosphor omitted.........................	30.00	
724		1d. lt olive (*shades*) (2 bands) (5.2.68).....	5	10
		a. Imperf (coil strip)†	£750	
		b. Part perf pane*		
		c. Imperf pane*		
		d. Uncoated paper (1970)**	85.00	
		Ey. Phosphor omitted.........................	1.00	
		l. Booklet pane. No. 724 × 2 *se-tenant* with 730 × 2 (6.4.68)	2.50	
		lEy. Booklet pane. Phosphor omitted......	75.00	
		m. Booklet pane. No. 724 × 4 *se-tenant* with 734 × 2 (6.1.69)	3.00	
		mEy. Booklet pane. Phosphor omitted......	£100	
		n. Booklet pane. No. 724 × 6, 734 × 3, 734Eb × 3 & 735 × 3 *se-tenant* (1.12.69)	11.00	
		na. Booklet pane. Uncoated paper (1970)**	£900	
		nEy. Booklet pane. Phosphor omitted......	£150	
725		1d. yellowish olive (1 centre band) (16.9.68)	25	40
		Eg. Gum arabic (27.8.69)	25	
		l. Booklet pane. No. 725 × 4 *se-tenant* with 732 × 2	3.50	
		lEy. Booklet pane. Phosphor omitted......	30.00	
		m. Coil strip. No. 728 × 2 *se-tenant* with 729, 725Eg & 733Eg (27.8.69)	1.10	
726		2d. lake-brown (Type I) (2 bands) (5.2.68)	10	12
		Ey. Phosphor omitted.........................	16.00	
727		2d. lake-brown (Type II) (2 bands) (1969)	15	12
		Ey. Phosphor omitted.........................	1.00	
728		2d. lake-brown (Type II) (1 centre band) (27.8.69)	40	60
729		3d. violet (*shades*) (1 centre band) (8.8.67)	10	10
		a. Imperf (pair)	£475	
		Ey. Phosphor omitted.........................	1.25	
		Ev. PVA gum (*shades*) (12.3.68).............	10	
		Evy. Phosphor omitted.........................	1.25	
730		3d. violet (2 bands) (6.4.68)	25	30
		a. Uncoated paper**	£900	
731	**282**	4d. dp sepia (*shades*) (2 bands)	8	8
		Ey. Phosphor omitted.........................	1.00	
		Ea. Dp olive-brown	8	8
		Eay. Phosphor omitted.........................	1.10	
		b. Part perf pane*	£550	
		Ev. PVA gum (*shades*) (22.1.68).............	8	
		Evy. Phosphor omitted.........................	1.00	
732		4d. dp olive-brown (*shades*) (1 centre band) (16.9.68)	8	8
		a. Part perf pane*	£450	
		l. Booklet pane. Two stamps plus two printed labels...............................	90	
		lEy. Booklet pane. Phosphor omitted......	45.00	
733		4d. brt vermilion (1 centre band) (6.1.69)	8	8
		a. Tête-bêche (horiz pair)	£2500	
		b. Uncoated paper (1970)**	10.00	
		Ey. Phosphor omitted.........................	1.10	
		Eg. Gum arabic (27.8.69)	12	
		Egy. Phosphor omitted.........................	£600	
		l. Booklet pane. Two stamps plus two printed labels (3.3.69).....................	90	
		lEy. Booklet pane. Phosphor omitted......	70.00	
734		4d. brt vermilion (1 band at left) (6.1.69) .	1.25	1.75
		a. Uncoated paper (1970)**	£175	
		Eb. One band at right (1.12.69)	2.00	3.25
		Eba. Ditto. Uncoated paper (1970)**	£175	

735	**282**	5d. royal blue (*shades*) (1.7.68).............	8	8
		a. Imperf pane*	£450	
		b. Part perf pane*	£400	
		c. Imperf (pair)††	£100	
		d. Uncoated paper (1970)**	18.00	
		Ey. Phosphor omitted.........................	1.10	
		Ee. Dp blue	8	10
		Eey. Phosphor omitted.........................	2.00	
736		6d. brt reddish purple (*shades*) (5.2.68) ..	20	25
		Ey. Phosphor omitted.........................	4.50	
		Ea. Brt magenta	2.00	40
		Eb. Claret	80	35
		Eby. Phosphor omitted.........................	10.00	
737	**282a**	7d. brt emerald (1.7.68)	40	20
		Ey. Phosphor omitted.........................	40.00	
738		8d. brt vermilion (1.7.68)	10	30
		Ey. Phosphor omitted.........................	£400	
739		8d. lt turquoise-blue (6.1.69)	40	45
		Ey. Phosphor omitted.........................	65.00	
740		9d. myrtle-green (8.8.67)	50	20
		Ey. Phosphor omitted.........................	18.00	
		Ev. PVA gum (29.11.68)	50	
		Evy. Phosphor omitted.........................	18.00	
741	**282**	10d. drab (1.7.68)	45	60
		a. Uncoated paper (1969)**	28.00	
		Ey. Phosphor omitted.........................	38.00	
742		1s. lt bluish violet (*shades*)	45	15
		Ey. Phosphor omitted.........................	55.00	
		Ea. Pale bluish violet	60	15
		Ev. Ditto. PVA gum (26.4.68)	50	
		Evy. Phosphor omitted.........................	3.50	
743		1s. 6d. greenish blue and deep blue (*shades*) (8.8.67)	65	12
		a. Greenish blue omitted	95.00	
		Ey. Phosphor omitted	7.00	
		Ev. PVA gum. (28.8.68)	60	
		Eva. Greenish blue omitted	80.00	
		Evy. Phosphor omitted	14.00	
		Evb. Prussian blue & indigo	1.50	
		Evby. Phosphor omitted	11.00	
		c. Phosphorised paper (Prussian blue & indigo) (10.12.69)	60	90
		ca. Prussian blue omitted	£225	
744		1s. 9d. dull orange & black (*shades*)	40	30
		Ey. Phosphor omitted.........................	25.00	
		Ea. Brt orange & black	1.50	30
		Ev. PVA gum (*brt orange & black*) (16.11.70)	40	
		Set of 16 (*one of each value & colour*)	3.00	2.75
		Presentation Pack (*one of each value*)	6.50	
		Presentation Pack (German)............	45.00	

*BOOKLET ERRORS. See note after No. 556.

**Uncoated paper. This does not respond to the chalky test, and may be further distinguished from the normal chalk-surfaced paper by the fibres which clearly show on the surface, resulting in the printing impression being rougher, and by the screening dots which are not so evident. The 1d., 4d. and 5d. come from the £1 "Stamps for Cooks" Booklet; the 3d. and 10d. from sheets. The 20p. and 50p. high values (Nos. 830/1) exist with similar errors.

†No. 724a occurs in a vertical strip of four, top stamp perforated on three sides, bottom stamp imperf three sides and the two middle stamps completely imperf.

††No. 735c comes from the original state of cylinder 15 which is identifiable by the screening dots which extend through the gutters of the stamps and into the margins of the sheet. This must not be confused with imperforate stamps from cylinder 10, a large quantity of which was stolen from the printers early in 1970.

The 1d. with centre band and PVA gum (725) only came in the September 1968 10s. booklet (No. XP6). The 1d., 2d. and 4d. with centre band and gum arabic (725Eg, 728 and 733Eg respectively) only came in

49

the coil strip (725m). The 5d. (No. 730) appeared in booklets on 6.4.68, from coils during Dec 68 and from sheets in Jan 1969. The 4d. with one side band at left (734) came from 10s. and £1 booklet se-tenant panes, and the 4d. with one side band at right (734Eb) came from the £1 booklet se-tenant panes only.

The 4d. (731) in shades of washed-out grey are colour changelings which we understand are caused by the concentrated solvents used in modern dry cleaning methods.

For decimal issue, see Nos. X841/980.

First Day Covers

5.6.67	4d., 1s., 1s. 9d. (731, 742, 744)	1.25
8.8.67	3d., 9d., 1s. 6d. (729, 740, 743)	1.25
5.2.68	½d., 1d., 2d., 6d. (723/4, 726, 736)	75
1.7.68	5d., 7d., 8d., 10d. (735, 737/8, 741)	1.10

283 "Master Lambton" (Sir Thomas Lawrence)

284 "Mares and Foals in a Landscape" (George Stubbs)

285 "Children Coming Out of School" (L. S. Lowry)

1967 (10 July). **British Paintings.** *Chalk-surfaced paper. Two phosphor bands. No wmk. P 14 × 15 (4d.) or 15 × 14 (others).*

748	**283**	4d. rose-red, lemon, brown, black, new blue & gold	5	8
		a. Gold (value & Queen's head) omitted	£160	
		b. New blue omitted	£550	
		Ey. Phosphor omitted	7.00	
749	**284**	9d. Venetian red, ochre, grey-black, new blue, greenish yellow & black	10	12
		a. Black (Queen's head & value) omitted	£450	
		b. Greenish yellow omitted	£600	
		Ey. Phosphor omitted	£450	
750	**285**	1s. 6d. greenish yellow, grey, rose, new blue, grey-black & gold	20	20
		a. Gold (Queen's head) omitted	£750	
		b. New blue omitted	£140	
		c. Grey omitted	75.00	
		Ey. Phosphor omitted	£300	
		Set of 3	30	30
		First Day Cover		1.10
		Presentation Pack	3.00	

Special First Day of Issue Postmark

G.P.O. Philatelic Bureau, Edinburgh 1 (Type C) 1.60

A First Day of Issue handstamp was provided at Bishop Auckland, Co. Durham, for this issue.

286 *Gypsy Moth IV*

(Des M. and Sylvia Goaman)

1967 (24 July). **Sir Francis Chichester's World Voyage.** *Chalk-surfaced paper. Three phosphor bands. No wmk. P 15 × 14.*

751	**286**	1s. 9d. black, brown-red, lt emerald & blue	12	12
		First Day Cover		45

Special First Day of Issue Postmarks

G.P.O. Philatelic Bureau, Edinburgh 1	1.10
Greenwich, London SE10	2.00
Plymouth, Devon	2.00

The Philatelic Bureau and Greenwich postmarks are similar in design to that for Plymouth. A First Day of Issue handstamp was provided at Chichester, Sussex for this issue.

287 Radar Screen

288 Penicillin Mould

289 "VC-10" Jet Engines

290 Television Equipment

(Des C. Abbott (4d., 1s.), Negus-Sharland team (others))

1967 (19 Sept). **British Discovery and Invention.** *Chalk-surfaced paper. Three phosphor bands (4d.) or two phosphor bands (others). W 179 (sideways on 1s. 9d.). P 14 × 15 (1s. 9d.) or 15 × 14 (others).*

752	**287**	4d. greenish yellow, black & vermilion...	5	8
		Ey. Phosphor omitted	1.75	

753	**288**	1s. blue-green, lt greenish blue, slate-purple & bluish violet	8	10
		Wi. Watermark inverted	10.00	
		Ey. Phosphor omitted	12.00	
754	**289**	1s. 6d. black, grey, royal blue, ochre & turquoise-blue	12	15
		Wi. Watermark inverted	30.00	
		Ey. Phosphor omitted	£500	
755	**290**	1s. 9d. black, grey-blue, pale olive-grey, violet & orange	20	20
		a. Grey-blue omitted		
		Ey. Phosphor omitted	£500	
		Set of 4	35	40
		First Day Cover		80
		Presentation Pack	1.50	

Special First Day of Issue Postmark
G.P.O. Philatelic Bureau, Edinburgh (Type C) 1.50

WATERMARK. All issues from this date are on unwatermarked paper.

291 "The Adoration of the Shepherds" (School of Seville)

292 "Madonna and Child" (Murillo)

293 "The Adoration of the Shepherds" (Louis le Nain)

1967. Christmas. *Chalk-surfaced paper. One phosphor band (3d.) or two phosphor bands (others). P 15 × 14 (1s. 6d.) or 14 × 15 (others).*

756	**291**	3d. olive-yellow, rose, blue, black & gold (27.11)	5	5
		a. Gold (value & Queen's head) omitted	50.00	
		b. Printed on the gummed side	£300	
		c. Rose omitted	£500	
		Ey. Phosphor omitted	1.00	
757	**292**	4d. brt purple, greenish yellow, new blue, grey-black & gold (18.10)	5	5
		a. Gold (value & Queen's head) omitted	60.00	
		b. Greenish yellow (Child, robe & Madonna's face) omitted		
		Ey. Phosphor omitted	£100	
758	**293**	1s. 6d. brt purple, bistre, lemon, black, orange-red, ultramarine & gold (27.11)	20	20
		a. Gold (value & Queen's head) omitted		
		b. Ultramarine omitted	£450	
		Ey. Phosphor omitted	10.00	
		Set of 3	25	25
		First Day Covers (2)		1.00

Distinct shades exist of the 4d. value but are not listable as there are intermediate shades. Stamps emanating from one machine show a darker background and give the appearance of the yellow colour being omitted but this is not so and these should not be confused with the true missing yellow No. 757b.

Special First Day of Issue Postmarks
G.P.O. Philatelic Bureau, Edinburgh, Edinburgh 1 (4d.) (18 Oct.) (Type C) 75
G.P.O. Philatelic Bureau, Edinburgh 1 (3d., 1s. 6d.) (27 Nov.) (Type C) 75
Bethlehem, Llandeilo, Carms (4d.) (18 Oct.) (Type C) 1.25
Bethlehem, Llandeilo, Carms (3d., 1s. 6d.) (27 Nov.) (Type C) 1.25

Gift Pack 1967

1967 (27 Nov). *Comprises Nos. 715p/22p and 748/58.*
GP758c Gift Pack 2.25

(Recess Bradbury, Wilkinson)

1967–68. *No wmk. White paper. P 11 × 12.*

759	**166**	2s. 6d. black-brown (1.7.68)	40	40
760	**167**	5s. red (10.4.68)	1.00	1.00
761	**168**	10s. brt ultramarine (10.4.68)	5.50	6.00
762	**169**	£1 black (4.12.67)	3.00	3.50
		Set of 4	9.00	10.00

PVA GUM. All the following issues from this date have PVA gum *except where footnotes state otherwise.*

294 Tarr Steps, Exmoor

295 Aberfeldy Bridge

296 Menai Bridge

297 M4 Viaduct

(Des A. Restall (9d.), L. Rosoman (1s. 6d.), J. Matthews (others))

1968 (29 Apr). **British Bridges.** *Chalk-surfaced paper. Two phosphor bands. P 15 × 14.*

763	**294**	4d. black, bluish violet, turquoise-blue & gold	5	5
		a. Printed on gummed side	22.00	
		Ey. Phosphor omitted	1.50	
764	**295**	9d. red-brown, myrtle-green, ultramarine, olive-brown, black & gold	8	10
		a. Gold (Queen's head) omitted	£180	
		b. Ultramarine omitted		
		Ey. Phosphor omitted	16.00	
765	**296**	1s. 6d. olive-brown, red-orange, brt green, turquoise-green & gold	12	15
		a. Gold (Queen's head) omitted	£180	
		b. Red-orange omitted	£225	
		Ey. Phosphor omitted	40.00	

766	297	1s.	9d. olive-brown, greenish yellow, dull green, dp ultramarine & gold	15	20
		a.	Gold (Queen's head) omitted	£275	
		Ey.	Phosphor omitted........................	10.00	
		Eya.	Gold (Queen's head) & phosphor omitted	£300	
			Set of 4	30	40
			First Day Cover		1.00
			Presentation Pack.........................	1.25	

Special First Day of Issue Postmarks

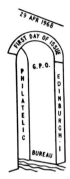

G.P.O. Philatelic Bureau, Edinburgh 1.................	1.50
Bridge, Canterbury, Kent	2.25
Aberfeldy, Perthshire (Type A) (9d. value only)	24.00
Menai Bridge, Anglesey (Type A) (1s. 6d. value only)	24.00

The Bridge, Canterbury, postmark is similar in design to that for the Philatelic Bureau.

769	300	1s.	olive-brown, blue, red, slate-blue & black	12	15
		Ey.	Phosphor omitted........................	9.00	
770	301	1s.	9d. yellow-ochre & blackish brown...	15	20
		Ey.	Phosphor omitted........................	£175	
			Set of 4	35	40
			First Day Cover		3.25
			Presentation Pack.........................	1.75	

Special First Day of Issue Postmarks

G.P.O. Philatelic Bureau, Edinburgh 1 (Type C)	3.50
Manchester	30.00
Aldeburgh, Suffolk	30.00
Hendon, London NW4	22.00
Whitby, Yorkshire...	25.00

298 "TUC" and Trades Unionists

299 Mrs. Emmeline Pankhurst (statute)

302 "Queen Elizabeth I" (unknown artist)

303 "Pinkie" (Lawrence)

300 Sopwith "Camel" and "Lightning" Fighters

301 Captain Cook's *Endeavour* and Signature

(Des D. Gentleman (4d.), C. Abbott (others))

1968 (29 May). **British Anniversaries.** *Events described on stamps. Chalk-surfaced paper. Two phosphor bands.* P 15 × 14.

767	298	4d.	emerald, olive, blue & black............	5	5
		Ey.	Phosphor omitted	10.00	
768	299	9d.	reddish violet, bluish grey & black ...	8	12
		Ey.	Phosphor omitted........................	8.00	

304 "Ruins of St. Mary Le Port" (Piper)

305 "The Hay Wain" (Constable)

1968 (12 Aug). **British Paintings.** *Queen's head embossed. Chalk-surfaced paper. Two phosphor bands. P 15 × 14 (1s. 9d.) or 14 × 15 (others).*

771	**302**	4d. black, vermilion, greenish yellow, grey & gold..................................	5	5
		a. Gold (value & Queen's head) omitted	£150	
		b. Vermilion omitted*	£200	
		Ec. Embossing omitted	30.00	
		Ey. Phosphor omitted..........................	1.00	
		Eya. Gold (value & Queen's head) & phosphor omitted	£175	
772	**303**	1s. mauve, new blue, greenish yellow, black, magenta & gold....................	10	15
		a. Gold (value & Queen's head) omitted	£175	
		Eb. Gold (value & Queen's head), embossing & phosphor omitted	£200	
		Ec. Embossing omitted		
		Ey. Phosphor omitted..........................	7.00	
773	**304**	1s. 6d. slate, orange, black, mauve, greenish yellow, ultramarine & gold .	12	15
		a. Gold (value & Queen's head) omitted	£175	
		Eb. Embossing omitted		
		Ey. Phosphor omitted..........................	7.00	
774	**305**	1s. 9d. greenish yellow, black, new blue, red & gold	15	20
		a. Gold (value & Queen's head) & embossing omitted	£400	
		b. Red omitted................................	£2000	
		Ey. Phosphor omitted..........................	20.00	
		Set of 4	40	40
		First Day Cover		1.00
		Presentation Pack	1.10	
		Presentation Pack (German)............	9.00	

No. 774a is only known with the phosphor also omitted.

*The effect of this is to leave the face and hands white and there is more yellow and olive in the costume.

The 4d. also exists with the value only omitted resulting from a colour shift.

Special First Day of Issue Postmark
G.P.O. Philatelic Bureau, Edinburgh 1 (Type C) 1.75

Gift Pack 1968

1968 (16 Sept). *Comprises Nos. 763/74.*

GP774c	Gift Pack	8.00
GP774d	Gift Pack (German)	20.00

Collectors Pack 1968

1968 (16 Sept). *Comprises Nos. 752/8 and 763/74.*

CP774e	Collectors Pack	6.50

306 Boy and Girl with Rocking Horse

307 Girl with Doll's House   **308** Boy with Train Set
(Des Rosalind Dease. Head printed in gold and then embossed)

1968 (25 Nov). **Christmas.** *Chalk-surfaced paper. One centre phosphor band (4d.) or two phosphor bands (others). P 15 × 14 (4d.) or 14 × 15 (others).*

775	**306**	4d. black, orange, vermilion, ultramarine, bistre & gold..........................	5	5
		a. Gold omitted	£1500	
		b. Vermilion omitted*	£140	
		c. Ultramarine omitted	£150	
		Ed. Embossing omitted	3.00	
		Ey. Phosphor omitted..........................	1.50	
776	**307**	9d. yellow-olive, black, brown, yellow, magenta, orange, turquoise-green & gold	8	12
		a. Yellow omitted.............................	60.00	
		Eb. Embossing omitted	5.00	
		Ey. Phosphor omitted..........................	6.00	
		Eya. Embossing & phosphor omitted	12.00	
777	**308**	1s. 6d. ultramarine, yellow-orange, brt purple, blue-green, black & gold	12	15
		Ea. Embossing omitted		
		Ey. Phosphor omitted..........................	15.00	
		Set of 3	20	25
		First Day Cover		60
		Presentation Pack	1.50	
		Presentation Pack (German)............	6.50	

*The effect of the missing vermilion is shown on the rocking horse, saddle and faces which appear orange instead of red.

A single used example of the 4d. exists with the bistre omitted.

No. 775c is only known with phosphor also omitted.

Two machines were used for printing the 4d. value:

Stamps from cylinders 1A–1B–2C–1D–1E in combination with 1F, 2F or 3F (gold) were printed entirely on the Rembrandt sheet-fed machine. They invariably have the Queen's head level with the top of the boy's head and the sheets are perforated through the left side margin.

Stamps from cylinders 2A–2B–3C–2D–2E in combination with 1F, 2F, 3F or 4F (gold) were printed on the reel-fed Thrissell machine in five colours (its maximum colour capacity) and subsequently sheet-fed on the Rembrandt machine for the gold Queen's head and the embossing. The position of the Queen's head is generally lower than on the stamps printed at one operation but it varies in different parts of the sheet and is not, therefore, a sure indication for identifying single stamps. Another small difference is that the boy's grey pullover is noticeably "moth-eaten" in the Thrissell printings and is normal on the Rembrandt. The Thrissell printings are perforated through the top margin.

Special First Day of Issue Postmarks
G.P.O. Philatelic Bureau, Edinburgh 1 (Type C) 1.10
Bethlehem, Llandeilo, Carms (Type C) 3.25

309 R.M.S. *Queen Elizabeth 2*

310 Elizabethan Galleon

311 East Indiaman

312 *Cutty Sark*

313 S.S. *Great Britain*

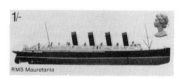

314 R.M.S. *Mauretania*

(Des D. Gentleman)

1969 (15 Jan). **British Ships.** *Chalk-surfaced paper. Two vertical phosphor bands at right (1s.), one horizontal phosphor band (5d.) or two phosphor bands (9d.). P* 15 × 14.

778	**309**	5d. black, grey, red & turquoise............		5	5
		a. Black (Queen's head, value, hull & inscr) omitted	£900		
		b. Grey (decks, etc.) omitted..............	£110		
		c. Red omitted................................	45.00		
		Ey. Phosphor omitted........................	2.00		
		Eya. Red & phosphor omitted	80.00		
779	**310**	9d. red, blue, ochre, brown, black & grey		10	15
		a. Strip of 3. Nos. 779/81.....................	60		75
		ab. Red & blue omitted........................	£1200		
		ac. Blue omitted................................	£1200		
		Ey. Phosphor omitted........................	12.00		
		Eya. Strip of 3. Nos. 779/81 phosphor omitted	40.00		
780	**311**	9d. ochre, brown, black & grey............		10	15
		Ey. Phosphor omitted........................	12.00		
781	**312**	9d. ochre, brown, black & grey............		10	15
		Ey. Phosphor omitted........................	12.00		
782	**313**	1s. brown, black, grey, green & greenish yellow		25	25
		a. Pair. Nos. 782/3	60		80
		ab. Greenish yellow omitted	£900		
		Ey. Phosphor omitted........................	25.00		
		Eya. Pair. Nos. 782/3. Phosphor omitted...	50.00		

783	**314**	1s. red, black, brown, carmine & grey ...		25	25
		a. Carmine (hull overlay) omitted			
		Ey. Phosphor omitted........................	25.00		
		Set of 6	1.10		85
		First Day Cover			3.25
		Presentation Pack...........................	2.00		
		Presentation Pack (German).............	22.00		

The 9d. and 1s. values were arranged in horizontal strips of three and pairs respectively throughout the sheet.

No. 779b is known only with the phosphor also omitted.

Special First Day of Issue Postmark
G.P.O. Philatelic Bureau, Edinburgh 1 (Type C) 4.50

315 "Concorde" in Flight

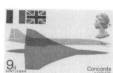

316 Plan and Elevation Views

317 "Concorde's" Nose and Tail

(Des M. and Sylvia Goaman (4d.), D. Gentleman (9d., 1s. 6d.))

1969 (3 Mar). **First Flight of "Concorde".** *Chalk-surfaced paper. Two phosphor bands. P* 15 × 14.

784	**315**	4d. yellow-orange, violet, greenish blue, blue-green & pale-green................		8	8
		a. Violet (value, etc.) omitted..............	£300		
		b. Yellow-orange omitted	£110		
		Ey. Phosphor omitted........................	1.00		
		Eya. Yellow-orange & phosphor omitted..	£120		
785	**316**	9d. ultramarine, emerald, red & grey-blue		10	20
		Ey. Phosphor omitted........................	£200		
786	**317**	1s. 6d. deep blue, silver-grey & lt blue ...		20	20
		a. Silver-grey omitted	£275		
		Ey. Phosphor omitted........................	5.00		
		Set of 3	30		40
		First Day Cover			90
		Presentation Pack...........................	2.00		
		Presentation Pack (German).............	20.00		

No. 786a affects the Queen's head which appears in the light blue colour.

Special First Day of Issue Postmarks
G.P.O. Philatelic Bureau, Edinburgh (Type C) 1.50
Filton, Bristol (Type C)....................................... 2.50

318 Queen Elizabeth II. (See also Type **357**)

(Des after plaster cast by Arnold Machin. Recess Bradbury, Wilkinson)

1969 (5 Mar). P 12.

787	**318**	2s. 6d. brown		50	20
788		5s. crimson-lake		3.00	50
789		10s. dp ultramarine		7.50	7.00
790		£1 bluish black		3.00	1.50
		Set of 4		12.50	8.25
		First Day Cover			20.00
		Presentation Pack		20.00	
		Presentation Pack (German)		45.00	

For decimal issue, see Nos. 829/31b and notes after No. 831b.

Special First Day of Issue Postmark
G.P.O. Philatelic Bureau, Edinburgh (Type C) 3.00

324 Durham Cathedral   **325** York Minster

319 Page from *Daily Mail*, and Vickers "Vimy" Aircraft

320 Europa and CEPT Emblems

326 St. Giles' Cathedral, Edinburgh   **327** Canterbury Cathedral

321 ILO Emblem

322 Flags of NATO Countries

328 St. Paul's Cathedral   **329** Liverpool Metropolitan Cathedral

323 Vickers "Vimy" Aircraft and Globe showing Flight

(Des P. Sharland (5d., 1s., 1s. 6d.), M. and Sylvia Goaman (9d., 1s. 9d.))

1969 (2 Apr). **Anniversaries.** *Events described on stamps. Chalk-surfaced paper. Two phosphor bands.* P 15 × 14.

791	**319**	5d. black, pale sage-green, chestnut & new blue	5	5
		Ey. Phosphor omitted		
792	**320**	9d. pale turquoise, dp blue, lt emerald-green & black	30	30
		Ey. Phosphor omitted	15.00	
793	**321**	1s. brt purple, dp blue & lilac	10	12
		Ey. Phosphor omitted	8.00	
794	**322**	1s. 6d. red, royal blue, yellow-green, black, lemon & new blue	15	15
		e. Black omitted	55.00	
		f. Yellow-green omitted	45.00	
		Ey. Phosphor omitted	8.00	
		Eya. Yellow-green & phosphor omitted	50.00	
795	**323**	1s. 9d. yellow-olive, greenish yellow & pale turquoise-green	20	20
		a. Uncoated paper*	£200	
		Ey. Phosphor omitted	5.00	
		Set of 5	50	60
		First Day Cover		1.25
		Presentation Pack	2.00	
		Presentation Pack (German)	45.00	

*Uncoated paper. The second note after No. 744 also applies here.

(Des P. Gauld)

1969 (28 May). **British Architecture.** *Cathedrals. Chalk-surfaced paper. Two phosphor bands.* P 15 × 14.

796	**324**	5d. grey-black, orange, pale bluish violet & black	8	8
		a. Block of 4. Nos. 796/9	50	75
		b. Pale bluish violet omitted	£750	
797	**325**	5d. grey-black, pale bluish violet, new blue & black	8	8
		b. Pale bluish violet omitted	£750	
798	**326**	5d. grey-black, purple, green & black	8	8
		c. Green omitted*	35.00	
799	**327**	5d. grey-black, green, new blue & black	8	8
800	**328**	9d. grey-black, ochre, pale drab, violet & black	12	12
		a. Black (value) omitted	90.00	
		Ey. Phosphor omitted	40.00	
801	**329**	1s. 6d. grey-black, pale turquoise, pale reddish violet, pale yellow-olive & black	15	15
		a. Black (value) omitted	£2000	
		b. Black (value) double		
		Ey. Phosphor omitted	20.00	
		Set of 6	70	55
		First Day Cover		1.60
		Presentation Pack	2.25	
		Presentation Pack (German)	24.00	

The 5d. values were issued together *se-tenant* in blocks of four throughout the sheet.

*The missing green on the roof top is known on R.2/5, R.8/5 and R.10/5 but all from different sheets and it only occurred in part of the printing, being "probably caused by a batter on the impression cylinder". Examples are also known with the green partly omitted.

Special First Day of Issue Postmark
G.P.O. Philatelic Bureau, Edinburgh (Type C) 2.75

330 The King's Gate, Caernarvon Castle

331 The Eagle Tower, Caernarvon Castle

332 Queen Eleanor's Gate, Caernarvon Castle

333 Celtic Cross, Margam Abbey

334 H.R.H. The Prince of Wales (after photo by G. Argent)

(Des D. Gentleman)

1969 (1 July). **Investiture of H.R.H. The Prince of Wales.** *Chalk-surfaced paper. Two phosphor bands. P 14 × 15.*

802	**330**	5d. dp olive-grey, lt olive-grey, dp grey, lt grey, red, pale turquoise-green, black & silver	5	10
		a. Strip of 3. Nos. 802/4	25	35
		b. Black (value & inscr) omitted	£325	
		c. Red omitted*	£200	
		d. Dp grey omitted*	£110	
		e. Pale turquoise-green omitted	£250	
		Ey. Phosphor omitted	3.50	
		Eya. Strip of 3. Nos. 802/4. Phosphor omitted	10.00	
803	**331**	5d. dp olive-grey, lt olive-grey, dp grey, lt grey, red, pale turquoise-green, black & silver	5	10
		b. Black (value and inscr) omitted	£325	
		c. Red omitted**	£200	
		d. Dp grey omitted**	£110	
		e. Pale turquoise-green omitted	£250	
		Ey. Phosphor omitted	3.50	

804	**332**	5d. dp olive-grey, lt olive-grey, dp grey, lt grey, red, pale turquoise-green, black & silver	5	10
		b. Black (value & inscr) omitted	£325	
		c. Red omitted**	£200	
		d. Dp grey omitted**	£110	
		e. Pale turquoise-green omitted	£250	
		Ey. Phosphor omitted	3.50	
805	**333**	9d. dp grey, lt grey, black & gold	10	10
		Ey. Phosphor omitted	20.00	
806	**334**	1s. blackish yellow-olive & gold	10	15
		Ey. Phosphor omitted	12.00	
		Set of 5	40	50
		First Day Cover		1.00
		Presentation Pack†	1.40	
		Presentation Pack (German)	18.00	

The 5d. values were issued together *se-tenant* in strips of three throughout the sheet.

*The 5d. value is also known with the red misplaced downwards and where this occurs the red printing does not take very well on the silver background and in some cases is so faint that it could be mistaken for a missing red. However, the red can be seen under a magnifying glass and caution should therefore be exercised when purchasing copies of Nos. 802/4c.

**The deep grey affects the dark portions of the windows and doors.

†In addition to the generally issued Presentation Pack a further pack in different colours and with all texts printed in both English and Welsh was made available exclusively through Education Authorities for free distribution to all schoolchildren in Wales and Monmouthshire (*Price £4*).

Special First Day of Issue Postmarks

G.P.O. Philatelic Bureau, Edinburgh 1 (Type C)	3.00	
Day of Investiture, Caernarvon	1.50	

335 Mahatma Gandhi

(Des B. Mullick)

1969 (13 Aug). **Gandhi Centenary Year.** *Chalk-surfaced paper. Two phosphor bands. P 15 × 14.*

807	**335**	1s. 6d. black, green, red-orange & grey .	20	20
		a. Printed on the gummed side	£275	
		Ey. Phosphor omitted	5.00	
		First Day Cover		50

Special First Day of Issue Postmark
G.P.O. Philatelic Bureau, Edinburgh (Type C) 1.00

Collectors Pack 1969

1969 (15 Sept). *Comprises Nos. 775/86 and 791/807.*
CP807b   Collectors Pack 25.00

336 National Giro "G" Symbol

337 Telecommunications-
International Subscriber Dialling

338 Telecommunications—
Pulse Code Modulation

339 Postal Mechanisation—
Automatic Sorting

(Des D. Gentleman. Litho De La Rue)

1969 (1 Oct). **Post Office Technology Commemoration.** *Chalk-sur-faced paper. Two phosphor bands. P 13½ × 14.*

808	336	5d. new blue, greenish blue, lavender & black	5	5
		Ey. Phosphor omitted.........................	5.00	
809	337	9d. emerald, violet-blue & black............	8	10
810	338	1s. emerald, lavender & black	12	15
		Ey. Phosphor omitted.........................	£300	
811	339	1s. 6d. brt purple, lt blue, grey-blue & black	25	30
		Set of 4	40	50
		First Day Cover		80
		Presentation Pack.........................	1.60	

Special First Day of Issue Postmark
G.P.O. Philatelic Bureau, Edinburgh (Type C) 1.75

340 Herald Angel

341 The Three Shepherds

342 The Three Kings

(Des F. Wegner. Queen's head (and stars 4d., 5d. and scroll-work 1s. 6d.) printed in gold and then embossed)

1969 (26 Nov). **Christmas.** *Chalk-surfaced paper. Two phosphor bands (5d., 1s. 6d.) or one centre band (4d.). P 15 × 14.*

812	340	4d. vermilion, new blue, orange, brt purple, lt green, bluish violet, blackish brown & gold..............................	5	8
		a. Gold (Queen's head etc.) omitted	£1300	
		Eb. Centre band 3½ mm	25	15
813	341	5d. magenta, lt blue, royal blue, olive-brown, green, greenish yellow, red & gold	5	8

(813)		a. Lt blue (sheep, etc.) omitted	55.00	
		b. Red omitted*	£450	
		c. Gold (Queen's head) omitted.........	£800	
		d. Green omitted	£225	
		Ee. Embossing omitted	20.00	
		Ey. Phosphor omitted.........................	1.00	
814	342	1s. 6d. greenish yellow, brt purple, bluish violet, dp slate, orange, green, new blue & gold	20	25
		a. Gold (Queen's head etc.) omitted....	£125	
		b. Dp slate (value) omitted.................	£350	
		c. Greenish yellow omitted	£125	
		d. Bluish violet omitted	£300	
		e. New blue omitted.........................	£100	
		Ef. Embossing omitted	8.00	
		Ey. Phosphor omitted.........................	7.00	
		Eya. Embossing & phosphor omitted.......	9.00	
		Set of 3	25	30
		First Day Cover		50
		Presentation Pack........................	1.60	

*The effect of the missing red is shown on the hat, leggings and purse which appear as dull orange.

No. 812 has one centre band 8 mm. wide but this was of no practical use in the automatic facing machines and after about three-quarters of the stamps had been printed the remainder were printed with a 3½mm. band (No. 812Eb).

Used copies of the 5d. have been seen with the olive-brown or greenish yellow omitted.

Special First Day of Issue Postmarks
P.O. Philatelic Bureau, Edinburgh (Type C)............ 1.25
Bethlehem, Llandeilo, Carms (Type C) 1.50

343 Fife Harling

344 Cotswold Limestone

345 Welsh Stucco

346 Ulster Thatch

(Des D. Gentleman (5d., 9d.), Sheila Robinson (1s., 1s. 6d.))

1970 (11 Feb). **British Rural Architecture.** *Chalk-surfaced paper. Two phosphor bands. P 15 × 14.*

815	343	5d. grey, grey-black, black, lemon, greenish blue, orange-brown, ultramarine & green	5	5
		a. Lemon omitted	60.00	
		b. Grey (Queen's head & cottage shading) omitted................................	£4000	
		Ey. Phosphor omitted.........................	1.75	
816	344	9d. orange-brown, olive-yellow, brt green, black, grey-black & grey........	15	15
		Ey. Phosphor omitted.........................	10.00	
817	345	1s. dp blue, reddish lilac, drab & new blue	12	15
		a. New blue omitted.........................	45.00	
		Ey. Phosphor omitted.........................	10.00	

818	**346**	1s. 6d. greenish yellow, black, turquoise-blue & lilac	20	20
		a. Turquoise-blue omitted	£1750	
		Ey. Phosphor omitted	2.75	
		Set of 4	50	50
		First Day Cover		1.00
		Presentation Pack	1.60	

Used examples of the 5d. have been seen with the grey-black or greenish blue colours omitted.

Special First Day of Issue Postmark
British Philatelic Bureau, Edinburgh (Type C) 1.75

347 Signing the Declaration of Arbroath

348 Florence Nightingale attending Patients

349 Signing of International Co-operative Alliance

350 Pilgrims and *Mayflower*

351 Sir William Herschel, Francis Baily, Sir John Herschel and Telescope

(Des F. Wegner (5d., 9d., and 1s. 6d.), Marjorie Saynor (1s., 1s. 9d.). Queen's head printed in gold and then embossed)

1970 (1 Apr). **Anniversaries.** *Events described on stamps. Chalk-surfaced paper. Two phosphor bands.* P 15 × 14.

819	**347**	5d. black, yellow-olive, blue, emerald, greenish yellow, rose-red, gold & orange-red	5	5
		a. Gold (Queen's head) omitted	£350	
		b. Emerald omitted	50.00	
		Ey. Phosphor omitted	£150	
820	**348**	9d. ochre, dp blue, carmine, black, blue-green, yellow-olive, gold & blue	8	12
		a. Ochre omitted	£150	
		Eb. Embossing omitted	10.00	
		Ey. Phosphor omitted	3.00	
821	**349**	1s. green, greenish yellow, brown, black, cerise, gold & lt blue	10	12
		a. Gold (Queen's head) omitted	45.00	
		b. Green & embossing omitted	£120	
		c. Green omitted	£110	
		d. Brown omitted	£125	
		Ee. Embossing omitted	10.00	
		Ey. Phosphor omitted	5.00	
		Eya. Brown & phosphor omitted	£110	
		Eyb. Embossing & phosphor omitted	20.00	

822	**350**	1s. 6d. greenish yellow, carmine, dp yellow-olive, emerald, black, blue, gold & sage-green	20	20
		a. Gold (Queen's head) omitted	90.00	
		b. Emerald omitted	38.00	
		Ec. Embossing omitted	2.50	
		Ey. Phosphor omitted	4.00	
823	**351**	1s. 9d. black, slate, lemon, gold & brt purple	25	25
		Ey. Phosphor omitted	3.50	
		Set of 5	60	60
		First Day Cover		1.25
		Presentation Pack	2.25	

The 1s. 9d. with the lemon colour omitted has been seen used on a First Day Cover.

Special First Day of Issue Postmark
British Philatelic Bureau, Edinburgh (Type C) 2.25
First Day of Issue handstamps were provided at Billericay, Essex; Boston, Lincs and Rochdale, Lancs for this issue.

352 "Mr. Pickwick and Sam" (*Pickwick Papers*)

353 "Mr. and Mrs. Micawber" (*David Copperfield*)

354 "David Copperfield and Betsy Trotwood" (*David Copperfield*)

355 "Oliver asking for more"(*Oliver Twist*)

356 "Grasmere" (from an engraving by J. Farrington, R.A.)

T **352/5** were issued together *se-tenant* in blocks of four throughout the sheet.

(Des Rosalind Dease. Queen's head printed in gold and then embossed)

1970 (3 June). **Literary Anniversaries.** *Death Centenary of Charles Dickens (novelist) (5d. × 4) and Birth Bicentenary of William Wordsworth (poet) (1s. 6d.). Chalk-surfaced paper. Two phosphor bands.* P 14 × 15.

824	**352**	5d. black, orange, silver, gold & magenta	8	10
		a. Block of 4. Nos. 824/7	65	80
		ab. Imperf (block of four)	£400	
825	**353**	5d. black, magenta, silver, gold & orange	8	10
826	**354**	5d. black, lt greenish blue, silver, gold & yellow-bistre	8	10
		b. Yellow-bistre (value) omitted	£750	

827	355	5d. black, yellow-bistre, silver, gold & lt greenish blue	8	10
		b. Yellow-bistre (background) omitted	£750	
		c. Lt greenish blue (value) omitted*	£400	
828	356	1s. 6d. lt yellow-olive, black, silver, gold & bright blue	20	20
		a. Gold (Queen's head) omitted	£225	
		b. Silver ("Grasmere") omitted	55.00	
		Ec. Embossing omitted	5.00	
		Ey. Phosphor omitted	5.00	
		Eya. Embossing & phosphor omitted	20.00	
		Set of 5	70	55
		First Day Cover		1.60
		Presentation Pack	2.25	

*No. 827c (unlike No. 826b) comes from a sheet on which the colour was only partially omitted so that, although No. 827 was completely without the light greenish blue colour, it was still partially present on No. 826.

Special First Day of Issue Postmark
British Philatelic Bureau, Edinburgh (Type C) 2.50
First Day of Issue handstamps were provided at Broadstairs, Kent; Cockermouth, Cumberland and Rochester, Kent, for this issue.

357 (Value redrawn)
(Des after plaster cast by Arnold Machin. Recess B.W.)

1970 (17 June)–72. *Decimal Currency. Chalk-surfaced paper or phosphorised paper (10p.). P 12.*

829	357	10p. cerise	1.40	70
830		20p. olive-green	80	10
		Ea. Thinner uncoated paper*		
831		50p. dp ultramarine	1.50	40
		Ea. Thinner uncoated paper*	38.00	
831b		£1 bluish black (6.12.72)	2.75	60
		Set of 4	6.00	1.60
		First Day Cover (829/31)		5.50
		First Day Cover (831b)		10.00
		Presentation Pack (829/31)	9.00	
		Presentation Pack (790 (or 831b), 830/1)	9.00	

*These are not as apparent as uncoated photogravure issues where there is normally a higher degree of chalk-surfacing. The 20p. is known only as a block of four with Plate No. 5. The 50p. comes from Plate No. 9.

The 10p. on phosphorised paper continued the experiments which started with the Machin 1s. 6d. When the experiment had ended a quantity of the 50p. value was printed on the phosphorised paper to use up the stock. These stamps were issued on 1 February 1973, but they cannot be distinguished from No. 831 by the naked eye. (*Price* £2.25).

A £1 was also issued in 1970, but it is difficult to distinguish it from the earlier No. 790. In common with the other 1970 values it was issued in sheets of 100.

A whiter paper was introduced in 1973. The £1 appeared on 27 Sept. 1973, the 20p. on 30 Nov. 1973 and the 50p. on 20 Feb. 1974.

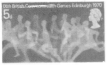

358 Runners

359 Swimmers

360 Cyclists

(Des A. Restall. Litho D.L.R.)

1970 (15 July). **Ninth British Commonwealth Games.** *Chalk-surfaced paper. Two phosphor bands. P 13½ × 14.*

832	358	5d. pink, emerald, greenish yellow & dp yellow-green	8	8
		a. Greenish yellow omitted		
		Ey. Phosphor omitted	£200	
833	359	1s. 6d. lt greenish blue, lilac, bistre-brown & Prussian blue	30	35
		Ey. Phosphor omitted	75.00	
834	360	1s. 9d. yellow-orange, lilac, salmon & dp red-brown	30	35
		Set of 3	60	70
		First Day Cover		80
		Presentation Pack	2.00	

Special First Day of Issue Postmark
British Philatelic Bureau, Edinburgh (Type C) 1.50

Collectors Pack 1970

1970 (14 Sept). *Comprises Nos. 808/28 and 832/4.*
CP834a Collectors Pack 28.00

361 1d. Black (1840)

362 1s. Green (1847)

363 4d. Carmine (1855)

(Des D. Gentleman)

1970 (18 Sept). **"Philympia 70" Stamp Exhibition.** *Chalk-surfaced paper. Two phosphor bands. P 14 × 14½.*

835	361	5d. grey-black, brownish bistre, black & dull purple	5	5
		Ey. Phosphor omitted	4.00	

836	362	9d. lt drab, bluish green, stone, black & dull purple	25	30
		Ey. Phosphor omitted........................	9.00	
837	363	1s. 6d. carmine, lt drab, black & dull purple	25	30
		Ey. Phosphor omitted........................	4.00	
		Set of 3	45	50
		First Day Cover		1.00
		Presentation Pack	2.00	

Special First Day of Issue Postmark

British Post Office Philatelic Bureau, Edinburgh....... 1.50

364 Shepherds and Apparition of the Angel

365 Mary, Joseph, and Christ in the Manger

366 The Wise Men bearing gifts

(Des Sally Stiff after De Lisle Psalter. Queen's head printed in gold and then embossed)

1970 (25 Nov). **Christmas.** *Chalk-surfaced paper. One centre phosphor band (4d.) or two phosphor bands (others). P 14 × 15.*

838	364	4d. brown-red, turquoise-green, pale chestnut, brown, grey-black, gold & vermilion	5	5
		Ea. Embossing omitted	40.00	
		Ey. Phosphor omitted........................	55.00	
839	365	5d. emerald, gold, blue, brown-red, ochre, grey-black & violet	5	5
		a. Gold (Queen's head) omitted	†	—
		b. Emerald omitted............................	60.00	
		c. Imperf (pair)	£250	
		Ed. Embossing omitted	15.00	
		Ey. Phosphor omitted........................	2.50	

840	366	1s. 6d. gold, grey-black, pale turquoise-green, salmon, ultramarine, ochre & yellow-green	25	25
		a. Salmon omitted.............................	£125	
		b. Ochre omitted	65.00	
		Ec. Embossing omitted	30.00	
		Ey. Phosphor omitted........................	5.00	
		Eya. Embossing & phosphor omitted		
		Set of 3	30	30
		First Day Cover		50
		Presentation Pack	2.00	

Special First Day of Issue Postmarks

British Post Office Philatelic Bureau, Edinburgh....... 1.10
Bethlehem, Llandeilo, Carms 1.00

(New Currency. 100 new pence=£1)

"X" NUMBERS. The following definitive series has been allocated ''X'' prefixes to the catalogue numbers to avoid re-numbering all subsequent issues.

367

367a

I

II

Two types of the 10p and 26p (Nos. X886/Eb and X948/Ea)

Figures of face value as I (all 10p and 26p sheet and booklet stamps except from booklets Nos. DX5 and GC1).
Figures of face value taller as in II (from booklets Nos. DX5 (10p.) or GC1 (26p.)).

(Des from plaster cast by Arnold Machin)

1971 (15 Feb)–**88.** *Decimal Currency. T 367. Chalk-surfaced paper.*

(a) *Photo Harrison (except for a printing of No. X879 in sheets produced by Enschedé in 1979). With phosphor bands. P 15 × 14.*

X841	½p. turquoise-blue (2 bands)................	5	5
	a. Imperf (pair)†..............................	£600	
	l. Booklet pane. No. X841 × 2 se-tenant vert with X849 × 2	5.50	
	lEy. Booklet pane. Phosphor omitted......	£150	
	la. Booklet pane. No. X841 × 2 se-tenant horiz with X849 × 2	70	
	laEy. Booklet pane. Phosphor omitted......	£350	

(X841)	m. Booklet pane. No. X841 × 5 plus label	2.25	
	mEy. Booklet pane. Phosphor omitted......	90.00	
	n. Coil strip No. X849Eg, X841Eg × 2 & X844Eg × 2	2.00	
	nEy. Coil strip. Phosphor omitted	30.00	
	nEv. Coil strip. PVA gum. No. X849, X841 × 2 & X844 × 2 (4.74)....................	25	
	nEvy. Coil strip. Phosphor omitted	9.00	
	o. Booklet pane. No. X841 × 3, X851 × 3, X852 × 3, X852Ea × 3 (24.5.72)..	18.00	
	oEy. Booklet pane. Phosphor omitted......	£1500	
	p. Booklet pane. No. X841 × 3, X842 × 2 (24.5.72)........................	70.00	
	pEy. Booklet pane. Phosphor omitted......		
	q. Coil strip. No. X870, X849, X844 & X841 × 2 (3.12.75)..........................	40	
	r. Booklet pane. No. X841 × 2, X844 × 3 & X870 (10.3.76).................	60	
	s. Booklet pane. No. X841 × 2, X844 × 2, X873 × 2 & X881 × 4 (8½p. values at right) (26.1.77).................	2.40	
	sa. Ditto but No. 873Ea & 8½p. values at left..	2.00	
	t. Booklet pane. No. X841, X844, X894 × 3 & X902 (14p. value at right) (26.1.81).......................................	1.60	
	tEy. Booklet pane. Phosphor omitted......	35.00	
	ta. Booklet pane. No. X841, X844, X894Ea × 3 & X902 (14p. value at left)...	1.60	
	taEy. Booklet pane. Phosphor omitted......	35.00	
	u. Booklet pane, No. X841, X857 × 4 & X899 × 3 (12½p. values at left) (1.2.82)	1.90	
	ua. Ditto but No. X899Ea & 12½p. values at right..	1.90	
	Eg. Gum arabic (from coil strip, & on 22.9.72 from sheets).......................	10	
	Egy. Phosphor omitted.........................	50.00	
X842	½p. turquoise-blue (1 side band at left) (24.5.72).......................................	60.00	32.00
X843	½p. turquoise-blue (1 centre band) (14.12.77).......................................	20	20
	l. Coil strip. No. X843 × 2, X875 & X845 × 2 (14.12.77)	45	
	m. Booklet pane. No. X843 × 2, X845 × 2 & X875 plus label (8.2.78) ...	60	
	mEy. Booklet pane. Phosphor omitted.....	25.00	
X844	1p. crimson (2 bands)	5	5
	a. Imperf (vert coil)		
	b. Pair, one imperf 3 sides (vert coil)		
	c. Imperf (pair)		
	l. Booklet pane. No. X844 × 2 se-tenant vert with X848 × 2	5.50	
	m. Ditto se-tenant horiz (14.7.71)..........	70	
	mEy. Booklet pane. Phosphor omitted......	80.00	
	n. Booklet pane. No. X844 × 2, X876 × 3 & X883 × 3 (9p. values at right) (13.6.77).......................................	4.00	
	na. Ditto but No. X876Ea & 9p. values at left..	2.00	
	Eg. Gum arabic (from coil strip)	20	
	Egy. Phosphor omitted.........................	45.00	
X845	1p. crimson (1 centre band) (14.12.77)...	10	10
	l. Booklet pane. No. X879 & X845 × 2 plus label (17.10.79)	40	
	m. Coil strip. No. X879 & X845 × 2 plus 2 labels (16.1.80)	35	
	n. Booklet pane. No. X845 × 2, X860 & X898 each × 3 (5.4.83)	4.00	
	nEy. Booklet pane. Phosphor omitted......	16.00	
	p. Booklet pane. No. X845 × 3, X863 × 2 & X900 × 3 (3.9.84)	1.60	

(X845)	pEy. Booklet pane. Phosphor omitted	£180	
	q. Booklet pane. No. X845 × 2 & X896 × 4 (29.7.86).....................................	1.40	
	s. Booklet pane. No. X845, X867 × 2 & X900 × 3 (20.10.86)	1.40	
	sa. Ditto, but with sides of pane imperf (29.9.87)	75	80
X846	1p. crimson ("all-over") (10.10.79)	10	15
X847	1p. crimson (1 side band at left) (20.10.86)	35	35
	Ea. Band at right (3.3.87).....................	45	50
	l. Booklet pane. No. X847, X901 & X906 × 2 (20.10.86)	1.40	
	lEy. Booklet pane. Phosphor omitted	90.00	
	m. Booklet pane. No. X847Ea, X901 × 2, X906 × 5 & X908 with margins all round (3.3.87).......................	4.00	
X848	1½p. black (2 bands)............................	10	12
	a. Uncoated paper (1971)*	£110	
	b. Imperf (pair)		
	c. Imperf 3 sides (horiz pair)		
	Ey. Phosphor omitted..........................	10.00	
X849	2p. myrtle-green (2 bands)	8	5
	l. Booklet pane. No. X849 × 2, X880 × 2 & X886 × 3 plus label (10p. values at right) (28.8.79)...............	1.60	
	la. Ditto but No. X880Ea & 10p. values at left	1.60	
	m. Booklet pane. No. X849 × 3, X889 × 2 & X895 × 2 plus label (12p. values at right) (4.2.80)	1.90	
	mEy. Booklet pane. Phosphor omitted......	30.00	
	ma. Booklet pane. No. X849 × 3, X889Ea × 2 & X895 × 2 plus label (12p. values at left)	1.90	
	maEy. Booklet pane. Phosphor omitted......	30.00	
	n. Booklet pane. No. X849, X888 × 3, X889Ea & X895 × 4 with margins all round (16.4.80).............................	2.60	
	nEy. Booklet pane. Phosphor omitted......	50.00	
	o. Booklet pane. No. X849 × 6 with margins all round (16.4.80)	45	
	oEy. Booklet pane. Phosphor omitted......	50.00	
	p. Booklet pane. No. X849, X857, X898, X899 × 3 and X899Ea × 3 with margins all round (19.5.82)...................	6.00	
	pEy. Booklet pane. Phosphor omitted......	£100	
	Eg. Gum arabic (from coil strip)	2.25	
	Egy. Phosphor omitted.........................	£170	
X850	2p. myrtle-green ("all over") (10.10.79)......	12	15
X851	2½p. magenta (1 centre band)	12	10
	a. Imperf (pair)†	£225	
	Ey. Phosphor omitted..........................	6.50	
	l. Booklet pane. No. X851 × 5 plus label	3.50	
	lEy. Booklet pane. Phosphor omitted......	35.00	
	m. Booklet pane. No. X851 × 4 plus two labels	4.00	
	mEy. Booklet pane. Phosphor omitted......	75.00	
	n. Booklet pane. No. X851 × 3, X852Ea × 3 & X855 × 6 (24.5.72)	12.00	
	nEy. Booklet pane. Phosphor omitted......		
	Eg. Gum arabic (13.9.72)	15	
X852	2½p. magenta (1 band at left)	1.25	1.50
	l. Booklet pane. No. X852 × 2 and X855 × 4	4.50	
	lEy. Booklet pane. Phosphor omitted......	90.00	
	Ea. Band at right (24.5.72).....................	1.90	2.25
X853	2½p. magenta (2 bands) (21.5.75)	20	30
X854	2½p. rose-red (2 bands) (26.8.81)	30	30
	l. Booklet pane. No. X854 × 3, X862 × 3 and X894 × 3, (11½p. values at left)...	3.50	
	la. Ditto but No. X894Ea and 11½p. values at right..	4.00	

X855	3p. ultramarine (2 bands)	20	8	
	a. Imperf (coil strip of 5)......................	£1000		
	b. Imperf (pair)†	£225		
	c. Uncoated paper (1972)*	40.00		
	Ey. Phosphor omitted..........................	2.00		
	l. Booklet pane. No. X855 × 5 plus label	2.75		
	lEy. Booklet pane. Phosphor omitted......	£250		
	Eg. Gum arabic (23.8.76)	75		
	Egy. Phosphor omitted..........................	7.00		
X856	3p. ultramarine (1 centre band) (10.9.73).	12	12	
	a. Imperf (pair)†	£250		
	b. Imperf between (vert pair)†	£375		
	c. Imperf horiz (vert pair)†	£150		
	Eg. Gum arabic	20		
	Egy. Phosphor omitted	75.00		
X857	3p. brt magenta (2 bands) (1.2.82)..........	20	25	
X858	3½p. olive-grey (2 bands) (shades)	30	30	
	a. Imperf (pair)	£350		
	Ey. Phosphor omitted..........................	3.50		
	Eb. Bronze-green (18.7.73)	50	40	
	Eby. Phosphor omitted..........................	8.00		
X859	3½p. olive-grey (1 centre band) (24.6.74) ...	20	15	
X860	3½p. purple-brown (1 centre band) (5.4.83)	1.10	90	
X861	4p. ochre-brown (2 bands)	12	15	
	a. Imperf (pair)†	£450		
	Ey. Phosphor omitted..........................	30.00		
	Eg. Gum arabic (1.11.72)	20		
X862	4p. greenish blue (2 bands) (26.8.81)	1.50	1.75	
X863	4p. greenish blue (1 centre band) (3.9.84)	35	60	
X864	4p. greenish blue (1 band at right) (8.1.85)	60	1.10	
	Ea. Band at left	60	1.10	
	l. Booklet pane. No. X864, X864Ea, X901/Ea, each × 2, X905 × 2 & X910 with margins all round (8.1.85)	6.00		
	lEy. Booklet pane. Phosphor omitted	£1000		
X865	4½p. grey-blue (2 bands) (24.10.73)	20	15	
	a. Imperf (pair)	£250		
	Ey. Phosphor omitted..........................	3.50		
X866	5p. pale violet (2 bands)	15	8	
X867	5p. claret (1 centre band) (20.10.86).......	25	25	
X868	5½p. violet (2 bands) (24.10.73)...............	25	25	
X869	5½p. violet (1 centre band) (17.3.75)	25	20	
	a. Uncoated paper*	£350		
	Ey. Phosphor omitted..........................	10.00		
X870	6p. lt emerald (2 bands)	20	10	
	a. Uncoated paper*	15.00		
	Ey. Phosphor omitted..........................	45.00		
	Eg. Gum arabic (6.6.73)	1.50		
X871	6½p. greenish blue (2 bands) (4.9.74)	40	45	
X872	6½p. greenish blue (1 centre band) (24.9.75)	20	12	
	a. Imperf (vert pair)	£300		
	b. Uncoated paper*	£160		
	Ey. Phosphor omitted..........................	10.00		
X873	6½p. greenish blue (1 band at right) (26.1.77)...	40	90	
	Ea. Band at left	35	55	
X874	7p. purple-brown (2 bands) (15.1.75)......	20	12	
	a. Imperf (pair)	£250		
	Ey. Phosphor omitted..........................	1.25		
X875	7p. purple-brown (1 centre band) (13.6.77)...	20	8	
	a. Imperf (pair)	£100		
	l. Booklet pane. No. X875 × 10 & X883 × 10 (15.11.78)	3.75		
X876	7p. purple-brown (1 band at right) (13.6.77)...	45	90	
	Ea. Band at left	20	30	
X877	7½p. pale chestnut (2 bands)...................	20	10	
	Ey. Phosphor omitted..........................	14.00		
X878	8p. rosine (2 bands) (24.10.73)...............	25	15	
	a. Uncoated paper*	10.00		

X879	8p. rosine (1 centre band) (20.8.79)	25	10	
	a. Uncoated paper*	£550		
	b. Imperf (pair)	£550		
	Ey. Phosphor omitted..........................	£110		
	l. Booklet pane. No. X879 × 10 & X886 × 10 (14.11.79)	4.75		
X880	8p. rosine (1 band at right) (29.8.79)	35	45	
	Ea. Band at left	35	45	
X881	8½p. lt yellowish green (2 bands) (shades) (24.9.75)...	35	30	
	a. Imperf (pair)	£750		
	Eb. Yellowish green (24.3.76)	25	10	
X882	9p. yellow-orange & black (2 bands)	40	15	
	Ey. Phosphor omitted..........................	65.00		
X883	9p. dp violet (2 bands) (25.2.76)............	25	10	
	a. Imperf (pair)	£175		
	Ey. Phosphor omitted..........................	1.60		
X884	9½p. purple (2 bands) (25.2.76)................	35	15	
	Ey. Phosphor omitted..........................	13.00		
X885	10p. orange-brown & chestnut (2 bands) (11.8.71)	30	10	
	a. Orange-brown omitted	£150		
	b. Imperf (horiz pair)	£1500		
	Ey. Phosphor omitted..........................	7.50		
X886	10p. orange-brown (Type I) (2 bands) (25.2.76)...	30	5	
	a. Imperf (pair)	£250		
	Eb. Type II (4.9.84)	1.10	1.10	
	l. Booklet pane. No. X886Eb, X901Ea & X905 × 7 with margins all round	5.50		
	lEy. Booklet pane. Phosphor omitted			
X887	10p. orange-brown ("all-over") (3.10.79) ..	30	30	
X888	10p. orange-brown (1 centre band) (4.2.80)	30	12	
	a. Imperf (pair)	£225		
	l. Booklet pane. No. X888 × 9 with margins all round (16.4.80)	2.25		
	lEy. Booklet pane. Phosphor omitted	40.00		
	m. Booklet pane. No. X888 & X895, each × 10 (12.11.80)	6.00		
	mEy. Booklet pane. Phosphor omitted	£125		
X889	10p. orange-brown (1 band at right) (4.2.80)...	40	60	
	Ea. Band at left	40	60	
X890	10½p. yellow (2 bands) (25.2.76)................	30	30	
X891	10½p. dp dull blue (2 bands) (26.4.78)	40	55	
X892	11p. brown-red (2 bands) (25.2.76)	35	15	
	a. Imperf (pair)	£1500		
X893	11½p. drab (1 centre band) (14.1.81)...........	30	30	
	a. Imperf (pair)	£175		
	Ey. Phosphor omitted..........................	5.50		
	l. Booklet pane. No. X893 & X900, each × 10 (11.11.81)	8.50		
X894	11½p. drab (1 band at right) (26.1.81)	35	45	
	Ea. Band at left	35	45	
	l. Booklet pane. No. X894/Ea, each × 2 & X900 × 6 (6.5.81)	4.25		
X895	12p. yellowish green (2 bands) (4.2.80).....	35	40	
	l. Booklet pane. No. X895 × 9 with margins all round (16.4.80)	2.75		
	lEy. Booklet pane. Phosphor omitted.:....	40.00		
X896	12p. brt emerald (1 centre band) (29.10.85)	30	25	
	Eu. Underprint Type 4 (29.10.85)	45		
	Ey. Phosphor omitted	8.00		
	l. Booklet pane. No. X896 × 9 with margins all round (18.3.86)..............	3.00		
	lEy. Booklet pane. Phosphor omitted	£160		
X897	12p. brt emerald (1 band at right) (14.1.86)...	35	45	
	Ea. Band at left	35	45	
	l. Booklet pane. No. X897/Ea, each × 2 & X905 × 6 (12p. values at left) (14.1.86)	4.00		

(X897)	la. Ditto. 12p. values at right	4.00		
	m. Booklet pane. No. X897/Ea, each × 3, X905 × 2 and X909 with margins all round (18.3.86)	5.00		
	mEy. Booklet pane. Phosphor omitted	£1000		
X898	12½p. lt emerald (1 centre band) (27.1.82)..	30	15
	a. Imperf (pair)	£100	
	Eu. Underprint Type 1 (10.11.82)	50	
	Eua. Underprint Type 2 (9.11.83)	45	
	Ey. Phosphor omitted	2.75	
	l. Booklet pane. No. X898Eu & X903Eu each × 10 (10.11.82)	9.00	
X899	12½p. lt emerald (1 band at right) (1.2.82) ..	35	40
	Ea. Band at left	35	40
	l. Booklet pane. No. X899/Ea, each × 2 & X903 × 6 (1.2.82)††	4.00	
	m. Booklet pane. No. X899/Ea, each × 3 with margins all round (19.5.82).......	1.90	
	mEy. Booklet pane. Phosphor omitted	25.00	
	n. Booklet pane. No. X899/Ea, each × 2 & X904 × 6 (12½p. values at left) (5.4.83)	9.00	
	na. Ditto. 12½p. values at right	9.00	
X900	13p. pale chestnut (1 centre band) (28.8.84)	35	20
	a. Imperf (pair)	£400	
	Eu. Underprint Type 2 (2.12.86)	40	
	Ey. Phosphor omitted	22.00	
	l. Booklet pane. No. X900 × 9 with margins all round (8.1.85)	2.90	
	lEy. Booklet pane. Phosphor omitted	£350	
	m. Booklet pane. No. X900 × 6 with margins all round (3.3.87)	1.90	
	n. Booklet pane. No. X900 × 4 with margins all round (4.8.87)	80	
	o. Booklet pane. No. X900 × 10 with margins all round (4.8.87)	2.00	
X901	13p. pale chestnut (1 band at right) (3.9.84)	35	45
	Ea. Band at left	35	45
	l. Booklet pane. No. X901/Ea, each × 2 & X905 × 6 (13p. values at left)	4.50	
	la. Ditto. 13p. values at right	4.50	
	m. Booklet pane. No. X901/Ea, each × 3 with margins all round (4.9.84)	1.90	
	mEy. Booklet pane. Phosphor omitted	£225	
	n. Booklet pane. No. X901Ea & X906 × 5 (20.10.86)	2.60	
	na. Ditto, but with sides of pane imperf (29.9.87)	1.50	
X902	14p. grey-blue (2 bands) (26.1.81)	50	45
X903	15½p. pale violet (2 bands) (1.2.82)	45	45
	Eu. Underprint Type 1 (10.11.82)	60	
	l. Booklet pane. No. X903 × 6 with margins all round (19.5.82)..............	2.50	
	lEy. Booklet pane. Phosphor omitted	75.00	
	m. Booklet pane. No. X903 × 9 with margins all round (19.5.82)	3.50	
	mEy. Booklet pane. Phosphor omitted	30.00	
X904	16p. olive-drab (2 bands) (5.4.83)	1.25	1.25
X905	17p. grey-blue (2 bands) (3.9.84)	50	45
	Eu. Underprint Type 4 (4.11.85)	55	
	l. Booklet pane. No. X905Eu × 3 plus label (4.11.85)	1.50	
	Ela. Booklet pane. No. X905 × 3 plus label (12.8.86)	1.90	
	lEy. Booklet pane. Phosphor omitted	50.00	
X906	18p. olive-grey (2 bands) (20.10.86)	50	60
X907	20p. dull purple (2 bands) (25.2.76)	60	15
X908	26p. rosine (2 bands) (3.3.87)	1.75	1.90
X909	31p. purple (2 bands) (18.3.86)	1.90	2.25
X910	34p. ochre-brown (2 bands) (8.1.85)	1.90	2.25

X911	50p. ochre-brown (2 bands) (2.2.77)........	1.40	15
	(b) Photo Harrison. On phosphorised paper. P 15 × 14		
X914	½p. turquoise-blue (10.12.80)	5	5
	a. Imperf (pair)	£125	
	l. Coil strip. No. X914 & X920 × 3 (30.12.81)	40	
X915	1p. crimson (12.12.79).........................	5	5
	l. Coil strip. No. X915 & X920 × 3 (14.8.84)	35	
X916	2p. myrtle-green (12.12.79)	8	5
X917	2½p. rose-red (14.1.81)	12	15
	l. Coil strip. No. X917 & X918 × 3 (6.81)	40	
X918	3p. brt magenta (10.12.80)	8	8
	a. Imperf (horiz pair)		
	l. Booklet pane. No. X918, X919 × 2 & X933 × 6 with margins all round (14.9.83)	6.00	
X919	3½p. purple-brown (30.3.83)	30	20
X920	4p. greenish blue (30.12.81)	20	20
X921	5p. pale violet (10.10.79)	20	15
X922	7p. red (29.10.85)	12	15
X923	8½p. yellowish green (24.3.76)	35	60
X924	10p. orange-brown (11.79)	15	30
X925	11p. brown-red (27.8.80)	50	75
X926	11½p. ochre-brown (15.8.79)	45	30
X927	12p. yellowish green (30.1.80)	35	15
X928	13p. olive-grey (15.8.79)	55	25
X929	13½p. purple-brown (30.1.80)	55	25
X930	14p. grey-blue (14.1.81)	40	12
X931	15p. ultramarine (15.8.79)	40	10
X932	15½p. pale violet (14.1.81)	40	25
	a. Imperf (pair)	£300	
X933	16p. olive-drab (30.3.83)	40	25
	a. Imperf (pair)	£160	
	Eu. Underprint Type 3 (10.8.83)	60	
	l. Booklet pane. No. X933 × 9 with margins all round (14.9.83)	3.50	
X934	16½p. pale chestnut (27.1.82)	60	60
X935	17p. lt emerald (30.1.80)	60	25
X936	17p. grey-blue (30.3.83)	40	20
	a. Imperf (pair)	£225	
	Eu. Underprint Type 3 (5.3.85)	60	
	l. Booklet pane. No. X936 × 6 with margins all round (4.9.84)	2.50	
	m. Booklet pane. No. X936 × 9 with margins all round (8.1.85)	3.75	
X937	17½p. pale chestnut (30.1.80)	60	35
X938	18p. dp violet (14.1.81)	60	75
X939	18p. olive-grey (28.8.84)	30	40
	a. Imperf. (pair)	£160	
	l. Booklet pane. No. X939 ×9 with margins all round (3.3.87)	3.75	
	m. Booklet pane. No. X939 × 4 with margins all round (4.8.87)	1.10	
	n. Booklet pane. No. X939 × 10 with margins all round (4.8.87)	2.50	
X940	19½p. olive-grey (27.1.82)	2.75	1.50
X941	20p. dull purple (10.10.79)	60	20
X942	20½p. ultramarine (30.3.82)	60	60
X943	22p. blue (22.10.80)	60	20
	a. Imperf pair	£150	
X944	22p. bright green (28.8.84)	35	45
	a. Imperf (horiz pair)		
X945	23p. brown-red (30.3.83)	1.10	55
X946	24p. violet (28.8.84)	40	45
X947	25p. purple (14.1.81)	75	75
X948	26p. rosine (27.1.82)	40	45
	Ea. Type II (4.8.87)	40	45
	l. Booklet pane. No. X948Ea × 4 with margins all round (4.8.87)	1.50	

63

X949	28p. dp violet (30.3.83)	45	45
	a. Imperf (pair)	£600	
X950	29p. ochre-brown (27.1.82)	2.50	1.10
X951	31p. purple (30.3.83)	50	45
	a. Imperf (pair)	£600	
X952	34p. ochre-brown (28.8.84)	55	45

(c) Photo Harrison. On ordinary paper. P 15 × 14

| X972 | 50p. ochre-brown (21.5.80) | 75 | 20 |
| | a. Imperf (pair) | £400 | |

(d) Litho J. W. (Nos. X974/5, X978/9), Questa (others). P 13½ × 14
(Nos. X973/7, X978/9, X980) or 15 × 14 (others)

X973	2p. emerald-green (*phosphorised paper*) (21.5.80)	8	15
	a. Perf 15 × 14 (10.7.84)	5	15
X973b	2p. brt green and dp green (smaller face value as in T **367**a) (*phosphorised paper*) (23.2.88)	5	5
X974	4p. greenish blue (2 *phosphor bands*) (30.1.80)	15	20
X975	4p. greenish blue (*phosphorised paper*) (11.81)	12	15
	a. Perf 15 × 14 (13.5.86)	8	12
X976	5p. lt violet (*phosphorised paper*) (21.5.80)	15	15
X977	5p. claret (*phosphorised paper*) (27.1.82)	15	15
	a. Perf 15 × 14 (21.2.84)	8	15
X977b	13p. pale chestnut (1 *centre band*) (9.2.88)	20	25
	ba. Booklet pane. No. X977b × 6 with margins all round	1.25	
X977c	13p. pale chestnut (1 *band at right*) (9.2.88)	25	25
	cEa. Band at left	25	25
	cb. Booklet pane. No. X977c/cEa, each × 3, X977e, X979b and X979c with margins all round	3.00	
X977d	18p. olive-grey (*phosphorised paper*) (9.2.88)	35	35
	da. Booklet pane No. X977d × 9 with margins all round	2.75	
	db. Booklet pane. No. X977d × 6 with margins all round	2.10	
X977e	18p. olive-grey (2 *bands*) (9.2.88)	35	35
X978	20p. dull purple (2 *phosphor bands*) (21.5.80)	55	35
X979	20p. dull purple (*phosphorised paper*) (11.81)	50	25
	a. Perf 15 × 14 (13.5.86)	30	40
X979b	22p. bright green (2 *bands*) (9.2.88)	45	50
X979c	34p. ochre-brown (2 *bands*) (9.2.88)	55	60
X980	75p. black (*ordinary paper*) (30.1.80)	1.90	45
	a. Perf 15 × 14 (21.2.84)	1.10	60
X981	75p. brownish grey and black (smaller face value as in T **367**a) (*ordinary paper*) (23.2.88)	1.10	1.25

*See footnote after No. 744.
†These come from sheets with gum arabic.
‡‡Examples of Booklet pane Nos. X899I, X901I and X901Ia are known on which the phosphor bands were printed on the wrong values in error with the result that the side bands appear on the 15½p. or 17p. and the two bands on the 12½p. or 13p. Similarly examples of the 1p. with phosphor band right, instead of left, exist from 50p. booklet pane No. X847I.

Nos. X844a/b come from a strip of eight of the vertical coil. It comprises two normals, one imperforate at sides and bottom, one completely imperforate, one imperforate at top, left and bottom and partly perforated at right due to the bottom three stamps being perforated twice. No. X844b is also known from another strip having one stamp imperforate at sides and bottom.

Nos. X848b/c come from the same sheet, the latter having perforations at the foot of the stamps only.

Coil strips Nos. X914I, X915I and X917I were produced by the Post Office for use by a large direct mail marketing firm. From 2 September 1981 No. X917I was available from the Philatelic Bureau, Edinburgh and, subsequently from a number of other Post Office counters.

Nos. X914I and X915I were sold at the Philatelic Bureau and Post Office philatelic counters.

PART–PERFORATED SHEETS. Since the introduction of the "Jumelle" press in 1972 a number of part-perforated sheets, both definitives and commemoratives, have been discovered. It is believed that these occur when the operation of the press is interrupted. Such sheets invariably show a number of "blind" perforations, where the pins have failed to cut the paper. Our listings of imperforate errors from these sheets are for pairs showing no traces whatsoever of the perforations. Examples showing "blind" perforations are outside our listings.

In cases where perforation varieties affect se-tenant stamps fuller descriptions will be found in Vol. 4 of the *G.B. Specialised Catalogue.*

WHITE PAPER. From 1972 printings appeared on fluorescent white paper giving a stronger chalk reaction than the original ordinary cream paper.

DEXTRIN GUM. From 1973 printings appeared with PVA gum to which dextrin, a bluish green substance had been added, giving a very mottled appearance.

PHOSPHOR OMITTED ERRORS. These are listed for those stamps or booklet panes which were not subsequently issued on phosphorised paper. The following phosphor omitted errors also exist, but can only be identified by the use of an ultra-violet lamp. Prices quoted are for mint examples:

½p. X841 (£1)	5p. X866 *(£175)	15½p. X903 (£4)
1p. X844 (£1.60)	8½p. X881 (£1.75)	16p. X904 (£95)
2p. X849 (£8)	10p. X886 (£1)	17p. X905 (£125)
3p. X857 (£60)	11p. X892 (£2.25)	18p. X906 (£40)
3½p. X860 (£5.50)	12p. X895 (£7)	31p. X909 (£600)
4p. X863 (£75)	14p. X902 (£25)	34p. X910 (£675)

"ALL–OVER" PHOSPHOR. To improve mechanised handling most commemoratives from the 1972 Royal Silver Wedding 3p. value to the 1979 Rowland Hill Death Centenary set had the phosphor applied by printing cylinder across the entire surface of the stamp, giving a matt effect. Printings of the 1, 2 and 10p. definitives, released in October 1979, also had "all-over" phosphor, but these were purely a temporary expedient pending the adoption of phosphorised paper. Nos. X883, X890 and X911 have been discovered with "all-over" phosphor in addition to the normal phosphor bands. These errors are outside the scope of this catalogue.

PHOSPHORISED PAPER. Following the experiments on Nos. 743b and 829 a printing of the 4½p. definitive was issued on 13 November 1974, which had, in addition to the normal phosphor bands, phosphor included in the paper coating. Because of difficulties in identifying this phosphorised paper with the naked eye this printing is not listed separately in this catalogue.

No. X923 was the first value printed on phosphorised paper without phosphor bands and was a further experimental issue to test the efficacy of this system. From 15 August 1979 phosphorised paper was accepted for use generally, this paper replacing phosphor bands on values other than those required for the second-class rate.

Stamps on phosphorised paper show a shiny surface instead of the matt areas of those printed with phosphor bands.

VARNISH COATING. Nos. X841 and X883 exist with and without a varnish coating. This cannot easily be detected without the use of an ultra-violet lamp as it merely reduces the fluorescent paper reaction.

First Day Covers

15.2.71	½p., 1p., 1½p., 2p., 2½p., 3p., 3½p., 4p., 5p., 6p., 7½p., 9p., (X841, X844, X848/9, X851, X855, X858, X861, X866, X870, X877, X882) (Covers carry "POSTING DELAYED BY THE POST OFFICE STRIKE 1971" cachet)	2.50
11.8.71	10p. (X885)	80
24.10.73	4½p., 5½p., 8p. (X865, X868, X878)	1.25
4.9.74	6½p. (X871)	1.25
15.1.75	7p. (X874)	60
24.9.75	8½p. (X881)	1.25
25.2.76	9p., 9½p., 10p., 10½p., 11p., 20p. (X883/4, X886, X890, X892, X907)	2.75
2.2.77	50p. (X911)	2.25
26.4.78	10½p. (X891)	1.00
15.8.79	11½p., 13p., 15p. (X926, X928, X931)..........	2.00
30.1.80	4p., 12p., 13½p., 17p., 17½p., 75p. (X974, X927, X929, X935, X937, X980)...................	4.00
22.10.80	3p., 22p. (X918, X943)	80
14.1.81	2½p., 11½p., 14p., 15½p., 18p., 25p. (X917, X893, X930, X932, X938, X947).................	2.25
27.1.82	5p., 12½p., 16½p., 19½p., 26p., 29p. (X977, X898, X934, X940, X948, X950).................	3.25
30.3.83	3½p., 16p., 17p., 20½p., 23p., 28p., 31p. (X919, X933, X936, X942, X945, X949, X951)	6.50
28.8.84	13p., 18p., 22p., 24p., 34p. (X900, X939, X944, X946, X952)	4.00
29.10.85	7p., 12p. (X922, X896)	1.75

Post Office Presentation Packs

15.2.71	P.O. Pack No. 26. ½p. (2 bands), 1p. (2 bands), 1½p. (2 bands), 2p. (2 bands), 2½p. magenta (1 centre band), 3p. ultramarine (2 bands), 3½p. olive-grey (2 bands), 4p. ochre-brown (2 bands), 5p. pale violet (2 bands), 6p. (2 bands), 7½p. (2 bands), 9p. yellow-orange and black (2 bands). (Nos. X841, X844, X848/9, X851, X855, X858, X861, X866, X870, X877, X882)	4.50
15.4.71**	"Scandinavia 71". Contents as above.......	38.00
25.11.71	P.O. Pack No. 37. ½p. (2 bands), 1p. (2 bands), 1½p. (2 bands), 2p. (2 bands), 2½p. magenta (1 centre band), 3p. ultramarine (2 bands) or (1 centre band), 3½p. olive-grey (2 bands) or (1 centre band), 4p. ochre-brown (2 bands), 4½p. (2 bands), 5p. pale violet (2 bands), 5½p. (2 bands) or (1 centre band), 6p. (2 bands), 6½p. (2 bands) or (1 centre band), 7p. (2 bands), 7½p. (2 bands), 8p. (2 bands), 9p. yellow-orange and black (2 bands), 10p. (2 bands). (Nos. X841, X844, X848/9, X851, X855 or X856, X858 or X859, X861, X865/6, X868 or X869, X870, X871 or X872, X874, X877/8, X882, X885)	4.00
2.2.77	P.O. Pack No. 90. ½p. (2 bands), 1p. (2 bands), 1½p. (2 bands), 2p. (2 bands), 2½p. magenta (1 centre band), 3p. ultramarine (1 centre band), 5p. pale violet (2 bands), 6½p. (1 centre band), 7p. (2 bands) or (1 centre band), 7½p. (2 bands), 8p. (2 bands), 8½p. (2 bands), 9p. deep violet (2 bands), 9½p. (2 bands), 10p. orange-brown (2 bands), 10½p. yellow (2 bands), 11p. (2 bands), 20p. (2 bands), 34p. (2 bands). (Nos. X841, X844, X848/9, X851, X856, X866, X872, X874 or X875, X877/8, X881, X883/4, X886, X890, X892, X907, X910).................	4.50
28.10.81	P.O. Pack No. 129a. 4p. greenish blue (2 bands), 10½p. deep dull blue (2 bands),	

11½p. (1 centre band), 2½p. (phos paper), 3p. (phos paper), 11½p. (phos paper), 12p. (phos paper), 13p. (phos paper), 13½p. (phos paper), 14p. (phos paper), 15p. (phos paper), 15½p. (phos paper), light emerald (phos paper), 17½p. (phos paper), 18p. deep violet (phos paper), 22p. blue (phos paper), 25p. (phos paper), 75p. (litho). (Nos. X862, X891, X893, X917/18, X926/32, X935, X937/8, X947, X980) ....

3.8.83	P.O. Pack No. 1. 10p. orange-brown (1 centre band), 12½p. (1 centre band), ½p. (phos paper), 1p. (phos paper), 3p. (phos paper), 3½p. (phos paper), 16½p. (phos paper), 17p. grey-blue (phos paper), 20½p. (phos paper), 23p. (phos paper), 26p. (phos paper), 28p. (phos paper), 31p. (phos paper), 50p. (ord paper), 2p. (litho phos paper), 4p. (litho phos paper), 5p. claret (litho phos paper), 20p. (litho phos paper), 75p. (litho). (Nos. X888, X898, X914/15, X918/19, X933/4, X936, X942, X945, X948/9, X951, X972/3, X975, X977, X979/80).....................................	15.00
23.10.84	P.O. Pack No. 5. 13p. (1 centre band), ½p. (phos paper), 1p. (phos paper), 10p. (phos paper), 16p. (phos paper), 17p. grey-blue (phos paper), 18p. olive-grey (phos paper), 22p. bright green (phos paper), 24p. (phos paper), 26p. (phos paper), 28p. (phos paper), 31p. (phos paper), 34p. (phos paper), 50p. (ord paper), 2p. (litho phos paper), 4p. (litho phos paper), 5p. claret (litho phos paper), 20p. (litho phos paper), 75p. (litho). (Nos. X900, X914/15, X918, X924, X933, X936, X939, X944, X946, X948/9, X951/2, X972, X973a, X975, X977a, X979, X980a)	12.00
3.3.87	P.O. Pack No. 9. 12p. (1 centre band), 13p. (1 centre band), 1p. (phos paper), 3p. (phos paper), 7p. (phos paper), 10p. (phos paper), 17p. grey-blue (phos paper), 18p. olive-grey (phos paper), 22p. bright green (phos paper), 24p. (phos paper), 26p. (phos paper), 28p. (phos paper), 31p. (phos paper), 34p. (phos paper), 50p. (ord paper), 2p. (litho phos paper), 4p. (litho phos paper), 5p. claret (litho phos paper), 20p. (litho phos paper), 75p. (litho). (Nos. X896, X900, X915, X918, X922, X924, X936, X939, X944, X946, X948/9, X951/2, X972, X973a, X975, X977a, X979, X980a)	10.00

**The "Scandinavia 71" is a special pack produced for sale during a visit to six cities in Denmark, Sweden and Norway by a mobile display unit between 15 April and 20 May 1971. The pack gives details of this tour and also lists the other stamps which were due to be issued in 1971, the text being in English. A separate insert gives translations in Danish, Swedish and Norwegian. The pack was also available at the Philatelic Bureau, Edinburgh.

DECIMAL MACHIN INDEX

Val.	Process	Colour	Phosphor	Cat. No.	Source
½p.	photo	turquoise-blue	2 bands	X841/Eg	(a) with P.V.A. gum—sheets, 5p. m/v coil (X841nEv), 10p. m/v coil (X841q), 10p. booklets (DN46/75, FA1/3), 25p. booklets (DH39/52), 50p. booklets (DT1/12, FB1, FB14/16, FB19/23), £1 Wedgwood booklet (DX1)
					(b) with gum arabic—sheets, 5p. m/v coil (X841n)
½p.	photo	turquoise-blue	1 band at left	X842	£1 Wedgwood booklet (DX1)
½p.	photo	turquoise-blue	1 centre band	X843	10p. m/v coil (X843l), 10p. booklets (FA4/8)
½p.	photo	turquoise-blue	phos paper	X914	sheets, 12½p. m/v coil (X914l)
1p.	photo	crimson	2 bands	X844/Eg	(a) with P.V.A. gum—sheets, coils, 5p. m/v coil (X841nEv), 10p. m/v coil (X841q), 10p. booklets (DN46/75, FA1/3), 50p. booklets (FB1/8, FB14/16)
					(b) with gum arabic—coils, 5p. m/v coil (X841n)
1p.	photo	crimson	1 centre band	X845	10p. m/v coils (X843l, X845m), 10p. booklets (FA4/11), 50p. booklets (FB24/30, 34/36, 43/6)
1p.	photo	crimson	"all-over"	X846	sheets
1p.	photo	crimson	phos paper	X915	sheets, coils, 13p. m/v coil (X915l)
1p.	photo	crimson	1 band at left	X847	50p. booklets (FB37/42)
1p.	photo	crimson	1 band at right	X847Ea¹	£5 P. & O. booklet (DX8)
1½p.	photo	black	2 bands	X848	sheets, 10p. booklets (DN46/75)
2p.	photo	myrtle-green	2 bands	X849/Eg	(a) with P.V.A. gum—sheets, 5p. m/v coil (X841nEv), 10p. m/v coil (X841q), 10p. booklets (DN46/75), 50p. booklets (FB9/13), £3 Wedgwood booklet (DX2), £4 SG booklet (DX3)
					(b) with gum arabic—5p. m/v coil (X841n)
2p.	photo	myrtle-green	"all-over"	X850	sheets
2p.	photo	myrtle-green	phos paper	X916	sheets
2p.	litho	emerald-green	phos paper	X973/a	sheets
2p.	litho	brt grn & dp grn	phos paper	X973b	sheets
2½p.	photo	magenta	1 centre band	X851/Eg	(a) with P.V.A. gum—sheets, coils, 25p. booklets (DH39/52), 50p. booklets (DT1/12), £1 Wedgwood booklet (DX1)
					(b) with gum arabic—sheets, coils
2½p.	photo	magenta	1 side band	X852/Ea	(a) band at left—50p. booklets (DT1/12), £1 Wedgwood booklet (DX1)
					(b) band at right—£1 Wedgwood booklet (DX1)
2½p.	photo	magenta	2 bands	X853	sheets
2½p.	photo	rose-red	phos paper	X917	sheets, 11½p. m/v coil (X917l)
2½p.	photo	rose-red	2 bands	X854	50p. booklets (FB17/18)
3p.	photo	ultramarine	2 bands	X855/Eg	(a) with P.V.A. gum—sheets, coils, 30p. booklets (DQ56/72), 50p. booklets (DT1/12), £1 Wedgwood booklet (DX1)
					(b) with gum arabic—sheets, coils
3p.	photo	ultramarine	1 centre band	X856/Eg	(a) with P.V.A. gum—sheets, coils, 30p. booklets (DQ73/4), 50p. booklets (DT13/14)
					(b) with gum arabic—sheets
3p.	photo	brt magenta	phos paper	X918	sheets, 11½p. m/v coil (X917l), £4 Royal Mint booklet (DX4)
3p.	photo	brt magenta	2 bands	X857	50p. booklets (FB19/23), £4 SG booklet (DX3)
3½p.	photo	olive-grey	2 bands	X858	sheets, coils, 35p. booklets (DP1/3), 50p. booklets (DT13/14)
3½p.	photo	olive-grey	1 centre band	X859	sheets, coils, 35p. booklets (DP4), 85p. booklet (DW1)
3½p.	photo	purple-brown	phos paper	X919	sheets, £4 Royal Mint booklet (DX4)
3½p.	photo	purple-brown	1 centre band	X860	50p. booklets (FB24/6)
4p.	photo	ochre-brown	2 bands	X861/Eg	(a) with P.V.A. gum—sheets. (b) with gum arabic—sheets
4p.	litho	greenish blue	2 bands	X974	sheets
4p.	photo	greenish blue	2 bands	X862	50p. booklets (FB17/18)
4p.	litho	greenish blue	phos paper	X975/a	sheets
4p.	photo	greenish blue	phos paper	X920	12½p. m/v coil (X914l), 13p. m/v coil (X915l)
4p.	photo	greenish blue	1 centre band	X863	50p. booklet (FB27/30)
4p.	photo	greenish blue	1 side band	X864/Ea	(a) band at right—£5 Times booklet (DX6)
					(b) band at left—£5 Times booklet (DX6)
4½p.	photo	grey-blue	2 bands	X865	sheets, coils, 45p. booklets (DS1/2), 85p. booklet (DW1)
5p.	photo	pale violet	2 bands	X866	sheets
5p.	photo	pale violet	phos paper	X921	sheets
5p.	litho	lt violet	phos paper	X976	sheets
5p.	litho	claret	phos paper	X977/a	sheets
5p.	photo	claret	1 centre band	X867	50p. booklets (FB35/36, 43/6)
5½p.	photo	violet	2 bands	X868	sheets
5½p.	photo	violet	1 centre band	X869	sheets
6p.	photo	lt emerald	2 bands	X870/Eg	(a) with P.V.A. gum—sheets, 10p. m/v coil (X841q), 10p. booklets (FA1/3)
					(b) with gum arabic—sheets
6½p.	photo	greenish blue	2 bands	X871	sheets
6½p.	photo	greenish blue	1 centre band	X872	sheets, coils, 65p. booklet (FC1)
6½p.	photo	greenish blue	1 side band	X873/Ea	(a) band at right—50p. booklet (FB1). (b) band at left—50p. booklet (FB1)
7p.	photo	purple-brown	2 bands	X874	sheets
7p.	photo	purple-brown	1 centre band	X875	sheets, coils, 10p. m/v coil (X843l), 10p. booklets (FA4/8), 70p. booklets (FD1/7), £1.60 Christmas booklet (FX1)

Val.	Process	Colour	Phosphor	Cat. No.	Source
7p.	photo	purple-brown	1 side band	X876/Ea	(a) band at right—50p. booklets (FB2/8)
					(b) band at left—50p. booklets (FB2/8)
7p.	photo	red	phos paper	X922	sheets
7½p.	photo	pale chestnut	2 bands	X877	sheets
8p.	photo	rosine	2 bands	X878	sheets
8p.	photo	rosine	1 centre band	X879	sheets, coils, 10p. m/v coil (X845m), 10p. booklets (FA10/11), 80p. booklet (FE1), £1.80 Christmas booklet (FX2)
8p.	photo	rosine	1 side band	X880/Ea	(a) band at right—50p. booklets (FB9/10)
					(b) band at left—50p. booklets (FB9/10)
8½p.	photo	lt yellowish green	2 bands	X881	sheets, coils, 50p. booklet (FB1), 85p. booklet (FF1)
8½p.	photo	yellowish green	phos paper	X923	sheets
9p.	photo	yellow-orange & black	2 bands	X882	sheets
9p.	photo	dp violet	2 bands	X883	sheets, coils, 50p. booklets (FB2/8), 90p. booklets (FG1/8), £1.60 Christmas booklet (FX1)
9½p.	photo	purple	2 bands	X884	sheets
10p.	recess	cerise	phos paper	829	sheets
10p.	photo	orange-brown & chestnut	2 bands	X885	sheets
10p.	photo	orange-brown	2 bands	X886/Eb	sheets, 50p. booklets (FB9/10), £1.80 Christmas booklet (FX2), £4 Christian Heritage booklet (DX5)
10p.	photo	orange-brown	"all-over"	X887	sheets, coils, £1 booklet (FH1)
10p.	photo	orange-brown	phos paper	X924	sheets
10p.	photo	orange-brown	1 centre band	X888	sheets, coils, £1 booklets (FH2/4), £2.20 Christmas booklet (FX3), £3 Wedgwood booklet (DX2)
10p.	photo	orange-brown	1 side band	X889/Ea	(a) band at right—50p. booklets (FB11/13)
					(b) band at left—50p. booklets (FB11/13), £3 Wedgwood booklet (DX2)
10½p.	photo	yellow	2 bands	X890	sheets
10½p.	photo	dp dull blue	2 bands	X891	sheets
11p.	photo	brown-red	2 bands	X892	sheets
11p.	photo	brown-red	phos paper	X925	sheets
11½p.	photo	ochre-brown	phos paper	X926	sheets
11½p.	photo	drab	1 centre band	X893	sheets, coils, £1.15 booklets (FI1/4), £2.55 Christmas booklet (FX4)
11½p.	photo	drab	1 side band	X894/Ea	(a) band at right—50p. booklets (FB14/18), £1.30 booklets (FL1/2)
					(b) band at left—50p. booklets (FB14/18), £1.30 booklets (FL1/2)
12p.	photo	yellowish green	phos paper	X927	sheets, coils, £1.20 booklets (FJ1/3)
12p.	photo	yellowish green	2 bands	X895	50p. booklets (FB11/13), £2.20 Christmas booklet (FX3), £3 Wedgwood booklet (DX2)
12p.	photo	brt emerald	1 centre band	X896	sheets, coils, £1.20 booklets (FJ4/5), £5 British Rail booklet (DX7)
12p.	photo	brt emerald	1 side band	X897	(a) band at right—£1.50 booklets (FP1/2), £5 British Rail booklet (DX7)
					(b) band at left—£1.50 booklets (FP1/2), £5 British Rail booklet (DX7)
12p.	photo	brt emerald	1 centre band Underprint T.4	X896Eu	sheets
12½p.	photo	lt emerald	1 centre band	X898	sheets, coils, 50p. booklets (FB24/6), £1.25 booklets (FK1/8), £4 SG booklet (DX3)
12½p.	photo	lt emerald	1 centre band Underprint T.1	X898Eu	£2.80 Christmas booklet (FX5)
12½p.	photo	lt emerald	1 centre band Underprint T.2	X898Eua	£2.50 Christmas booklet (FX6)
12½p.	photo	lt emerald	1 side band	X899/Ea	(a) band at right—50p. booklets (FB19/23), £1.43 booklets (FN1/6), £1.46 booklets (FO1/3), £4 SG booklet (DX3), £4 Royal Mint booklet (DX4)
					(b) band at left—50p. booklets (FB19/23), £1.43 booklets (FN1/6), £1.46 booklets (FO1/3), £4 SG booklet (DX3), £4 Royal Mint booklet (DX4).
13p.	photo	olive-grey	phos paper	X928	sheets
13p.	photo	pale chestnut	1 centre band	X900	sheets, coils, 50p. booklets (FB27/30, 35/6, 43/6), 52p. booklet (GA1), £1.30 booklets (FL3/12, GD1), £5 Times booklet (DX6), £5 P & O booklet (DX8)
13p.	photo	pale chestnut	1 centre band Underprint T.2	X900Eu	£1.30 Christmas booklet (FX9)
13p.	photo	pale chestnut	1 side band	X901/Ea	(a) band at right— 50p. booklets (FB37/42), £1.54 booklets (FQ1/4), £4 Christian Heritage booklet (DX5), £5 Times booklet (DX6), £5 P & O booklet (DX8)
					(b) band at left—£1 booklets (FH6/11), £1.54 booklets (FQ1/4), £4 Christian Heritage booklet (DX5), £5 Times booklet (DX6)
13p.	litho	pale chestnut	1 centre band	X977b	£5 Financial Times booklet (DX9)
13p.	litho	pale chestnut	1 side band	X977c/cEa	£5 Financial Times booklet (DX9)
13½p.	photo	purple-brown	phos paper	X929	sheets
14p.	photo	grey-blue	phos paper	X930	sheets, coils, £1.40 booklets (FM1/4)
14p.	photo	grey-blue	2 bands	X902	50p. booklets (FB14/16), £1.30 booklets (FL1/2), £2.55 Christmas booklet (FX4)
15p.	photo	ultramarine	phos paper	X931	sheets
15½p.	photo	pale violet	phos paper	X932	sheets, coils, £1.55 booklets (FR1/6)

Val.	Process	Colour	Phosphor	Cat. No.	Source
15½p.	photo	pale violet	2 bands	X903	£1.43 booklets (FN1/6), £4 SG booklet (DX3)
15½p.	photo	pale violet	2 bands Underprint T.1	X903/Eu	£2.80 Christmas booklet (FX5)
16p.	photo	olive-drab	phos paper	X933	sheets, coils, £1.60 booklets (FS1/3), £4 Royal Mint booklet (DX4)
16p.	photo	olive-drab	phos paper Underprint T.3	X933Eu	£1.60 booklet (FS2)
16p.	photo	olive-drab	2 bands	X904	£1.46 booklets (FO1/3)
16½p.	photo	pale chestnut	phos paper	X934	sheets
17p.	photo	lt emerald	phos paper	X935	sheets
17p.	photo	grey-blue	phos paper	X936	sheets, coils, £1 booklet (FH5), £1.70 booklets (FT1/3, 5/7), £4 Christian Heritage booklet (DX5), £5 Times booklet (DX6), £5 British Rail booklet (DX7)
17p.	photo	grey-blue	phos paper Underprint T.3	X936Eu	£1.70 booklet (FT2)
17p.	photo	grey-blue	2 bands	X905	50p. booklet (FB33), £1.50 booklets (FP1/3), £1.54 booklets (FQ1/4), £4 Christian Heritage booklet (DX5), £5 Times booklet (DX6), £5 British Rail booklet (DX7)
17p.	photo	grey-blue	2 bands Underprint T.4	X905Eu	50p. booklets (FB31/33)
17½p.	photo	pale chestnut	phos paper	X937	sheets
18p.	photo	dp violet	phos paper	X938	sheets
18p.	photo	olive-grey	phos paper	X939	sheets, coils, 72p. booklet (GB1), £1.80 booklets (FU1/6, GB1), £5 P & O booklet (DX8)
18p.	photo	olive-grey	2 bands	X906	50p. booklets (FB37/42), £1 booklets (FH6/11), £5 P & O booklet (DX8)
18p.	litho	olive-grey	phos paper	X977d	£5 Financial Times booklet (DX9)
18p.	litho	olive-grey	2 bands	X977e	£5 Financial Times booklet (DX9)
19½p.	photo	olive-grey	phos paper	X940	sheets
20p.	recess	olive-green	none	830	sheets
20p.	photo	dull purple	2 bands	X907	sheets
20p.	photo	dull purple	phos paper	X941	sheets
20p.	litho	dull purple	2 bands	X978	sheets
20p.	litho	dull purple	phos paper	X979/a	sheets
20½p.	photo	ultramarine	phos paper	X942	sheets
22p.	photo	blue	phos paper	X943	sheets
22p.	photo	brt green	phos paper	X944	sheets
22p.	litho	brt green	2 bands	X979b	£5 Financial Times booklet (DX9)
23p.	photo	brown-red	phos paper	X945	sheets
24p.	photo	violet	phos paper	X946	sheets
25p.	photo	purple	phos paper	X947	sheets
26p.	photo	rosine	phos paper	X948/Ea	sheets, £1.04 booklet (GC1)
26p.	photo	rosine	2 bands	X908	£5 P & O booklet (DX8)
28p.	photo	dp violet	phos paper	X949	sheets
29p.	photo	ochre-brown	phos paper	X950	sheets
31p.	photo	purple	phos paper	X951	sheets
31p.	photo	purple	2 bands	X909	£5 British Rail booklet (DX7)
34p.	photo	ochre-brown	phos paper	X952	sheets
34p.	photo	ochre-brown	2 bands	X910	£5 Times booklet (DX6)
34p.	litho	ochre-brown	2 bands	X979c	£5 Financial Times booklet (DX9)
50p.	recess	dp ultramarine	none or phos paper	831	sheets
50p.	photo	ochre-brown	2 bands	X911	sheets
50p.	photo	ochre-brown	none	X972	sheets
75p.	litho	black	none	X980/a	sheets
75p.	litho	brnish grey & blk	none	X981	sheets
£1	recess	bluish black	none	831b	sheets
£1	photo	brt yellow-green & blackish olive	none	1026	sheets
£1.30	photo	drab & dp greenish blue	none	1026b	sheets
£1.33	photo	pale mauve & grey-black	none	1026c	sheets
£1.41	photo	drab & dp greenish blue	none	1026d	sheets
£1.50	photo	pale mauve & grey-black	none	1026e	sheets
£1.60	photo	pale drab & dp greenish blue	none	1026f	sheets
£2	photo	lt emerald & purple-brown	none	1027	sheets
£5	photo	salmon & chalky blue	none	1028	sheets

Abbreviations used in the diagrams: 2B = 2 bands, CB = centre band, LB = left band and RB = right band. The shaded squares represent printed labels. Panes completed by blank labels are outside the scope of this catalogue.

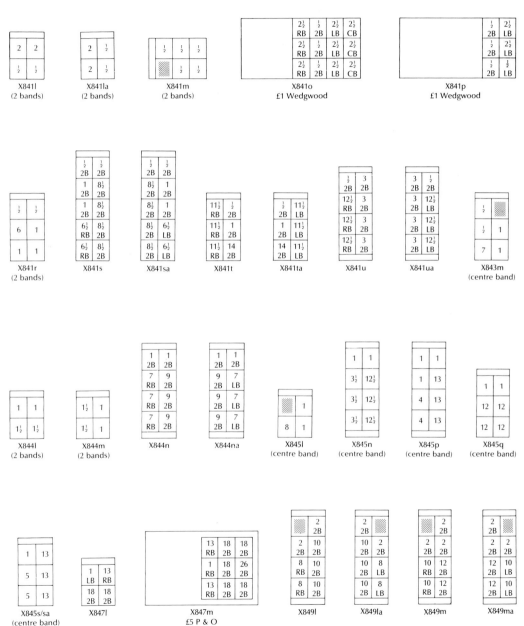

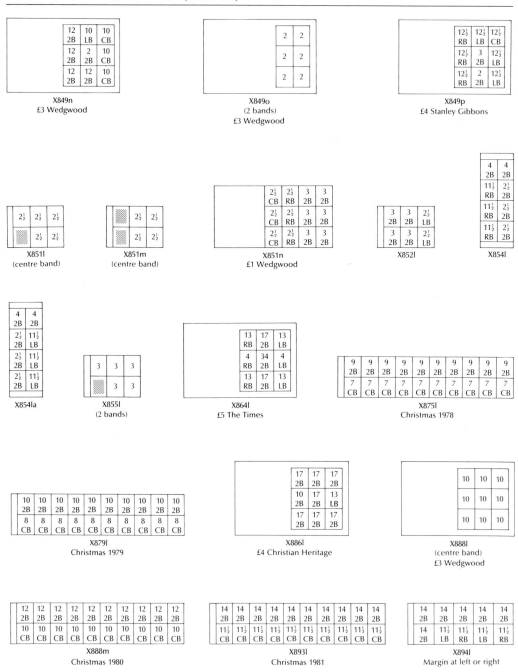

X849n
£3 Wedgwood

X849o
(2 bands)
£3 Wedgwood

X849p
£4 Stanley Gibbons

X851l
(centre band)

X851m
(centre band)

X851n
£1 Wedgwood

X852l

X854l

X854la

X855l
(2 bands)

X864l
£5 The Times

X875l
Christmas 1978

X879l
Christmas 1979

X886l
£4 Christian Heritage

X888l
(centre band)
£3 Wedgwood

X888m
Christmas 1980

X893l
Christmas 1981

X894l
Margin at left or right

12	12	12
12	12	12
12	12	12

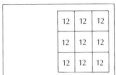

X895l
(2 bands)
£3 Wedgwood

12	12	12
12	12	12
12	12	12

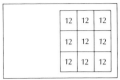

X896l
(centre band)
£5 British Rail

17 2B	17 2B	17 2B	17 2B	17 2B
12 LB	12 RB	12 LB	12 RB	17 2B

X897l

17 2B	17 2B	17 2B	17 2B	17 2B
17 2B	12 LB	12 RB	12 LB	12 RB

X897la

12 RB	17 2B	12 LB
12 RB	31 2B	12 LB
12 RB	17 2B	12 LB

X897m
£5 British Rail

15½ 2B	15½ 2B	15½ 2B	15½ 2B	15½ 2B	15½ 2B	15½ 2B	15½ 2B	15½ 2B	15½ 2B
12½ CB	12½ CB	12½ CB	12½ CB	12½ CB	12½ CB	12½ CB	12½ CB	12½ CB	12½ CB

X898l
Christmas 1982

15½ 2B	15½ 2B	15½ 2B	15½ 2B	15½ 2B
15½ 2B	12½ LB	12½ RB	12½ LB	12½ RB

X899l
Margin at left or right

12½ RB	12½ LB
12½ RB	12½ LB
12½ RB	12½ LB

X899m
£4 Stanley Gibbons
£4 Royal Mint

16 2B	16 2B	16 2B	16 2B	16 2B
12½ LB	12½ RB	12½ LB	12½ RB	16 2B

X899n

16 2B	16 2B	16 2B	16 2B	16 2B
16 2B	12½ LB	12½ RB	12½ LB	12½ RB

X899na

13	13	13
13	13	13
13	13	13

X900l
(centre band)
£5 The Times
£5 P & O

13	13
13	13

X900n
(centre band)
52p. Window Booklet

13	13	13	13	13
13	13	13	13	13

X900o
(centre band)
£1.30 Window Booklet

17 2B	17 2B	17 2B	17 2B	17 2B
13 LB	13 RB	13 LB	13 RB	17 2B

X901l

17 2B	17 2B	17 2B	17 2B	17 2B
17 2B	13 LB	13 RB	13 LB	13 RB

X901la

13 RB	13 LB
13 RB	13 LB
13 RB	13 LB

X901m
£4 Christian Heritage
£5 P & O (X900 6 × CB)
£5 Financial Times (X977ba 6 × CB)

13 LB	18 2B
18 2B	18 2B
18 2B	18 2B

X901n/na

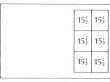

$15\frac{1}{2}$	$15\frac{1}{2}$
$15\frac{1}{2}$	$15\frac{1}{2}$
$15\frac{1}{2}$	$15\frac{1}{2}$

X903l
(2 bands)
£4 Stanley Gibbons

$15\frac{1}{2}$	$15\frac{1}{2}$	$15\frac{1}{2}$
$15\frac{1}{2}$	$15\frac{1}{2}$	$15\frac{1}{2}$
$15\frac{1}{2}$	$15\frac{1}{2}$	$15\frac{1}{2}$

X903m
(2 bands)
£4 Stanley Gibbons

X905l
(2 bands)

16	16	16
$3\frac{1}{2}$	3	$3\frac{1}{2}$
16	16	16

X918l
(phosphorised paper)
£4 Royal Mint

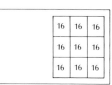

16	16	16
16	16	16
16	16	16

X933l
(phosphorised paper)
£4 Royal Mint

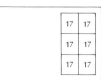

17	17
17	17
17	17

X936l
(phosphorised paper)
£4 Christian Heritage
£5 The Times
£5 British Rail

17	17	17
17	17	17
17	17	17

X936m
(phosphorised paper)
£5 The Times
£5 British Rail

18	18	18
18	18	18
18	18	18

X939l, X977da
(phosphorised paper)
£5 P & O
£5 Financial Times

18	18
18	18

X939m
(phosphorised paper)
72p. Window Booklet

18	18	18	18	18
18	18	18	18	18

X939n
(phosphorised paper)
£1.80 Window Booklet

26	26
26	26

X948l
(phosphorised paper)
£1.04 Window Booklet

13 RB	22 2B	13 LB
13 RB	34 2B	13 LB
13 RB	18 2B	13 LB

X977cb
£5 Financial Times

18	18
18	18

X977db
(phosphorised paper)
£5 Financial Times

368 "A Mountain Road"
(T. P. Flanagan)

369 "Deer's Meadow"
(Tom Carr)

371 John Keats
(150th Death Anniv)

372 Thomas Gray
(Death Bicentenary)

370 "Slieve na brock"
(Colin Middleton)

373 Sir Walter Scott (Birth Centenary)

1971 (16 June). **"Ulster 1971" Paintings.** *Chalk-surfaced paper. Two phosphor bands. P* 15 × 14.

881	368	3p. yellow-buff, pale yellow, Venetian red, black, blue and drab		10	10
		Ey. Phosphor omitted		3.25	
882	369	7½p. olive-brown, brownish grey, pale olive-grey, dp blue, cobalt & grey-blue		75	75
		a. Pale olive-grey omitted*		60.00	
		Ey. Phosphor omitted		17.00	
883	370	9p. greenish yellow, orange, grey, lavender-grey, bistre, black, pale ochre-brown, and ochre-brown		75	75
		a. Orange omitted		£150	
		Ey. Phosphor omitted		15.00	
		Set of 3		1.40	1.40
		First Day Cover			1.75
		Presentation Pack		2.75	

A used example of the 3p. has been seen with the Venetian red omitted.

*This only affects the boulder in the foreground, which appears whitish and it only applied to some stamps in the sheet.

Special First Day of Issue Postmarks

FIRST DAY OF ISSUE
16 JUNE 1971
BELFAST

British Post Office Philatelic Bureau, Edinburgh	2.25
Armagh	35.00
Ballymena	35.00
Belfast	2.75
Coleraine	42.00
Cookstown	35.00
Enniskillen	35.00
Londonderry	15.00
Newry	25.00
Omagh	45.00
Portadown	28.00

Postmarks for the other towns in Northern Ireland are similar in design to that for Belfast.

(Des Rosalind Dease. Queen's head printed in gold and then embossed)

1971 (28 July). **Literary Anniversaries.** *Chalk-surfaced paper. Two phosphor bands. P* 15 × 14.

884	371	3p. black, gold & greyish blue		10	10
		a. Gold (Queen's head) omitted		70.00	
		Ey. Phosphor omitted		2.00	
885	372	5p. black, gold & yellow-olive		75	75
		a. Gold (Queen's head) omitted		£160	
		Ey. Phosphor omitted		27.00	
886	373	7½p. black, gold & yellow-brown		75	80
		Eb. Embossing omitted		15.00	
		Ey. Phosphor omitted		17.00	
		Set of 3		1.40	1.40
		First Day Cover			1.60
		Presentation Pack		2.25	

Special First Day of Issue Postmarks

British Post Office Philatelic Bureau, Edinburgh	2.25
London EC	3.00

374 Servicemen and Nurse of 1921

375 Roman Centurion

73

376 Rugby Football, 1871

(Des F. Wegner)

1971 (25 Aug). **British Anniversaries.** *Events described on stamps. Chalk-surfaced paper. Two phosphor bands.* P 15 × 14.

887	**374**	3p.	red-orange, grey, dp blue, olive-green, olive-brown, black, rosine & violet-blue	10	10
		a.	Dp blue omitted*	£750	
		b.	Red-orange (nurse's cloak) omitted ..	£275	
		c.	Olive-brown (faces, etc.) omitted.....	£125	
		d.	Black omitted..............................	£10000	
		Ey.	Phosphor omitted..........................	1.10	
888	**375**	7½p.	grey, yellow-brown, vermilion, mauve, grey-black, black silver, pale ochre & ochre	80	90
		a.	Grey omitted	75.00	
		Ey.	Phosphor omitted..........................	6.00	
889	**376**	9p.	new blue, myrtle-green, grey-black, lemon, olive-brown, magenta & yellow-olive	90	1.00
		a.	Olive-brown omitted	£110	
		b.	New blue omitted..........................	£1400	
		c.	Myrtle-green omitted	£1200	
		Ey.	Phosphor omitted..........................	£500	
			Set of 3	1.60	1.75
			First Day Cover		1.75
			Presentation Pack.........................	2.75	

*The effect of the missing deep blue is shown on the sailor's uniform, which appears as grey.

A used example has been seen of the 3p. with grey omitted.

Special First Day of Issue Postmarks

British Post Office Philatelic Bureau, Edinburgh....... 3.00
Maidstone.. 7.50
Twickenham 7.50
York 7.50

377 Physical Sciences Building University College of Wales, Aberystwyth

378 Faraday Building, Southampton University

379 Engineering Department Leicester University

380 Hexagon Restaurant, Essex University

(Des N. Jenkins)

1971 (22 Sept). **British Architecture.** *Modern University Buildings. Chalk-surfaced paper. Two phosphor bands.* P 15 × 14.

890	**377**	3p.	olive-brown, ochre, lemon, black & yellow-olive..................................	10	10
		a.	Lemon omitted	£450	
		b.	Black (windows) omitted		
		Ey.	Phosphor omitted.........................	3.50	
891	**378**	5p.	rose, black, chestnut & lilac	20	25
		Ey.	Phosphor omitted.........................	55.00	
892	**379**	7½p.	ochre, black & purple-brown...........	80	80
		Ey.	Phosphor omitted.........................	7.00	
893	**380**	9p.	pale lilac, black, sepia-brown & dp blue	1.40	1.50
		Ey.	Phosphor omitted.........................	15.00	
			Set of 4	2.40	2.40
			First Day Cover		2.50
			Presentation Pack.........................	3.25	

Special First Day of Issue Postmarks

British Post Office Philatelic Bureau, Edinburgh	3.50
Aberystwyth	9.00
Colchester	9.00
Leicester	9.00
Southampton	9.00

Collectors Pack 1971

1971 (29 Sept). *Comprises Nos. 835/40 and 881/93.*
CP893a   Collectors Pack 35.00

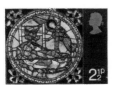

381 "Dream of the Wise Men"   382 "Adoration of the Magi"

383 "Ride of the Magi"

(Des Clarke-Clements-Hughes design team, from stained-glass windows, Canterbury Cathedral. Queen's head printed in gold and then embossed)

1971 (13 Oct).   **Christmas.** *Ordinary paper. One centre phosphor band (2½p.) or two phosphor bands (others). P 15 × 14.*

894	**381**	2½p. new blue, black, lemon, emerald, reddish violet, carmine-red, carmine-rose & gold	8	8
		a. Imperf (pair)	£275	
895	**382**	3p. black, reddish violet, lemon, new blue, carmine-rose, emerald, ultramarine & gold	10	10
		a. Gold (Queen's head) omitted	£250	
		b. Carmine-rose omitted	£275	
		c. Lemon omitted	60.00	
		d. New blue omitted	†	—
		Ee. Embossing omitted	3.50	
		Ey. Phosphor omitted	1.60	
		Eya. Embossing & phosphor omitted	45.00	
896	**383**	7½p. black, lilac, lemon, emerald, new blue, rose, green & gold	80	90
		a. Gold (Queen's head) omitted	90.00	
		b. Lilac omitted	£375	
		c. Emerald omitted	£190	
		Ed. Embossing omitted	17.00	
		Ee. Embossing double	30.00	
		Ey. Phosphor omitted	8.00	
		Eya. Embossing & phosphor omitted	20.00	
		Set of 3	90	1.00
		First Day Cover		1.25
		Presentation Pack	2.75	

The 3p. is known with reddish violet and embossing omitted, used in Llandudno and with lemon and carmine-rose both omitted used in Falkirk.

Special First Day of Issue Postmarks

British Post Office Philatelic Bureau, Edinburgh	2.50
Bethlehem, Llandeilo, Carms	6.00
Canterbury	3.50

WHITE CHALK-SURFACED PAPER. From No. 897 all issues, with the exception of Nos. 904/8, were printed on fluorescent white paper, giving a stronger chalk reaction than the original cream paper.

384 Sir James Clark Ross   **385** Sir Martin Frobisher

386 Henry Hudson   **387** Capt. Scott

(Des Marjorie Saynor. Queen's head printed in gold and then embossed)

1972 (16 Feb). **British Polar Explorers.** *Two phosphor bands.* P 14 × 15.

897	**384**	3p. yellow-brown, indigo, slate-black, flesh, lemon, rose, brt blue & gold ...	8	8
		a. Gold (Queen's head) omitted	60.00	
		b. Slate-black (hair, etc.) omitted	£800	
		c. Lemon omitted		
		Ed. Embossing omitted	15.00	
		Ee. Gold (Queen's head) & embossing omitted	65.00	
		Ey. Phosphor omitted........................	1.75	
		Eya. Embossing & phosphor omitted	20.00	
898	**385**	5p. salmon, flesh, purple-brown, ochre, black & gold	20	20
		a. Gold (Queen's head) omitted	90.00	
		Eb. Embossing omitted	6.00	
		Ey. Phosphor omitted........................	7.00	
		Eya. Gold & phosphor omitted	£100	
		Eyb. Embossing & phosphor omitted		
899	**386**	7½p. reddish violet, blue, dp slate, yellow-brown, buff, black & gold	55	60
		a. Gold (Queen's head) omitted	£190	
		Ey. Phosphor omitted........................	16.00	
900	**387**	9p. dull blue, ultramarine, black, greenish yellow, pale pink, rose-red & gold	90	95
		Ey. Phosphor omitted........................	£300	
		Set of 4	1.60	1.60
		First Day Cover		2.00
		Presentation Pack	3.00	

An example of the 3p. is known used on piece with the flesh colour omitted.

Special First Day of Issue Postmarks

Philatelic Bureau, Edinburgh	5.00
London WC	7.00

388 Statuette of Tutankhamun   **389** 19th-century Coastguard

390 Ralph Vaughan Williams and Score

(Des Rosalind Dease (3p.), F. Wegner (7½p.), C. Abbott (9p.). Queen's head printed in gold and then embossed (7½p., 9p.))

1972 (26 Apr). **General Anniversaries.** *Events described on stamps. Two phosphor bands.* P 15 × 14.

901	**388**	3p. black, grey, gold, dull bistre-brown, blackish brown, pale stone & lt brown	8	8
902	**389**	7½p. pale yellow, new blue, slate-blue, violet-blue, slate & gold	70	75
		Ea. Embossing omitted		
		Ey. Phosphor omitted........................	£250	
903	**390**	9p. bistre-brown, black, sage-green, dp slate, yellow-ochre, brown & gold....	70	65
		a. Gold (Queen's head) omitted..........	£550	
		b. Brown (facial features) omitted	£1100	
		c. Deep slate omitted		
		Ey. Phosphor omitted........................	25.00	
		Set of 3	1.25	1.25
		First Day Cover		2.00
		Presentation Pack	3.00	

Special First Day of Issue Postmarks

Philatelic Bureau, Edinburgh	3.00
London EC	4.50

391 St. Andrew's,
Greensted-juxta-Ongar, Essex

392 All Saints, Earls Barton,
Northants

393 St. Andrew's,
Letheringsett, Norfolk

394 St. Andrew's,
Helpringham, Lincs

395 St. Mary the Virgin, Huish
Episcopi, Somerset

(Des R. Maddox. Queen's head printed in gold and then embossed)

1972 (21 June). **British Architecture.** *Village Churches. Ordinary paper. Two phosphor bands.* P 14 × 15.

904	**391**	3p. violet-blue, black, lt yellow-olive, emerald-green, orange-vermilion & gold	8	8
		a. Gold (Queen's head) omitted	75.00	
		Eb. Embossing omitted	9.00	
		Ey. Phosphor omitted	3.50	
		Eya. Gold (Queen's head) & phosphor omitted	80.00	
		Eyb. Embossing & phosphor omitted	7.50	
905	**392**	4p. dp yellow-olive, black, emerald, violet-blue, orange-vermilion & gold	15	20
		a. Gold (Queen's head) omitted	£2250	
		b. Violet-blue omitted	£110	
		Ec. Embossing omitted	5.00	
		Ey. Phosphor omitted	12.00	
906	**393**	5p. dp emerald, black, royal blue, lt yellow-olive, orange-vermilion & gold	20	25
		a. Gold (Queen's head) omitted	£150	
		Eb. Embossing omitted	10.00	
		Ey. Phosphor omitted	18.00	

907	**394**	7½p. orange-red, black, dp yellow-olive, royal blue, lt emerald & gold	1.40	1.40
		Ey. Phosphor omitted	10.00	
908	**395**	9p. new blue, black, emerald-green, dp yellow-olive, orange-vermilion & gold	1.60	1.60
		Ea. Embossing omitted	8.00	
		Ey. Phosphor omitted	16.00	
		Set of 5	3.00	3.25
		First Day Cover		3.50
		Presentation Pack	5.00	

Nos. 905a and 906a only exist with the phosphor omitted.

Special First Day of Issue Postmarks

Philatelic Bureau, Edinburgh	4.50
Canterbury	7.50

"Belgica '72" Souvenir Pack

1972 (24 June). *Comprises Nos. 894/6 and 904/8.*
CP908b Souvenir Pack 14.00
This pack was specially produced for sale at the "Belgica '72" Stamp Exhibition, held in Brussels between 24 June and 9 July. It contains information on British stamps with a religious theme with text in English, French and Flemish, and was put on sale at Philatelic Bureaux in Britain on 26 June.

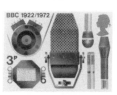

396 Microphones, 1924–69

397 Horn Loudspeaker

398 T.V. Camera, 1972

399 Oscillator and Spark
Transmitter, 1897

(Des D. Gentleman)

1972 (13 Sept). **Broadcasting Anniversaries.** *75th Anniv of Marconi and Kemp's Radio Experiments* (9p.)*, and 50th Anniv of Daily Broadcasting by the B.B.C.* (others). *Two phosphor bands.* P 15 × 14.

909	**396**	3p. pale brown, black, grey, greenish yellow & brownish slate	15	8
		a. Greenish yellow (terminals) omitted	£400	

910	**397**	5p. brownish slate, lake-brown, salmon, lt brown, black & red-brown	20	20
		Ey. Phosphor omitted.........................	3.50	
		Eya. Phosphor on back but omitted on front	25.00	
911	**398**	7½p. lt grey, slate, brownish slate, magenta & black	90	95
		Ey. Phosphor omitted.........................	6.00	
912	**399**	9p. lemon, brown, brownish slate, dp brownish slate, bluish slate & black ..	90	95
		a. Brownish slate (Queen's head) omitted	£600	
		Ey. Phosphor omitted.........................	20.00	
		Set of 4	2.00	2.00
		First Day Cover		2.00
		Presentation Pack	3.00	

In addition to the generally issued Presentation Pack a further pack exists inscribed "1922–1972". This pack of stamps commemorating the 50th Anniversary of the B.B.C. was specially produced as a memento of the occasion for the B.B.C. staff. It was sent with the good wishes of the Chairman and Board of Governors, the Director-General and Board of Management. The pack contains Nos. 909/11 only. (*Price*|£35.)

Special First Day of Issue Postmarks

Philatelic Bureau, Edinburgh	3.00
London W1..	4.50

400 Angel holding Trumpet   **401** Angel playing Lute

402 Angel playing Harp

(Des Sally Stiff. Photo and embossing)

1972 (18 Oct). **Christmas.** *One centre phosphor band (2½p.) or two phosphor bands (others).* P 14 × 15.

913	**400**	2½p. cerise, pale reddish brown, yellow-orange, orange-vermilion, lilac, gold, red-brown and dp grey..................	8	8
		a. Gold omitted	£375	
		Eb. Embossing omitted	6.00	
		c. Dp grey omitted		
		Ey. Phosphor omitted.........................	6.50	
914	**401**	3p. ultramarine, lavender, lt turquoise-blue, brt green, gold, red-brown & bluish violet..............................	8	8
		a. Red-brown omitted.......................	£375	
		b. Brt green omitted	60.00	
		c. Bluish violet omitted	75.00	
		Ed. Embossing omitted	2.50	
		Ey. Phosphor omitted.........................	2.25	
		Eya. Embossing & phosphor omitted	5.00	
915	**402**	7½p. dp brown, pale lilac, lt cinnamon, ochre, gold, red-brown & blackish violet..............................	40	45
		a. Ochre omitted	45.00	
		Eb. Embossing omitted	7.00	
		Ey. Phosphor omitted.........................	7.00	
		Eya. Embossing & phosphor omitted	15.00	
		Set of 3	50	50
		First Day Cover		1.25
		Presentation Pack	2.00	

The gold printing on the 3p. is from two cylinders: 1E and 1F. Examples have been seen with the gold of the 1F cylinder omitted, but these are difficult to detect on single stamps.

Special First Day of Issue Postmarks

Philatelic Bureau, Edinburgh	1.75
Bethlehem, Llandeilo, Carms	2.75

403 Queen Elizabeth and   **404** "Europe"
Duke of Edinburgh

(Des J. Matthews from photo by N. Parkinson)

1972 (20 Nov). **Royal Silver Wedding.** *"All-over" phosphor (3p.) or without phosphor (20p.). P 14 × 15.*

I. "REMBRANDT" Machine

916	**403**	3p. brownish black, dp blue & silver	10	10
		a. Silver omitted	£300	
917		20p. brownish black, reddish purple & silver	65	70

II. "JUMELLE" Machine

918	**403**	3p. brownish black, dp blue & silver	20	25
		Set of 2	75	80
		Gutter Pair (No. 918)	1.00	
		Traffic Light Gutter Pair..................	20.00	
		First Day Cover		1.25
		Presentation Pack	2.00	
		Presentation Pack (Japanese)...........	4.50	
		Souvenir Book	3.50	

The souvenir book is a twelve-page booklet containing photographs of the Royal Wedding and other historic events of the royal family and accompanying information.

The 3p. "JUMELLE" has a lighter shade of the brownish black than the 3p. "Rembrandt". It also has the brown cylinders less deeply etched, which can be distinguished in the Duke's face which is slightly lighter, and in the Queen's hair where the highlights are sharper.

3p. "REMBRANDT". Cyls. 3A–1B–11C no dot. Sheets of 100 (10 × 10).
3p. "JUMELLE". Cyls. 1A–1B–3C dot and no dot. Sheets of 100 (two panes 5 × 10, separated by gutter margin).

Special First Day of Issue Postmarks

Philatelic Bureau, Edinburgh	2.25
Windsor, Berks	3.75

Collectors Pack 1972

1972 (20 Nov). *Comprises Nos. 897/917.*
CP918*a* Collectors pack 35.00

(Des P. Murdoch)

1973 (3 Jan). *Britain's Entry into European Communities. Two phosphor bands. P 14 × 15.*

919	**404**	3p. dull orange, brt rose-red, ultramarine, lt lilac & black	10	10
920		5p. new blue, brt rose-red, ultramarine, cobalt-blue & black........................	25	35
		a. Pair. Nos. 920/1	1.50	1.50
921	**404**	5p. lt emerald-green bright rose-red, ultramarine, cobalt-blue and black ...	25	35
		Set of 3	1.50	70
		First Day Cover		1.50
		Presentation Pack.........................	2.25	

Nos. 920/1 were printed horizontally *se-tenant* throughout the sheet.

Philatelic Bureau, Edinburgh 2.75

405 Oak Tree

(Des D. Gentleman)

1973 (28 Feb). **Tree Planting Year. British Trees (1st issue).** *Two phosphor bands. P 15 × 14.*

922	**405**	9p. brownish black, apple-green, dp olive, sepia, blackish green & brownish grey......................................	35	30
		a. Brownish black (value & inscr) omitted	£550	
		b. Brownish grey (Queen's head) omitted	£400	
		E*y*. Phosphor omitted.........................	90.00	
		First Day Cover		60
		Presentation Pack.........................	2.25	

See also No. 949.

Special First Day of Issue Postmark

Philatelic Bureau, Edinburgh 1.50

CHALK-SURFACED PAPER. The following issues are printed on chalk-surfaced paper but where "all-over" phosphor has been applied there is no chalk reaction except in the sheet margins outside the phosphor area.

79

406 David Livingstone **407** H. M. Stanley

T **406/7** were printed together, horizontally *se-tenant* within the sheet

408 Sir Francis Drake **409** Walter Raleigh

410 Charles Sturt

(Des Marjorie Saynor. Queen's head printed in gold and then embossed)

1973 (18 Apr). **British Explorers.** *"All-over" phosphor.* P 14 × 15.

923	**406**	3p. orange-yellow, lt orange-brown, grey-black, lt turquoise-blue, turquoise-blue & gold		25	20
		a. Pair. Nos. 923/4		1.60	1.75
		b. Gold (Queen's head) omitted		32.00	
		c. Turquoise-blue (background & inscr) omitted		£350	
		d. Lt orange-brown omitted		£250	
		Ee. Embossing omitted		10.00	
924	**407**	3p. orange-yellow, lt orange-brown, grey-black, lt turquoise-blue, turquoise-blue & gold		25	20
		b. Gold (Queen's head) omitted		32.00	
		c. Turquoise-blue (background & inscr) omitted		£350	
		d. Lt orange-brown omitted		£250	
		Ee. Embossing omitted		10.00	

925	**408**	5p. lt flesh, chrome-yellow, orange-yellow, sepia, brownish grey, grey-black, violet-blue & gold		30	30
		a. Gold (Queen's head) omitted		75.00	
		b. Grey-black omitted		£475	
		c. Sepia omitted		£375	
		Ed. Embossing omitted		5.00	
926	**409**	7½p. lt flesh, reddish brown, sepia, ultramarine, grey-black, brt lilac & gold		35	30
		a. Gold (Queen's head) omitted			
		b. Ultramarine (eyes) omitted		—	£350
927	**410**	9p. flesh, pale stone, grey-blue, grey-black, brown-grey, Venetian red, brown-red & gold		40	40
		a. Gold (Queen's head) omitted		75.00	
		b. Brown-grey printing double .....*from*		85.00	
		c. Grey-black omitted		£225	
		Ed. Embossing omitted		20.00	
		Set of 5		2.50	1.25
		First Day Cover			2.50
		Presentation Pack		4.00	

Caution is needed when buying missing gold heads in this issue as they can be removed by using a hard eraser, etc., but this invariably affects the "all-over" phosphor. Genuine examples have the phosphor intact. Used examples off cover cannot be distinguished as much of the phosphor is lost in the course of floating.

In the 5p. value the missing grey-black affects the doublet, which appears as brownish grey, and the lace ruff, which is entirely missing. The missing sepia affects only Drake's hair, which appears much lighter.

The double printing of the brown-grey (cylinder 1F) on the 9p. is a most unusual type of error to occur in a multicoloured photogravure issue. Two sheets are known and it is believed that they stuck to the cylinder and went through a second time. This would result in the following two sheets missing the colour but at the time of going to press this error has not been reported. The second print is slightly askew and more prominent in the top half of the sheets. Examples from the upper part of the sheet showing a clear double impression of the facial features are worth a substantial premium over the price quoted.

Special First Day of Issue Postmark

Philatelic Bureau, Edinburgh 3.50
First Day of Issue handstamps were provided at Blantyre, Glasgow, and Denbigh for this issue.

411 **412**

413

416 "Nelly O'Brien"
(Reynolds)

417 "Rev. R. Walker
(The Skater)" (Raeburn)

(T **411/13** show sketches of W. G. Grace by Harry Furniss)

(Des S. Rose. Queen's head printed in gold and then embossed)

(Des E. Ripley. Queen's head printed in gold and then embossed)

1973 (16 May).   **County Cricket 1873–1973.** "All-over" phosphor.
P 14 × 15.

928	**411**	3p. black, ochre & gold.......................	8	8
		a. Gold (Queen's head) omitted..........	£2250	
		Eb. Embossing omitted	6.00	
929	**412**	7½p. black, light sage-green & gold	1.25	1.25
		Eb. Embossing omitted	15.00	
930	**413**	9p. black, cobalt & gold	1.25	1.25
		Eb. Embossing omitted	50.00	
		Set of 3	2.25	2.25
		First Day Cover		2.25
		Presentation Pack...........................	2.75	
		Souvenir Book	8.00	
		P.H.Q. Card (No. 928)	60.00	£150

The souvenir book is a 24-page illustrated booklet containing a
history of County Cricket with text by John Arlott.

Special First Day of Issue Postmarks

Philatelic Bureau, Edinburgh	2.75
Lords, London NW	3.75

414 "Self-portrait"
(Reynolds)

415 "Self-portrait"
(Raeburn)

1973 (4 July).   **British Paintings.** 250th Birth Anniv of Sir Joshua Reynolds and 150th Death Anniv of Sir Henry Raeburn. "All-over"
phosphor. P 14 × 15.

931	**414**	3p. rose, new blue, jet-black, magenta, greenish yellow, black, ochre & gold	8	8
		a. Gold (Queen's head) omitted..........	60.00	
		Ec. Gold (Queen's head) & embossing omitted	65.00	
932	**415**	5p. cinnamon, greenish yellow, new blue, lt magenta, black, yellow-olive & gold	20	25
		a. Gold (Queen's head) omitted..........	75.00	
		b. Greenish yellow omitted	£300	
933	**416**	7½p. greenish yellow, new blue, lt magen-ta, black, cinnamon & gold	60	65
		a. Gold (Queen's head) omitted..........	75.00	
		b. Cinnamon omitted	£650	
		Ec. Embossing omitted	6.00	
934	**417**	9p. brownish rose, black, dull rose, pale yellow, brownish grey, pale blue & gold	80	85
		b. Brownish rose omitted	25.00	
		Ec. Embossing omitted	80.00	
		Set of 4	1.50	1.60
		First Day Cover		1.75
		Presentation Pack..........................	2.00	

Secial First Day of Issue Postmark

Philatelic Bureau, Edinburgh	2.75

418 Court Masque Costumes

419 St. Paul's Church, Covent Garden

420 Prince's Lodging, Newmarket   **421** Court Masque Stage Scene

T **418/19** and T **420/1** were printed horizontally *se-tenant* within the sheet.

(Des Rosalind Dease. Litho and typo B.W.)

1973 (15 Aug). **400th Birth Anniv of Inigo Jones (architect and designer).** *"All-over" phosphor.* P 15 × 14.

935	**418**	3p. dp mauve, black & gold	10	15
		a. Pair. Nos. 935/6	30	40
		Eb. 9 mm. phosphor band*	10.00	
936	**419**	3p. dp brown, black & gold	10	15
937	**420**	5p. blue, black & gold	40	45
		a. Pair. Nos. 937/8	2.25	2.25
		Eb. 9 mm. phosphor band*	10.00	
938	**421**	5p. grey-olive, black & gold	40	45
		Set of 4	2.40	1.10
		First Day Cover		2.50
		Presentation Pack	2.75	
		P.H.Q. Card (No. 936)	£125 ǀ 70.00	

*On part of the printings for both values the "all-over" phosphor band missed the first vertical row and a 9 mm. phosphor band was applied to correct this.

Special First Day of Issue Postmark

Philatelic Bureau, Edinburgh 3.50

422 Palace of Westminster
seen from Whitehall

423 Palace of Westminster
seen from Millbank

(Des R. Downer. Recess and typo B.W.)

1973 (12 Sept). **19th Commonwealth Parliamentary Conference.** *"All-over" phosphor.* P 15 × 14.

939	**422**	8p. black, brownish grey & stone	30	30
940	**423**	10p. gold & black	40	40
		Set of 2	65	65
		First Day Cover		1.25
		Presentation Pack	2.00	
		Souvenir Book	9.00	
		P.H.Q. Card (No. 939)	40.00	90.00

The souvenir book is a twelve-page booklet containing a history of the Palace of Westminster.

Special First Day of Issue Postmark

Philatelic Bureau, Edinburgh 2.00

424 Princess Anne and Capt. Mark Phillips

(Des C. Clements and E. Hughes from photo by Lord Litchfield)

1973 (14 Nov). **Royal Wedding.** *"All-over" phosphor.* P 15 × 14.

941	**424**	3½p. dull violet & silver.........................	10	10
		a. Imperf (pair)	£900	
942		20p. dp brown & silver	70	70
		a. Silver omitted	£900	
		Set of 2	80	80
		Set of 2 Gutter Pairs	8.00	
		Set of 2 Traffic Light Gutter Pairs	£120	
		First Day Cover		1.25
		Presentation Pack	2.00	
		P.H.Q. Card (No. 941)	12.00	22.00

Special First Day of Issue Postmarks

Philatelic Bureau, Edinburgh 1.75
Westminster Abbey, London SW1 .... 3.75
Windsor, Berks 2.75

425

426

427

428

429

T **425/9** depict the carol "Good King Wenceslas" and were printed horizontally *se-tenant* within the sheet.

430 "Good King Wenceslas, the Page and Peasant"

(Des D. Gentleman)

1973 (28 Nov). **Christmas.** *One centre phosphor band* (3p.) *or "all-over" phosphor* (3½p.). P 15 × 14.

943	**425**	3p. grey-black, blue, brownish grey, lt brown, brt rose-red, turquoise-green, salmon-pink & gold.............		15	15
		a. Strip of 5. Nos. 943/7		2.90	2.75
		b. Imperf (horiz strip of 5)			
		Eg. Gum arabic..................................		20	
		Ega. Strip of 5. Nos. 943Eg/47Eg		3.50	
		Egb. Imperf (strip of 5. Nos. 943Eg/7Eg)			
944	**426**	3p. grey-black, violet-blue, slate, brown, rose-red, rosy mauve, turquoise-green, salmon-pink & gold.............		15	15
		a. Rosy mauve omitted			
		Eg. Gum arabic..................................		20	
945	**427**	3p. grey-black, violet-blue, slate, brown, rose-red, rosy mauve, turquoise-green, salmon-pink & gold.............		15	15
		a. Rosy mauve omitted			
		Eg. Gum arabic..................................		20	
946	**428**	3p. grey-black, violet-blue, slate, brown, rose-red, rosy mauve, turquoise-green, salmon-pink & gold.............		15	15
		a. Rosy mauve omitted			
		Eg. Gum arabic..................................		20	
947	**429**	3p. grey-black, violet-blue, slate, brown, rose-red, rosy mauve, turquoise-green, salmon-pink & gold.............		15	15
		a. Rosy mauve omitted			
		Eg. Gum arabic..................................		20	
948	**430**	3½p. salmon-pink, grey-black, red-brown, blue, turquoise-green, brt rose-red, rosy mauve, lavender-grey & gold		15	15
		a. Imperf (pair)		£450	
		b. Grey-black (value & inscr, etc.) omitted		75.00	
		c. Salmon-pink omitted		60.00	
		d. Blue (leg, robes) omitted		£110	
		e. Rosy mauve (robe at right) omitted...		70.00	
		f. Blue & rosy mauve omitted		£225	
		g. Brt rose-red (King's robe) omitted		75.00	
		h. Red-brown (logs, basket, etc.) omitted			
		Set of 6		2.90	80
		First Day Cover			2.75
		Presentation Pack		3.00	

An example of the 3½p. with the gold background colour omitted has been seen used on cover; another has been seen with the turquoise-green omitted (used on piece); and a pair with the lavender-grey omitted (used on piece).

The 3p. and 3½p. are normally with PVA gum with added dextrin but the 3½p. also exists with normal PVA gum.

Special First Day of Issue Postmarks

Philatelic Bureau, Edinburgh		3.50
Bethlehem, Llandeilo, Carms		5.00

Collectors Pack 1973

1973 (28 Nov). *Comprises Nos. 919/48.*

CP948*i*	Collectors Pack	30.00

431 Horse Chestnut

(Des D. Gentleman)

1974 (27 Feb). **British Trees (2nd issue).** *"All-over"* phosphor.
P 15 × 14.

949 **431** 10p. lt emerald, brt green, greenish yellow, brown-olive, black & brownish grey 35 30
Gutter Pair 3.25
Traffic Light Gutter Pair.................... 42.00
First Day Cover 1.00
Presentation Pack......................... 2.00
P.H.Q. Card £140 60.00

Special First Day of Issue Postmark

Philatelic Bureau, Edinburgh 2.00

953 **435** 10p. grey-black, pale reddish brown, lt brown, orange-yellow & grey 80 30
Set of 4 .... 1.40 1.50
Set of 4 Gutter Pairs 3.25
Set of 4 Traffic Light Gutter Pairs 40.00
First Day Cover 3.00
Presentation Pack......................... 2.00
P.H.Q. Card (No. 950) £140 60.00

The 3½p. exists with ordinary PVA gum.

Special First Day of Issue Postmark

Philatelic Bureau, Edinburgh 3.50

436 P & O Packet, *Peninsular*, 1888

437 Farman Biplane, 1911

438 Airmail-blue Van and Postbox, 1930

439 Imperial Airways "C" Class Flying-boat, 1937

432 First Motor Fire-engine, 1904   **433** Prize-winning Fire-engine, 1863

434 First Steam Fire-engine, 1830   **435** Fire-engine, 1766

(Des D. Gentleman)

1974 (24 Apr). **Bicentenary of the Fire Prevention (Metropolis) Act.** *"All-over"* phosphor. P 15 × 14.

950 **432** 3½p. grey-black, orange-yellow, greenish yellow, dull rose, ochre & grey 8 8
a. Imperf (pair) £500
951 **433** 5½p. greenish yellow, dp rosy magenta, orange-yellow, lt emerald, grey-black & grey...................................... 25 25
952 **434** 8p. greenish yellow, lt blue-green, lt greenish blue, lt chestnut, grey-black & grey....................................... 60 60

(Des Rosalind Dease)

1974 (12 June). **Centenary of Universal Postal Union.** *"All-over"* phosphor. P 15 × 14.

954 **436** 3½p. dp brownish grey, brt mauve, grey-black & gold 8 8
955 **437** 5½p. pale orange, lt emerald, grey-black & gold 15 20
956 **438** 8p. cobalt, brown, grey-black & gold 25 30
957 **439** 10p. dp brownish grey, orange, grey-black & gold 40 35
Set of 4 .... 80 80
Set of 4 Gutter Pairs 3.25
Set of 4 Traffic Light Gutter Pairs 40.00
First Day Cover 1.25
Presentation Pack......................... 2.00

Special First Day of Issue Postmark

Philatelic Bureau, Edinburgh 2.25

440 Robert the Bruce

441 Owain Glyndŵr

442 Henry the Fifth

443 The Black Prince

(Des F. Wegner)

1974 (10 July). **Medieval Warriors.** *"All-over"* phosphor. P 15 × 14.

958	**440**	4½p. greenish yellow, vermilion, slate-blue, red-brown, reddish brown, lilac-grey & gold	10	10
959	**441**	5½p. lemon, vermilion, slate-blue, red-brown, reddish brown, olive-drab & gold	20	25
960	**442**	8p. dp grey, vermilion, greenish yellow, new blue, red-brown, dp cinnamon & gold	80	85
961	**443**	10p. vermilion, greenish yellow, new blue, red-brown, reddish brown, lt blue & gold	80	85
		Set of 4	1.75	1.75
		Set of 4 Gutter Pairs	9.00	
		Set of 4 Traffic Light Gutter Pairs	60.00	
		First Day Cover		2.00
		Presentation Pack	3.25	
		P.H.Q. Cards (set of 4)	32.00	25.00

Special First Day of Issue Postmark

Philatelic Bureau, Edinburgh 3.25

444 Churchill in Royal Yacht Squadron Uniform

445 Prime Minister, 1940

446 Secretary for War and Air, 1919

447 War Correspondent, South Africa, 1899

(Des C. Clements and E. Hughes)

1974 (9 Oct). **Birth Centenary of Sir Winston Churchill.** *"All-over"* phosphor. P 14 × 15.

962	**444**	4½p. Prussian blue, pale turquoise-green & silver	12	12
963	**445**	5½p. sepia, brownish grey & silver	20	25
964	**446**	8p. crimson, lt claret & silver	40	40
965	**447**	10p. lt brown, stone & silver	45	45
		Set of 4	1.10	1.10
		Set of 4 Gutter Pairs	5.50	
		Set of 4 Traffic Light Gutter Pairs	38.00	
		First Day Cover		1.60
		Presentation Pack	1.50	
		Souvenir Book	2.50	
		P.H.Q. Card (No. 963)	7.50	10.00

The souvenir book consists of an illustrated folder containing a biography of Sir Winston.

Nos. 962/5 come with PVA gum containing added dextrin, but the 8p. also exists with normal PVA.

Special First Day of Issue Postmarks

Philatelic Bureau, Edinburgh 2.75
Blenheim, Woodstock, Oxford 4.50
House of Commons, London SW 4.50

Philatelic Bureau, Edinburgh 3.00
Bethlehem, Llandeilo, Carms 4.50

Collectors Pack 1974

1974 (27 Nov). *Comprises Nos. 949/69.*
CP969a   Collectors Pack 10.00

448 "Adoration of the Magi" (York Minster, *circa* 1355)

449 "The Nativity" (St. Helen's Church, Norwich, *circa* 1480)

452 Invalid in Wheelchair

(Des P. Sharland)

1975 (22 Jan). **Health and Handicap Funds.** *"All-over" phosphor.*
P 15 × 14.
970 **452** 4½p. + 1½p. azure & grey-blue 10   12
                Gutter Pair 35
                Traffic Light Gutter Pair.................. 85
                First Day Cover   60

Special First Day of Issue Postmark

Philatelic Bureau, Edinburgh 1.60

450 "Virgin and Child" (Ottery St. Mary Church, *circa* 1350)

451 "Virgin and Child" (Worcester Cathedral, *circa* 1224)

(Des Peter Hatch Partnership)

1974 (27 Nov).   **Christmas.** *Church Roof Bosses. One phosphor band*
(3½p.) or "all-over" phosphor (others). P 15 × 14.
966 **448**   3½p. gold, lt new blue, lt brown, grey-
                   black & lt stone   8   8
           a. Lt stone (background shading) omit-
                   ted ....
           Ey. Phosphor omitted 7.00
967 **449**   4½p. gold, yellow-orange, rose-red, lt
                   brown, grey-black, & lt new blue   10   10
968 **450**   8p. blue, gold, lt brown, rose-red, dull
                   green & grey-black   30   35
969 **451**   10p. gold, dull rose, grey-black, lt new
                   blue, pale cinnamon & lt brown.......   30   35
                   Set of 4   75   80
                   Set of 4 Gutter Pairs 5.50
                   Set of 4 Traffic Light Gutter Pairs 42.00
                   First Day Cover 1.40
                   Presentation Pack.........................   1.50
The phosphor band on the 3½p. was first applied down the centre of
the stamp but during the printing this was deliberately placed to the
right between the roof boss and the value; however, intermediate
positions, due to shifts, are known.

453 "Peace—Burial at Sea"

454 "Snowstorm—Steamer off a Harbour's Mouth"

455 "The Arsenal, Venice"   **456** "St. Laurent"

461 National Theatre, London

(Des S. Rose)

(Des P. Gauld)

1975 (19 Feb). **Birth Bicentenary of J. M. W. Turner (painter).** "All-over" phosphor. P 15 × 14.

971	453	4½p. grey-black, salmon, stone, blue & grey	10	10
972	454	5½p. cobalt, greenish yellow, lt yellow-brown, grey-black & rose	15	15
973	455	8p. pale yellow-orange, greenish yellow, rose, cobalt & grey-black	20	25
974	456	10p. dp blue, lt yellow-ochre, lt brown, dp cobalt & grey-black	30	35
		Set of 4	70	80
		Set of 4 Gutter Pairs	1.75	
		Set of 4 Traffic Light Gutter Pairs	5.50	
		First Day Cover		1.25
		Presentation Pack	1.50	
		P.H.Q. Card (No. 972)	30.00	†10.00

Special First Day of Issue Postmarks

      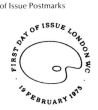

Philatelic Bureau, Edinburgh	2.50
London WC	3.00

457 Charlotte Square, Edinburgh   **458** The Rows, Chester

T **457/8** were printed horizontally se-tenant within the sheet.

459 Royal Observatory, Greenwich

460 St. George's Chapel, Windsor

1975 (23 Apr). **European Architectural Heritage Year.** "All-over" phosphor. P 15 × 14.

975	457	7p. greenish yellow, brt orange, grey-black, red-brown, new blue, lavender & gold	20	20
		a. Pair. Nos. 975/6	55	65
976	458	7p. grey-black, greenish yellow, new blue, brt orange, red-brown & gold	20	20
977	459	8p. magenta, dp slate, pale magenta, lt yellow-olive, grey-black & gold	20	25
978	460	10p. bistre-brown, greenish yellow, dp slate, emerald-green, grey-black & gold	25	25
979	461	12p. grey-black, new blue, pale magenta & gold	30	35
		Set of 5	1.10	1.10
		Set of 5 Gutter Pairs	2.75	
		Set of 5 Traffic Light Gutter Pairs	13.00	
		First Day Cover		1.60
		Presentation Pack	2.00	
		P.H.Q. Cards (Nos. 975/7)	8.50	9.00

Special First Day of Issue Postmark

Philatelic Bureau, Edinburgh	3.25

462 Sailing Dinghies   **463** Racing Keel Yachts

464 Cruising Yachts   **465** Multihulls

87

(Des A. Restall. Recess and photo)

1975 (11 June). **Sailing.** *"All-over" phosphor.* P 15 × 14.

980	**462**	7p. black, bluish violet, scarlet, orange-vermilion, orange & gold	15	15
981	**463**	8p. black, orange-vermilion, orange, lavender, brt mauve, brt blue, dp ultramarine & gold	20	20
		a. Black omitted............................	60.00	
982	**464**	10p. black, orange, bluish emerald, lt olive-drab, chocolate & gold	25	25
983	**465**	12p. black, ultramarine, turquoise-blue, rose, grey, steel-blue & gold	35	45
		Set of 4	85	1.00
		Set of 4 Gutter Pairs	2.25	
		Set of 4 Traffic Light Gutter Pairs	20.00	
		First Day Cover		1.25
		Presentation Pack	1.25	
		P.H.Q. Card (No. 981)	4.00	9.00

On No. 981a the recess-printed black colour is completely omitted.

Special First Day of Issue Postmark

Philatelic Bureau, Edinburgh 2.50
A First Day of Issue handstamp was provided at Weymouth for this issue.

1825 Stockton and Darlington Railway

466 Stephenson's *Locomotion*, 1825

1876 North British Railway Drummond

467 *Abbotsford*, 1876

1923 Great Western Railway Castle Class

468 *Caerphilly Castle*, 1923

1975 British Rail Inter-City Service HST

469 High Speed Train, 1975

(Des B. Craker)

1975 (13 Aug). **150th Anniv of Public Railways.** *"All-over" phosphor.* P 15 × 14.

984	**466**	7p. red-brown, grey-black, greenish yellow, grey & silver.........................	30	30

985	**467**	8p. brown, orange-yellow, vermilion, grey-black, grey & silver	30	35
986	**468**	10p. emerald-green, grey-black, yellow-orange, vermilion, grey & silver	40	40
987	**469**	12p. grey-black, pale lemon, vermilion, blue, grey & silver.........................	50	55
		Set of 4	1.40	1.40
		Set of 4 Gutter Pairs	2.90	
		Set of 4 Traffic Light Gutter Pairs	10.00	
		First Day Cover		2.50
		Presentation Pack	2.25	
		Souvenir Book	3.50	
		P.H.Q. Cards (set of 4)	60.00	25.00

The souvenir book is an eight-page booklet containing a history of the railways.

Special First Day of Issue Postmarks

Philatelic Bureau, Edinburgh 3.50
Darlington, Co. Durham..................................... 4.50
Shildon, Co. Durham 5.50
Stockton-on-Tees, Cleveland............................... 4.50

470 Palace of Westminster

(Des R. Downer)

1975 (3 Sept). **62nd Inter-Parliamentary Union Conference.** *"All-over" phosphor.* P 15 × 14.

988	**470**	12p. lt new blue, black, brownish grey & gold	30	35
		Gutter Pair	75	
		Traffic Light Gutter Pair...................	2.25	
		First Day Cover		60
		Presentation Pack	1.00	

Special First Day of Issue Postmark

Philatelic Bureau, Edinburgh 1.25

Special First Day of Issue Postmark

Philatelic Bureau, Edinburgh 1.75
Steventon, Basingstoke, Hants 2.75

471 "Emma and Mr.
Woodhouse" (Emma)

472 "Catherine Morland"
(Northanger Abbey)

473 "Mr. Darcy"
(Pride and Prejudice)

474 "Mary and Henry
Crawford"
(Mansfield Park)

(Des Barbara Brown)

1975 (22 Oct).   **Birth Bicentenary of Jane Austen (novelist).** *"All-over"*
phosphor. P 14 × 15.

989	471	8½p. blue, slate, rose-red, lt yellow, dull green, grey-black & gold................	20	20
990	472	10p. slate, brt magenta, grey, lt yellow, grey-black & gold	25	25
991	473	11p. dull blue, pink, olive-sepia, slate, pale greenish yellow, grey-black & gold	40	45
992	474	13p. brt magenta, lt new blue, slate, buff, dull blue-green, grey-black & gold ...	35	40
		Set of 4	1.00	1.10
		Set of 4 Gutter Pairs	2.25	
		Set of 4 Traffic Light Gutter Pairs	7.50	
		First Day Cover		1.25
		Presentation Pack	2.00	
		P.H.Q. Cards (set of 4)	15.00	15.00

475 Angels with Harp and Lute   476 Angel with Mandolin

477 Angel with Horn   478 Angel with Trumpet

(Des R. Downer)

1975 (26 Nov).   **Christmas.** *One phosphor band* (6½p.), *phosphor-
inked background* (8½p.), *"all-over" phosphor* (others). *P* 15 × 14.

993	475	6½p. bluish violet, brt reddish violet, light lavender & gold...........................	15	15
994	476	8½p. turquoise-green, brt emerald-green, slate, lt turquoise-green & gold........	20	20
995	477	11p. vermilion, cerise, pink & gold..........	40	40
996	478	13p. drab, brown, brt orange, buff & gold	40	40
		Set of 4	1.00	1.00
		Set of 4 Gutter Pairs	2.10	
		Set of 4 Traffic Light Gutter Pairs	7.50	
		First Day Cover		1.25
		Presentation Pack	2.00	

The 6½p. exists with both ordinary PVA gum and PVA containing
added dextrin.

Special First Day of Issue Postmarks

Philatelic Bureau, Edinburgh 2.00
Bethlehem, Llandeilo, Dyfed 2.50

Collectors Pack 1975

1975 (26 Nov). *Comprises Nos. 970/96.*
CP996a Collectors Pack 9.00

479 Housewife

480 Policeman

481 District Nurse

482 Industrialist

(Des P. Sharland)

1976 (10 Mar). **Telephone Centenary.** *"All-over" phosphor.*
P 15 × 14.

997	**479**	8½p. greenish blue, dp rose, black & blue	20	20
		a. Dp rose omitted	£2250	
998	**480**	10p. greenish blue, black & yellow-olive ..	25	25
999	**481**	11p. greenish blue, dp rose, black & brt mauve	40	40
1000	**482**	13p. olive-brown, dp rose, black & orange-red..	40	40
		Set of 4	1.10	1.10
		Set of 4 Gutter Pairs	2.25	
		Set of 4 Traffic Light Gutter Pairs	7.50	
		First Day Cover		1.25
		Presentation Pack........................	2.00	

Special First Day of Issue Postmark

Philatelic Bureau, Edinburgh 2.25

483 Hewing Coal
(Thomas Hepburn)

484 Machinery (Robert Owen)

485 Chimney Cleaning
(Lord Shaftesbury)

486 Hands clutching Prison Bars
(Elizabeth Fry)

(Des D. Gentleman)

1976 (28 Apr). **Social Reformers.** *"All-over" phosphor.* P 15 × 14.

1001	**483**	8½p. lavender-grey, grey-black, black & slate-grey	20	20
1002	**484**	10p. lavender-grey, grey-black, grey & slate-violet	25	25
1003	**485**	11p. black, slate-grey & drab	40	40
1004	**486**	13p. slate-grey, black & dp dull green......	40	40
		Set of 4	1.10	1.10
		Set of 4 Gutter Pairs	2.25	
		Set of 4 Traffic Light Gutter Pairs	7.50	
		First Day Cover		1.25
		Presentation Pack	2.00	
		P.H.Q. Card (No. 1001)..................	6.00	7.00

Special First Day of Issue Postmark

Philatelic Bureau, Edinburgh 2.25

487 Benjamin Franklin (bust by Jean-Jacques Caffieri)

(Des P. Sharland)

1976 (2 June). **Bicentenary of American Revolution.** *"All-over" phosphor.* P 14 × 15.

1005	**487**	11p. pale bistre, slate-violet, pale blue-green, black & gold......................	30	30
		Gutter Pair	65	
		Traffic Light Gutter Pair..................	1.50	
		First Day Cover		60
		Presentation Pack..........................	1.00	
		P.H.Q. Card	4.00	8.50

Special First Day of Issue Postmark

Philatelic Bureau, Edinburgh 1.50

Special First Day of Issue Postmark

Philatelic Bureau, Edinburgh 2.50

488 "Elizabeth of Glamis"

489 "Grandpa Dickson"

492 Archdruid

493 Morris Dancing

490 "Rosa Mundi"

491 "Sweet Briar"

494 Scots Piper

495 Welsh Harpist

(Des Kristin Rosenberg)

1976 (30 June). **Centenary of Royal National Rose Society.** "All-over" phosphor. P 14 × 15.

1006	488	8½p. bright rose-red, greenish yellow, emerald, grey-black & gold.................	20	20
1007	489	10p. greenish yellow, brt green, reddish brown, grey-black & gold...............	30	30
1008	490	11p. brt magenta, greenish yellow, emerald, grey-blue, grey-black & gold	35	40
1009	491	13p. rose-pink, lake-brown, yellow-green, pale greenish yellow, grey-black & gold	35	35
		a. Value omitted*.............................		
		Set of 4	1.10	1.10
		Set of 4 Gutter Pairs	2.25	
		Set of 4 Traffic Light Gutter Pairs	10.00	
		First Day Cover		1.50
		Presentation Pack.........................	2.00	
		P.H.Q. Cards (set of 4)	28.00	13.00

*The value was not etched in one position of the cylinder but the error was discovered before issue and most examples were removed from the sheets.

(Des Marjorie Saynor)

1976 (4 Aug). **British Cultural Traditions.** "All-over" phosphor. P 14 × 15.

1010	492	8½p. yellow, sepia, brt rose, dull ultramarine, black & gold	20	20
1011	493	10p. dull ultramarine, brt rose-red, sepia, greenish yellow, black & gold..........	30	30
1012	494	11p. bluish green, yellow-brown, yellow-orange, black, brt rose-red & gold....	35	35
1013	495	13p. dull violet-blue, yellow-orange, yellow, black, bluish green & gold	35	35
		Set of 4	1.10	1.10
		Set of 4 Gutter Pairs	2.25	
		Set of 4 Traffic Light Gutter Pairs	7.50	
		First Day Cover		1.25
		Presentation Pack.........................	1.60	
		P.H.Q. Cards (set of 4)	15.00	8.50

The 8½p. and 13p. commemorate the 800th Anniv of the Royal National Eisteddfod.

Special First Day of Issue Postmarks

Special First Day of Issue Postmarks

Philatelic Bureau, Edinburgh 2.25
Cardigan, Dyfed 3.50

Philatelic Bureau, Edinburgh 2.00
London SW1 .... 2.50

496 Woodcut from
The Canterbury Tales

497 Extract from
The Tretyse of Love

500 Virgin and Child   **501** Angel with Crown

498 Woodcut from
The Game and Playe of Chesse

499 Early Printing Press

502 Angel appearing to Shepherds   **503** The Three Kings

(Des Enid Marx)

1976 (24 Nov). **Christmas.** *English Medieval Embroidery.* One phosphor band (6½p.), "all-over" phosphor (others). P 15 × 14.

1018	**500**	6½p. blue, bistre-yellow, brown & orange.	15	15
		a. Imperf (pair)	£450	
1019	**501**	8½p. sage-green, yellow, brown-ochre, chestnut & olive-black	20	20
1020	**502**	11p. dp magenta, brown-orange, new blue, black & cinnamon.................	35	35
		a. Uncoated paper*	50.00	20.00
1021	**503**	13p. bright purple, new blue, cinnamon, bronze-green & olive-grey	40	40
		Set of 4	1.00	1.00
		Set of 4 Gutter Pairs	2.10	
		Set of 4 Traffic Light Gutter Pairs	6.50	
		First Day Cover		1.25
		Presentation Pack	2.00	
		P.H.Q. Cards (set of 4)	3.25	10.00

*See footnote after No. 744.

(Des R. Gay. Queen's head printed in gold and then embossed)

1976 (29 Sept). **500th Anniv of British Printing.** *"All-over"* phosphor. P 14 × 15.

1014	**496**	8½p. black, lt new blue & gold	20	20
1015	**497**	10p. black, olive-green & gold...............	25	30
1016	**498**	11p. black, brownish grey & gold............	35	40
1017	**499**	13p. chocolate, pale ochre & gold...........	40	40
		Set of 4	1.10	1.10
		Set of 4 Gutter Pairs	2.25	
		Set of 4 Traffic Light Gutter Pairs	6.50	
		First Day Cover		1.25
		Presentation Pack	2.00	
		P.H.Q. Cards (set of 4)	14.00	8.50

Special First Day of Issue Postmarks

Special First Day of Issue Postmark

Philatelic Bureau, Edinburgh 2.00

Philatelic Bureau, Edinburgh 2.00
Bethlehem, Llandeilo, Dyfed 2.50

Collectors Pack 1976

1976 (24 Nov). *Comprises Nos. 997/1021.*
CP1021a Collectors Pack 14.00

504 Lawn Tennis

505 Table Tennis

506 Squash

507 Badminton

(Des A. Restall)

1977 (12 Jan). **Racket Sports.** *Phosphorised paper. P 15 × 14.*
1022	**504**	8½p.	emerald-green, black, grey & bluish green	20	20
			a. Imperf (horiz pair)	£850
1023	**505**	10p.	myrtle-green, black, grey-black & dp blue-green	30	30
1024	**506**	11p.	orange, pale yellow, black, slate-black & grey	35	40
1025	**507**	13p.	brown, grey-black, grey & brt reddish violet....................................	40	40
			Set of 4	1.10	1.10
			Set of 4 Gutter Pairs	2.25
			Set of 4 Traffic Light Gutter Pairs	6.50
			First Day Cover		1.25
			Presentation Pack	2.00
			P.H.Q. Cards (set of 4)	6.00	9.00

508
(Des after plaster cast by Arnold Machin)

1977 (2 Feb)–**87.** *P 14 × 15.*
1026	**508**	£1	brt yellow-green & blackish olive	1.50	20
			a. Imperf (pair)	£650
1026b		£1.30	pale drab & dp greenish blue (3.8.83)	6.00	5.00
1026c		£1.33	pale mauve & grey-black (28.8.84)	5.00	3.75
1026d		£1.41	pale drab & dp greenish blue (17.9.85)	4.00	3.25
1026e		£1.50	pale mauve & grey-black (2.9.86)	2.25	2.75
1026f		£1.60	pale drab & dp grnish blue (15.9.87)	2.40	2.75
1027		£2	light emerald & purple-brown	3.00	60
1028		£5	salmon & chalky blue	7.50	3.00
			Set of 8	30.00	18.00
			Set of 8 Gutter Pairs	60.00
			Set of 8 Traffic Light Gutter Pairs	70.00
			First Day Cover (1026, 1027/8)...........		22.00
			First Day Cover (1026b)		8.00
			First Day Cover (1026c)		6.00
			First Day Cover (1026d)		6.00
			First Day Cover (1026e)...................		6.50
			First Day Cover (1026f)		5.50
			Presentation Pack (1026, 1027/8)	12.50
			Presentation Pack (1026f)	5.50

509 Steroids—Conformational
Analysis

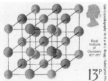

510 Vitamin C—Synthesis

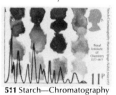

511 Starch—Chromatography

512 Salt—Crystallography

93

(Des J. Karo)

1977 (2 Mar). **Royal Institute of Chemistry Centenary.** *"All-over"* *phosphor.* P 15 × 14.

1029 **509**	8½p. rosine, new blue, olive-yellow, brt mauve, yellow-brown, black & gold..	20	20
	a. Imperf (horiz pair)	£850	
1030 **510**	10p. brt orange, rosine, new blue, brt blue, black & gold	30	30
1031 **511**	11p. rosine, greenish-yellow, new blue, dp violet, black & gold	35	35
1032 **512**	13p. new blue, brt green, black & gold	40	40
	Set of 4	1.10	1.10
	Set of 4 Gutter Pairs	2.25	
	Set of 4 Traffic Light Gutter Pairs	6.50	
	First Day Cover		1.25
	Presentation Pack.........................	2.40	
	P.H.Q. Cards (set of 4)	6.00	9.00

Special First Day of Issue Postmark

Philatelic Bureau, Edinburgh 2.00

513

514

515

516

T **513/16** differ in the decorations of "ER".

(Des R. Guyatt)

1977 (11 May–15 June). **Silver Jubilee.** *"All-over"* *phosphor.* P 15 × 14.

1033 **513**	8½p. blackish green, black, silver, olive-grey & pale turquoise-green............	20	20
	a. Imperf (pair)	£750	

1034 **513**	9p. maroon, black, silver, olive-grey & lavender (15 June)...........................	20	25
1035 **514**	10p. blackish blue, black, silver, olive-grey & ochre.................................	25	30
	a. Imperf (horiz pair)		
1036 **515**	11p. brown-purple, black, silver, olive-grey & rose-pink..........................	30	35
	a. Imperf (horiz pair)	£1250	
1037 **516**	13p. sepia, black, silver, olive-grey & bistre-brown	40	40
	a. Imperf (pair)	£1250	
	Set of 5	1.25	1.40
	Set of 5 Gutter Pairs	2.75	
	Set of 5 Traffic Light Gutter Pairs	4.00	
	First Day Covers (2)		1.60
	Presentation Pack (Nos. 1033, 1035/7)	1.75	
	Souvenir Book	3.00	
	P.H.Q. Cards (set of 5)	13.00	10.00

The souvenir book is a 16-page booklet containing a history of the Queen's reign.

Special First Day of Issue Postmarks

Philatelic Bureau, Edinburgh (1033, 1035/7) (11 May)	1.50
Philatelic Bureau, Edinburgh (1034) (15 June)	60
Windsor, Berks (1033, 1035/7) (11 May)	3.50
Windsor, Berks (1034) (15 June)	55

517 "Gathering of Nations"

(Des P. Murdoch. Recess and photo)

1977 (8 June). **Commonwealth Heads of Government Meeting, London.** *"All-over"* phosphor. P 14 × 15.

1038 **517**	13p. black, blackish green, rose-carmine & silver	30	30
	Gutter Pair	75	
	Traffic Light Gutter Pair...................	1.10	
	First Day Cover		80
	Presentation Pack.........................	1.00	
	P.H.Q. Card	3.00	3.50

Special First Day of Issue Postmarks

Philatelic Bureau, Edinburgh 1.10
London SW... 1.40

518 Hedgehog   **519** Brown Hare

520 Red Squirrel   **521** Otter

522 Badger

T **518/22** were printed horizontally *se-tenant* within the sheet.

(Des P. Oxenham)

1977 (5 Oct). **British Wildlife.** *"All-over"* phosphor. P 14 × 15.
1039 **518**   9p. reddish brown, grey-black, pale le-
              mon, brt turquoise-blue, brt magenta
              & gold 25   20
       a. Strip of 5. Nos. 1039/43 .... 1.40   1.40
       b. Imperf (vert pair) ....
       c. Imperf (horiz pair. Nos. 1039/40) ......

1040 **519**	9p. reddish brown, grey-black, pale lemon, brt turquoise-blue, brt magenta & gold		25	20
1041 **520**	9p. reddish brown, grey-black, pale lemon, brt turquoise-blue, brt magenta & gold		25	20
1042 **521**	9p. reddish brown, grey-black, pale lemon, brt turquoise-blue, brt magenta & gold		25	20
1043 **522**	9p. grey-black, reddish brown, pale lemon, brt turquoise-blue, brt magenta & gold		25	20
	Set of 5		1.40	90
	Gutter Strip of 10		4.25	
	Traffic Light Gutter Strip of 10		4.50	
	First Day Cover			2.00
	Presentation Pack		2.00	
	P.H.Q. Cards (set of 5)		4.00	4.00

Special First Day of Issue Postmark

Philatelic Bureau, Edinburgh 2.50

523 "Three French Hens, Two Turtle Doves and a Partridge in a Pear Tree"   **524** "Six Geese-a-laying, Five Gold Rings, Four Colly Birds"

525 "Eight Maids a-milking, Seven Swans a-swimming"   **526** "Ten Pipers piping, Nine Drummers drumming"

527 "Twelve Lords a-leaping, Eleven Ladies dancing"

T **523/7** depict the carol "The Twelve Days of Christmas" and were printed horizontally *se-tenant* within the sheet.

528 "A Partridge in a Pear Tree"

(Des D. Gentleman)

1977 (23 Nov). **Christmas.** *One centre phosphor band (7p.) or "all-over" phosphor (9p.). P* 15 × 14.

1044 **523**	7p.	slate, grey, brt yellow-green, new blue, rose-red & gold	15	15
	a.	Strip of 5. Nos. 1044/8	95	1.10
	ab.	Imperf (strip of 5. Nos. 1044/8)	£900	
1045 **524**	7p.	slate, brt yellow-green, new blue & gold	15	15
1046 **525**	7p.	slate, grey, brt yellow-green, new blue, rose-red & gold	15	15
1047 **526**	7p.	slate, grey, brt yellow-green, new blue, rose-red & gold	15	15
1048 **527**	7p.	slate, grey, bright yellow-green, new blue, rose-red & gold	15	15
1049 **528**	9p.	pale brown, pale orange, brt emerald, pale greenish yellow, slate-black & gold	20	20
	a.	Imperf (pair)	£750	
		Set of 6	1.10	85
		Set of 6 Gutter Pairs	2.50	
		Traffic Light Gutter Pairs	4.50	
		First Day Cover		1.25
		Presentation Pack	2.00	
		P.H.Q. Cards (set of 6)	3.25	3.75

Special First Day of Issue Postmarks

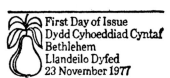

First Day of Issue
Dydd Cyhoeddiad Cyntaf
Bethlehem
Llandeilo Dyfed
23 November 1977

Philatelic Bureau, Edinburgh	1.50
Bethlehem, Llandeilo, Dyfed	3.25

Collectors Pack 1977

1977 (23 Nov). *Comprises Nos. 1022/5 and 1029/49.*
CP1049*b* Collectors Pack 7.50

529 Oil—North Sea
Production Platform

530 Coal—Modern Pithead

531 Natural Gas—Flame Rising from Sea	**532** Electricity—Nuclear Power Station and Uranium Atom

(Des P. Murdoch)

1978 (25 Jan). **Energy Resources.** *"All-over" phosphor. P* 14 × 15.

1050 **529**	9p.	dp brown, orange-vermilion, grey-black, greenish yellow, rose-pink, new blue & silver...........................	25	20
1051 **530**	10½p.	lt emerald-green, grey-black, red-brown, slate-grey, pale apple-green & silver	25	35
1052 **531**	11p.	greenish blue, brt violet, violet-blue, blackish brown, grey-black & silver ..	35	35
1053 **532**	13p.	orange-vermilion, grey-black, dp brown, greenish yellow, lt brown, lt blue & silver	35	40
		Set of 4	1.10	1.10
		Set of 4 Gutter Pairs	2.25	
		Set of 4 Traffic Light Gutter Pairs	4.50	
		First Day Cover		1.25
		Presentation Pack.........................	2.00	
		P.H.Q. Cards (set of 4)	3.25	4.25

Special First Day of Issue Postmark

Philatelic Bureau, Edinburgh 2.50

533 The Tower of London

534 Holyroodhouse

535 Caernarvon Castle

536 Hampton Court Palace

(Des R. Maddox (stamps), J. Matthews (miniature sheet))

1978 (1 Mar). **British Architecture.** *Historic Buildings. "All-over" phosphor.* P 15 × 14.

1054 **533**	9p.	black, olive-brown, new blue, brt green, lt yellow-olive & rose-red	25	20
1055 **534**	10½p.	black, brown-olive, orange-yellow, brt green, lt yellow-olive & violet-blue	25	30
1056 **535**	11p.	black, brown-olive, violet-blue, brt green, lt yellow-olive & dull blue	35	35
1057 **536**	13p.	black, orange-yellow, lake-brown, brt green & lt yellow-olive	40	40
		Set of 4	1.10	1.10
		Set of 4 Gutter Pairs	2.25	
		Set of 4 Traffic Light Gutter Pairs	4.25	
		First Day Cover		1.25
		Presentation Pack	2.00	
		P.H.Q. Cards (set of 4)	3.00	3.50
MS1058	121 × 89 mm. Nos. 1054/7 (sold at 53½p.)		1.25	1.60
	a. Imperforate		1800	
	b. Lt yellow-olive (Queen's head) omitted		£1800	
	c. Rose-red (Union Jack on 9p.) omitted		£1200	
	d. Orange-yellow omitted		£1000	
	First Day Cover			2.00

The premium on No. **MS**1058 was used to support the London 1980 International Stamp Exhibition.

No. **MS**1058d is most noticeable on the 10½p. (spheres absent on towers) and around the roadway and arch on the 13p.

Special First Day of Issue Postmarks

Philatelic Bureau, Edinburgh (stamps)	1.75
Philatelic Bureau, Edinburgh (miniature sheet)	2.50
London EC (stamps)	2.00
London EC (miniature sheet)	3.50

537 State Coach   **538** St. Edward's Crown

539 The Sovereign's Orb   **540** Imperial State Crown

(Des J. Matthews)

1978 (31 May). **25th Anniv of Coronation.** *"All-over" phosphor.* P 14 × 15.

1059 **537**	9p.	gold & royal blue	20	20
1060 **538**	10½p.	gold & brown-lake	25	30
1061 **539**	11p.	gold & dp dull green	30	35
1062 **540**	13p.	gold & reddish violet.....................	35	40
		Set of 4	1.00	1.10
		Set of 4 Gutter Pairs	2.25	
		Set of 4 Traffic Light Gutter Pairs	4.25	
		First Day Cover		1.25
		Presentation Pack	1.50	
		Souvenir Book	3.50	
		P.H.Q. Cards (set of 4)	2.50	2.50

The souvenir book is a 16-page booklet illustrated with scenes from the Coronation.

Special First Day of Issue Postmarks

Philatelic Bureau, Edinburgh	2.00
London SW1	1.50

541 Shire Horse   **542** Shetland Pony

543 Welsh Pony   **544** Thoroughbred

(Des P. Oxenham)

1978 (5 July). **Horses.** *"All-over" phosphor.* P 15 × 14.

1063 **541**	9p.	black, pale reddish brown, grey-black, greenish yellow, lt blue, vermilion & gold	25	30
1064 **542**	10½p.	pale chestnut, magenta, brownish grey, greenish yellow, greenish blue, grey-black & gold	30	35
1065 **543**	11p.	reddish brown, black, lt green, greenish yellow, bistre, grey-black & gold	40	45
1066 **544**	13p.	reddish brown, pale reddish brown, emerald, greenish yellow, grey-black & gold	45	50
		Set of 4	1.25	1.40
		Set of 4 Gutter Pairs	2.75	
		Set of 4 Traffic Light Gutter Pairs	4.50	
		First Day Cover		1.50
		Presentation Pack	1.75	
		P.H.Q. Cards (set of 4)	2.50	4.50

Special First Day of Issue Postmarks

Philatelic Bureau, Edinburgh 2.25
Peterborough 2.75

545 "Penny-farthing" and 1884 Safety Bicycle

546 1920 Touring Bicycles

547 Modern Small-wheel Bicycles

548 1978 Road-racers

(Des F. Wegner)

1978 (2 Aug). **Centenaries of Cyclists Touring Club and British Cycling Federation.** *"All-over" phosphor.* P 15 × 14.

1067 **545**	9p.	brown, dp dull blue, rose-pink, pale olive, grey-black & gold	20	20
		a. Imperf (pair)	£300	

1068 **546**	10½p.	olive, pale yellow-orange, orange-vermilion, rose-red, lt brown, grey-black & gold	25	30
1069 **547**	11p.	orange-vermilion, greenish blue, lt brown, pale greenish yellow, dp grey, grey-black & gold	30	35
1070 **548**	13p.	new blue, orange-vermilion, lt brown, olive-grey, grey-black & gold	35	40
		a. Imperf (pair)	£650	
		Set of 4	1.00	1.10
		Set of 4 Gutter Pairs	2.25	
		Set of 4 Traffic Light Gutter Pairs	4.25	
		First Day Cover		1.25
		Presentation Pack	1.50	
		P.H.Q. Cards (set of 4)	1.75	2.50

Special First Day of Issue Postmarks

Philatelic Bureau, Edinburgh 1.75
Harrogate, North Yorkshire................................... 2.25

549 Singing Carols round the Christmas Tree

550 The Waits

551 18th-century Carol Singers

552 "The Boar's Head Carol"

(Des Faith Jaques)

1978 (22 Nov). **Christmas.** *One centre phosphor band (7p.) or "all-over" phosphor (others).* P 15 × 14.

1071 **549**	7p.	brt green, greenish yellow, magenta, new blue, black & gold	20	20
		a. Imperf (vert pair)		
1072 **550**	9p.	magenta, greenish yellow, new blue, sage-green, black & gold	25	25
		a. Imperf (horiz pair)		
1073 **551**	11p.	magenta, new blue, greenish yellow, yellow-brown, black & gold	30	35
		a. Imperf (horiz pair)		

1074 **552**	13p.	salmon-pink, new blue, greenish yellow, magenta, black & gold	35	35
		Set of 4	1.00	1.00
		Set of 4 Gutter Pairs	2.10	
		Set of 4 Traffic Light Gutter Pairs	3.25	
		First Day Cover		1.00
		Presentation Pack	1.40	
		P.H.Q. Cards (set of 4)	1.75	3.25

Special First Day of Issue Postmarks

Philatelic Bureau, Edinburgh	1.50
Bethlehem, Llandeilo, Dyfed	1.25

Collectors Pack 1978
1978 (22 Nov). Comprises Nos. 1050/7 and 1059/74.
CP1074a Collectors Pack 9.00

553 Old English Sheepdog   **554** Welsh Springer Spaniel

555 West Highland Terrier   **556** Irish Setter

(Des P. Barrett)

1979 (7 Feb). **Dogs.** "All-over" phosphor. P 15 × 14.

1075 **553**	9p.	grey-black, sepia, turquoise-green, pale greenish yellow, pale greenish blue & grey	20	20
1076 **554**	10½p.	grey-black, lake-brown, apple-green, pale greenish yellow, pale greenish blue & grey	25	30
1077 **555**	11p.	grey-black, claret, yellowish green, pale greenish yellow, cobalt & grey ..	30	35
	a.	Imperf (horiz pair)		
1078 **556**	13p.	grey-black, lake-brown, green, pale greenish yellow & dp turquoise-blue	35	40
		Set of 4	1.00	1.10
		Set of 4 Gutter Pairs	2.25	
		Set of 4 Traffic Light Gutter Pairs	3.75	
		First Day Cover		1.25
		Presentation Pack	1.50	
		P.H.Q. Cards (set of 4)	3.50	3.50

Special First Day of Issue Postmarks

Philatelic Bureau, Edinburgh	1.75
London SW	2.00

557 Primrose   **558** Daffodil

559 Bluebell   **560** Snowdrop

(Des P. Newcombe)

1979 (21 Mar). **Spring Wild Flowers.** "All-over" phosphor. P 14 × 15.

1079 **557**	9p.	slate-black, dp brown, pale greenish yellow, dp olive, pale new blue & silver	20	20
	a.	Imperf (pair)	£400	
1080 **558**	10½p.	greenish yellow, grey-green, steel-blue, slate-black, new blue & silver ..	30	30
	a.	Imperf (vert pair)		
1081 **559**	11p.	slate-black, dp brown, ultramarine, lt greenish blue, pale greenish yellow & silver	30	35
	a.	Imperf (horiz pair)	£850	
1082 **560**	13p.	slate-black, indigo, grey-green, sepia, ochre & silver	35	40
	a.	Imperf (horiz pair)	£750	
		Set of 4	1.00	1.10
		Set of 4 Gutter Pairs	2.25	
		Set of 4 Traffic Light Gutter Pairs	3.75	
		First Day Cover		1.25
		Presentation Pack	1.50	
		P.H.Q. Cards (set of 4)	1.50	3.50

Special First Day of Issue Postmark

Philatelic Bureau, Edinburgh 1.75

Special First Day of Issue Postmarks

Philatelic Bureau, Edinburgh 1.75
London SW... 1.50

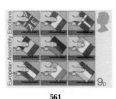

561

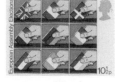

562

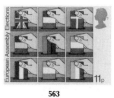

563

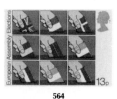

564

T 561/4 show Hands placing National Flags in Ballot Boxes.

(Des S. Cliff)

1979 (9 May).   **First Direct Elections to European Assembly.** *Phosphorised paper. P* 15 × 14.

1083	561	9p. grey-black, vermilion, cinnamon, pale greenish yellow, pale turquoise-green & dull ultramarine..............	20	20
1084	562	10½p. grey-black, vermilion, cinnamon, pale greenish yellow, dull ultramarine, pale turquoise-green & chestnut	25	30
1085	563	11p. grey-black, vermilion, cinnamon, pale greenish yellow, dull ultramarine, pale turquoise-green & grey-green	30	35
1086	564	13p. grey-black, vermilion, cinnamon, pale greenish yellow, dull ultramarine, pale turquoise-green & brown...	35	40
		Set of 4	1.00	1.10
		Set of 4 Gutter Pairs	2.25	
		Set of 4 Traffic Light Gutter Pairs	3.75	
		First Day Cover		1.25
		Presentation Pack..........................	1.50	
		P.H.Q. Cards (set of 4)	1.50	3.50

565 "Saddling 'Mahmoud' for the Derby, 1936" (Sir Alfred Munnings)

566 "The Liverpool Great National Steeple Chase, 1839" (aquatint by F. C. Turner)

567 "The First Spring Meeting, Newmarket, 1793" (J. N. Sartorius)

568 "Racing at Dorsett Ferry, Windsor, 1684" (Francis Barlow)

(Des S. Rose)

1979 (6 June).   **Horseracing Paintings.** *Bicentenary of the Derby (9p.). "All-over" phosphor. P* 15 × 14.

1087	565	9p. lt blue, red-brown, rose-pink, pale greenish yellow, grey-black & gold...	25	25
1088	566	10½p. bistre-yellow, slate-blue, salmon-pink, lt blue, grey-black & gold........	35	40
1089	567	11p. rose, vermilion, pale greenish yellow, new blue, grey-black & gold...........	40	45
1090	568	13p. bistre-yellow, rose, turquoise, grey-black & gold	45	50
		Set of 4	1.25	1.40
		Set of 4 Gutter Pairs	2.75	
		Set of 4 Traffic Light Gutter Pairs	4.00	
		First Day Cover		1.50
		Presentation Pack..........................	1.75	
		P.H.Q. Cards (set of 4)	1.50	2.50

Special First Day of Issue Postmarks

Special First Day of Issue Postmark

Philatelic Bureau, Edinburgh 1.75
Epsom, Surrey... 1.75

Philatelic Bureau, Edinburgh 2.00
First Day of Issue handstamps were provided at Hartfield,
East Sussex and Stourbridge, West Midlands for this issue.

569 *The Tale of Peter Rabbit*
(Beatrix Potter)

570 *The Wind in the Willows*
(Kenneth Grahame)

573 Sir Rowland Hill

574 Postman, *circa* 1839

571 *Winnie-the-Pooh*
(A. A. Milne)

572 *Alice's Adventures in Wonderland*
(Lewis Carroll)

575 London Postman,
circa 1839

576 Woman and Young Girl
with Letters, 1840

(Des E. Hughes)

(Des E. Stemp)

1979 (11 July). **International Year of the Child.** *Children's Book Illustrations.* "All-over" phosphor. P 14 × 15.

1091	**569**	9p.	dp bluish green, grey-black, bistre-brown, brt rose, greenish yellow & silver	35	20
1092	**570**	10½p.	dull ultramarine, grey-black, olive-brown, brt rose, yellow-orange, pale greenish yellow & silver................	30	30
1093	**571**	11p.	drab, grey-black, greenish yellow, new blue, yellow-orange, agate & silver	35	35
1094	**572**	13p.	pale greenish yellow, grey-black, brt rose, dp bluish green, olive-brown, new blue & silver..........................	40	40
			Set of 4	1.25	1.10
			Set of 4 Gutter Pairs	2.50	
			Set of 4 Traffic Light Gutter Pairs	3.75	
			First Day Cover		1.25
			Presentation Pack..........................	2.00	
			P.H.Q. Cards (set of 4)	1.50	2.25

1979 (22 Aug–24 Oct). **Death Centenary of Sir Rowland Hill.** "All-over" phosphor. P 14 × 15.

1095	**573**	10p.	grey-black, brown-ochre, myrtle-green, pale greenish yellow, rosine, brt blue & gold............................	25	25
1096	**574**	11½p.	grey-black, brown-ochre, brt blue, rosine, bistre-brown, pale greenish yellow & gold............................	30	35
1097	**575**	13p.	grey-black, brown-ochre, bright blue, rosine, bistre-brown, pale greenish yellow & gold..................	35	35
1098	**576**	15p.	grey-black, brown-ochre, myrtle-green, bistre-brown, rosine, pale greenish yellow & gold..................	40	40
			Set of 4	1.25	1.25
			Set of 4 Gutter Pairs	2.60	
			Set of 4 Traffic Light Gutter Pairs	3.75	
			First Day Cover		1.25
			Presentation Pack..........................	1.50	
			P.H.Q. Cards (set of 4)	1.50	2.25

MS1099 89 × 121 mm. Nos. 1095/8 (*sold at 59½p.*)
(24 Oct) 1.10 1.25
  a. Imperforate £1000
  b. Brown-ochre (15p. background, etc.)
    omitted £950
  c. Gold (Queen's head) omitted £225
  d. Brown-ochre, myrtle-green & gold
    omitted £3000
  e. Brt blue (13p. background, etc.) omit-
    ted £1100
  f. Myrtle-green (10p. (background),
    15p.) omitted £1250
  g. Pale greenish yellow omitted £175
  h. Rosine omitted............................. £700
  i. Bistre-brown omitted £900
  First Day Cover 1.25
The premium on No. **MS**1099 was used to support the London 1980 International Stamp Exhibition.

Special First Day of Issue Postmarks

Philatelic Bureau, Edinburgh (stamps) (22 Aug.).... 1.50
Philatelic Bureau, Edinburgh (miniature sheet)
(24 Oct.) 1.50
London EC (stamps) (22 Aug.) 1.50
London EC (miniature sheet) (24 Oct.) 1.50
First Day of Issue handstamps were provided at Kidderminster, Worcs on 22 August (pictorial) and 24 October (Type C) and at Sanquhar, Dumfries on 22 August (Type C).

577 Policeman on the Beat

578 Policeman directing Traffic

579 Mounted Policeman

580 River Patrol Boat

(Des B. Sanders)

1979 (26 Sept). **150th Anniv of Metropolitan Police.** *Phosphorised paper.* P 15 × 14.
1100 **577** 10p. grey-black, red-brown, emerald,
  greenish yellow, brt blue & magenta 25 25

1101 **578** 11½p. grey-black, brt orange, purple-
  brown, ultramarine, greenish yellow
  & dp bluish green 30 35
1102 **579** 13p. grey-black, red-brown, magenta,
  olive-green, greenish yellow & dp
  dull blue 35 35
1103 **580** 15p. grey-black, magenta, brown, slate-
  blue, dp brown & greenish black 40 40
  Set of 4 .... 1.10 1.25
  Set of 4 Gutter Pairs 2.50
  Set of 4 Traffic Light Gutter Pairs 3.75
  First Day Cover 1.25
  Presentation Pack 1.50
  P.H.Q. Cards (set of 4) 1.50 2.25

Special First Day of Issue Postmarks

Philatelic Bureau, Edinburgh 1.50
London SW.. 1.75

581 The Three Kings

582 Angel appearing to the Shepherds

583 The Nativity

584 Mary and Joseph travelling to Bethlehem

585 The Annunciation

(Des F. Wegner)

1979 (21 Nov). **Christmas.** *One centre phosphor band (8p.) or phosphorised paper (others).* P 15 × 14.
1104 **581** 8p. blue, grey-black, ochre, slate-violet &
  gold 20 20
  a. Imperf (pair) £550

1105 **582**	10p.	brt rose-red, grey-black, chestnut, chrome-yellow, dp violet & gold	25	25
	a.	Imperf between (vert pair)	£450	
	b.	Imperf (pair)		
1106 **583**	11½p.	orange-vermilion, steel-blue, drab, grey-black, dp blue-green & gold.....	30	30
1107 **584**	13p.	brt blue, orange-vermilion, bistre, grey-black & gold	35	35
1108 **585**	15p.	orange-vermilion, blue, bistre, grey-black, green & gold........................	40	40
		Set of 5	1.40	1.40
		Set of 5 Gutter Pairs	3.00	
		Set of 5 Traffic Light Gutter Pairs	3.75	
		First Day Cover		1.40
		Presentation Pack..........................	1.75	
		P.H.Q. Cards (set of 5)	1.50	2.25

Special First Day of Issue Postmarks

Philatelic Bureau, Edinburgh	1.75
Bethlehem, Llandeilo, Dyfed	1.50

Collectors Pack 1979

1979 (21 Nov). *Comprises Nos. 1075/98 and 1100/8.*
CP1108a Collectors Pack 10.00

586 Common Kingfisher

587 Dipper

588 Moorhen

589 Yellow Wagtails

(Des M. Warren)

1980 (16 Jan). **Centenary of Wild Bird Protection Act.** *Phosphorised paper. P 14 × 15.*

1109 **586**	10p.	brt blue, brt yellow-green, vermilion, pale greenish yellow, grey-black & gold	25	25
1110 **587**	11½p.	sepia, grey-black, dull ultramarine, vermilion, grey-green, pale greenish yellow & gold...............................	30	35
1111 **588**	13p.	emerald-green, grey-black, brt blue, vermilion, pale greenish yellow & gold	40	45
1112 **589**	15p.	greenish yellow, brown, lt green, slate-blue, grey-black & gold	45	50
		Set of 4	1.25	1.40
		Set of 4 Gutter Pairs	2.50	
		First Day Cover		1.40
		Presentation Pack..........................	1.60	
		P.H.Q. Cards (set of 4)	1.50	2.25

Special First Day of Issue Postmarks

Philatelic Bureau, Edinburgh	1.75
Sandy, Beds...	1.75

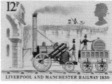

590 *Rocket* approaching Moorish Arch, Liverpool

591 First and Second Class Carriages passing through Olive Mount cutting

592 Third Class Carriage and Cattle Truck crossing Chat Moss

593 Horsebox and Carriage Truck near Bridgewater Canal

594 Goods Truck and Mail-Coach at Manchester

T **590/4** were printed together, *se-tenant*, in horizontal strips of 5 throughout the sheet.

(Des D. Gentleman)

1980 (12 Mar). **150th Anniv of Liverpool and Manchester Railway.** *Phosphorised paper.* P 15 × 14.

1113 **590**	12p.	lemon, lt brown, rose-red, pale blue & grey-black	25	25
		a. Strip of 5. Nos. 1113/17	1.50	1.50
		ab. Imperf (horiz strip of 5. Nos. 1113/17)	£1200	
1114 **591**	12p.	rose-red, lt brown, lemon, pale blue & grey-black	25	25
1115 **592**	12p.	pale blue, rose-red, lemon, lt brown & grey-black	25	25
1116 **593**	12p.	lt brown, lemon, rose-red, pale blue & grey-black	25	25
1117 **594**	12p.	lt brown, rose-red, pale blue, lemon & grey-black	25	25
		Set of 5	1.50	1.10
		Gutter Strip of 10	3.50	
		First Day Cover		1.50
		Presentation Pack	2.00	
		P.H.Q. Cards (set of 5)	1.75	2.50

Special First Day of Issue Postmarks

Philatelic Bureau, Edinburgh	1.75
Liverpool	1.75
Manchester	1.75

INTERNATIONAL STAMP EXHIBITION

595 Montage of London Buildings

During the printing of No. 1118 the die was re-cut resulting in the following two types:

Type I (original). Top and bottom lines of shading in portrait oval broken. Hatched shading below left arm of Tower Bridge and hull of ship below right arm. Other points: Hatched shading on flag on Westminster Abbey, bottom right of Post Office Tower and archway of entrance to Westminster Abbey.

Type II (re-engraved). Lines in oval unbroken. Solid shading on bridge and ship. Also solid shading on flag, Post Office Tower and archway.

(Des J. Matthews. Recess)

1980 (9 Apr–7 May). **"London 1980" International Stamp Exhibition.** *Phosphorised paper. P* 14½ × 14.

1118	**595**	50p. agate (I)		1.25	1.25
		Ea. Type II		1.25	1.25
		Gutter Pair		2.50	
		First Day Cover			1.25
		Presentation Pack		1.75	
		P.H.Q. Card		50	1.50
MS1119		90 × 123 mm. No. 1118 (sold at 75p.)			
		(7 May)		1.25	1.40
		a. Error. Imperf		£650	
		First Day Cover			1.40

Examples of No. 1118 are known in various shades of green. Such shades result from problems with the drying of the printed sheets on the press, but are not listed as similar colours can be easily faked.

Special First Day of Issue Postmarks

Philatelic Bureau, Edinburgh (stamp) (9 Apr.)	1.75
Philatelic Bureau, Edinburgh (miniature sheet) (7 May)	2.00
London SW (stamp) (9 Apr.)	1.50
London SW (miniature sheet) (7 May)	1.50

596 Buckingham Palace

597 The Albert Memorial

598 Royal Opera House

599 Hampton Court

600 Kensington Palace

(Des Sir Hugh Casson)

1980 (7 May). **London Landmarks.** *Phosphorised paper. P* 14 × 15.

1120	**596**	10½p. grey, pale blue, rosine, pale greenish yellow, yellowish green & silver		25	25
1121	**597**	12p. grey-black, bistre, rosine, yellowish green, pale greenish yellow & silver		30	30
		a. Imperf (vert pair)		£500	
1122	**598**	13½p. grey-black, pale salmon, pale olive-green, slate-blue & silver		35	35
		a. Imperf (pair)		£500	
1123	**599**	15p. grey-black, pale salmon, slate-blue, dull yellowish green, olive-yellow & silver		40	45
1124	**600**	17½p. grey, slate-blue, red-brown, sepia, yellowish green, pale greenish yellow & silver		50	50
		a. Silver (Queen's head) omitted		£225	
		Set of 5		1.60	1.60
		Set of 5 Gutter Pairs		3.50	
		First Day Cover			1.60
		Presentation Pack		2.00	
		P.H.Q. Cards (set of 5)		1.50	2.25

No. 1124a shows the Queen's head in pale greenish yellow, this colour being printed beneath the silver for technical reasons.

Special First Day of Issue Postmarks

Philatelic Bureau, Edinburgh	1.75
Kingston-upon-Thames	1.75

601 Charlotte Brontë
(Jane Eyre)

602 George Eliot
(The Mill on the Floss)

603 Emily Brontë   **604** Mrs. Gaskell
(*Wuthering Heights*)   (*North and South*)

T **601/4** show authoresses and scenes from their novels. T **601/2** also include the "Europa" C.E.P.T. emblem.

(Des Barbara Brown)

1980 (9 July). **Famous Authoresses.** *Phosphorised paper.* P 15 × 14.

1125 **601**	12p. red-brown, brt rose, brt blue, greenish yellow, grey & silver	30	20
	Ea. Missing "P" in value (R. 4/6)	20.00	
1126 **602**	13½p. red-brown, dull vermilion, pale blue, pale greenish yellow, grey & silver	35	35
	a. Pale blue omitted	£600	
1127 **603**	15p. red-brown, vermilion, blue, lemon, grey & silver	40	45
1128 **604**	17½p. dull vermilion, slate-blue, ultramarine, pale greenish yellow, grey & silver	50	50
	a. Imperf & slate-blue omitted (pair)	£600	
	Set of 4	1.40	1.40
	Set of 4 Gutter Pairs	3.00	
	First Day Cover		1.40
	Presentation Pack	1.75	
	P.H.Q. Cards (set of 4)	1.50	2.00

Special First Day of Issue Postmarks

Philatelic Bureau, Edinburgh	1.50
Haworth, Keighley, W. Yorks	1.50

605 Queen Elizabeth the Queen Mother

(Des J. Matthews from photograph by N. Parkinson)

1980 (4 Aug). **80th Birthday of Queen Elizabeth the Queen Mother.** *Phosphorised paper.* P 14 × 15.

1129 **605**	12p. brt rose, greenish yellow, new blue, grey & silver	35	35
	a. Imperf (horiz pair)		
	Gutter Pair	75	
	First Day Cover		50
	P.H.Q. Card	50	90

Special First Day of Issue Postmarks

Philatelic Bureau, Edinburgh	1.00
Glamis Castle, Forfar	1.10

606 Sir Henry Wood   **607** Sir Thomas Beecham

608 Sir Malcolm Sargent   **609** Sir John Barbirolli

(Des P. Gauld)

1980 (10 Sept). **British Conductors.** *Phosphorised paper.* P 14 × 15.

1130 **606**	12p. slate, rose-red, greenish yellow, bistre & gold	30	30
1131 **607**	13½p. grey-black, vermilion, greenish yellow, pale carmine-rose & gold	35	35
1132 **608**	15p. grey-black, bright rose-red, greenish yellow, turquoise-green & gold	45	45
1133 **609**	17½p. black, bright rose-red, greenish yellow, dull violet-blue & gold	50	50
	Set of 4	1.40	1.40
	Set of 4 Gutter Pairs	3.00	
	First Day Cover		1.40
	Presentation Pack	1.75	
	P.H.Q. Cards (set of 4)	1.50	2.25

Special First Day of Issue Postmarks

Philatelic Bureau, Edinburgh 1.75
London SW.. 1.75

Special First Day of Issue Postmarks

Philatelic Bureau, Edinburgh 1.75
Cardiff 1.50

610 Running

611 Rugby

614 Christmas Tree   **615** Candles

612 Boxing

613 Cricket

616 Apples and Mistletoe   **617** Crown, Chains and B. 'l

(Des R. Goldsmith. Litho Questa)

1980 (10 Oct). **Sport Centenaries.** *Phosphorised paper.* P 14 × 14½.

1134	**610**	12p.	pale new blue, greenish yellow, magenta, lt brown, reddish purple & gold	30	25
			a. Gold (Queen's head) omitted		
1135	**611**	13½p.	pale new blue, olive-yellow, brt purple, orange-vermilion, blackish lilac & gold	35	35
1136	**612**	15p.	pale new blue, greenish yellow, brt purple, chalky blue & gold.............	40	45
1137	**613**	17½p.	pale new blue, greenish yellow, magenta, dp olive, grey-brown & gold ..	50	50

Set of 4 .... 1.40   1.40
Set of 4 Gutter Pairs 2.90
First Day Cover 1.40
Presentation Pack........................ 1.75
P.H.Q. Cards (set of 4) 1.50   2.00

Centenaries:—12p. Amateur Athletics Association; 13½p. Welsh Rugby Union; 15p. Amateur Boxing Association; 17½p. First England–Australia Test Match.

No. 1134a was caused by a paper fold.

618 Holly
(Des J. Matthews)

1980 (19 Nov). **Christmas.** *One centre phosphor band* (10p.) *or phosphorised paper* (others). P 15 × 14.

1138	**614**	10p.	black, turquoise-green, greenish yellow, vermilion & blue....................	25	25
			a. Imperf (horiz pair).........................		
1139	**615**	12p.	grey, magenta, rose-red, greenisn grey & pale orange........................	30	30
1140	**616**	13½p.	grey-black, dull yellow-green, brown, greenish yellow & pale olive-bistre	35	35
1141	**617**	15p.	grey-black, bistre-yellow, brt orange, magenta & new blue	40	45

1142	618	17½p. black, vermilion, dull yellowish green & greenish yellow	45	50
		Set of 5	1.60	1.60
		Set of 5 Gutter Pairs	3.50	
		First Day Cover		1.60
		Presentation Pack	2.00	
		P.H.Q. Cards (set of 5)	1.50	2.00

Special First Day of Issue Postmarks

Philatelic Bureau, Edinburgh 1.75
Bethlehem, Llandeilo, Dyfed 1.75

Collectors Pack 1980

1980 (19 Nov). *Comprises Nos. 1109/18 and 1120/42.*
CP1142a Collectors Pack 14.00

619 St. Valentine's Day

620 Morris Dancers

621 Lammastide

622 Medieval Mummers

T **619/20** also include the "Europa" C.E.P.T. emblem.

(Des F. Wegner)

1981 (6 Feb). **Folklore.** *Phosphorised paper.* P 15 × 14.

1143	619	14p. cerise, green, yellow-orange, salmon-pink, black & gold	35	35
1144	620	18p. dull ultramarine, lemon, lake-brown, brt green, black & gold	45	45
1145	621	22p. chrome-yellow, rosine, brown, new blue, black & gold	60	60

1146	622	25p. brt blue, red-brown, brt rose-red, greenish yellow, black & gold	65	65
		Set of 4	1.90	1.90
		Set of 4 Gutter Pairs	4.00	
		First Day Cover		2.00
		Presentation Pack	2.25	
		P.H.Q. Cards (set of 4)	1.50	2.00

Special First Day of Issue Postmarks

Philatelic Bureau, Edinburgh 2.25
London WC 2.10

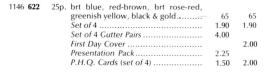

623 Blind Man with Guide Dog

624 Hands spelling "Deaf" in Sign Language

625 Disabled Man in Wheelchair

626 Disabled Artist painting with Foot

(Des J. Gibbs)

1981 (25 Mar). **International Year of the Disabled.** *Phosphorised paper.* P 15 × 14.

1147	623	14p. drab, greenish yellow, brt rose-red, dull purple & silver	35	35
1148	624	18p. dp blue-green, brt orange, dull vermilion, grey-black & silver	45	45
1149	625	22p. brown-ochre, rosine, purple-brown, greenish blue, black & silver	60	60
1150	626	25p. vermilion, lemon, pale salmon, olive-brown, new blue, black & silver	65	70
		Set of 4	1.90	1.90
		Set of 4 Gutter Pairs	4.00	
		First Day Cover		2.00
		Presentation Pack	2.25	
		P.H.Q. Cards (set of 4)	1.50	2.00

Special First Day of Issue Postmarks

Special First Day of Issue Postmarks

Edinburgh Philatelic Bureau 2.25
Windsor.. 2.25

Philatelic Bureau, Edinburgh 2.25
London SW... 2.10

631 Glenfinnan, Scotland   **632** Derwentwater, England

627 Small Tortoiseshell   **628** Large Blue

633 Stackpole Head, Wales   **634** Giant's Causeway,
Northern Ireland

629 Peacock   **630** Chequered Skipper

635 St. Kilda, Scotland

(Des M. Fairclough)

(Des G. Beningfield)

1981 (13 May). **Butterflies.** *Phosphorised paper. P* 14 × 15.

1151	627	14p. greenish yellow, yellow-green, brt rose, brt blue, emerald & gold.........	35	35
1152	628	18p. black, greenish yellow, dull yellowish green, brt mauve, brt blue, brt green & gold	50	50
1153	629	22p. black, greenish yellow, bronze-green, rosine, ultramarine, lt green & gold	60	60
1154	630	25p. black, greenish yellow, bronze-green, brt rose-red, ultramarine, brt emerald & gold	70	70
		Set of 4	2.00	2.00
		Set of 4 Gutter Pairs	4.25	
		First Day Cover		2.00
		Presentation Pack.........................	2.50	
		P.H.Q. Cards (set of 4)	1.50	2.40

1981 (24 June). **50th Anniv of National Trust for Scotland.** *British Landscapes. Phosphorised paper. P* 15 × 14.

1155	631	14p. lilac, dull blue, reddish brown, bistre-yellow, black & gold......................	35	35
1156	632	18p. bottle green, brt blue, brown, bistre-yellow, black & gold......................	50	50
1157	633	20p. dp turquoise-blue, dull blue, greenish yellow, reddish brown, black & gold	55	55
1158	634	22p. chrome-yellow, reddish brown, new blue, yellow-brown, black & gold.....	60	60
1159	635	25p. ultramarine, new blue, olive-green, olive-grey & gold	65	65
		Set of 5	2.50	2.50
		Set of 5 Gutter Pairs	5.50	
		First Day Cover		2.50
		Presentation Pack.........................	2.75	
		P.H.Q. Cards (set of 5)	2.00	2.50

Special First Day of Issue Postmarks

Special First Day of Issue Postmarks

Philatelic Bureau, Edinburgh 2.25
Caernarfon, Gwynedd.. 2.25
London EC 2.25

Philatelic Bureau, Edinburgh 2.75
Glenfinnan.. 3.00
Keswick 3.00

637 "Expeditions"   **638** "Skills"

639 "Service"   **640** "Recreation"

636 Prince Charles and Lady Diana Spencer

(Des J. Matthews from photograph by Lord Snowdon)

(Des P. Sharland. Litho J.W.)

1981 (22 July). **Royal Wedding.** *Phosphorised paper.* P 14 × 15.

1160	**636**	14p. grey-black, greenish yellow, brt rose-red, ultramarine, pale blue, blue & silver	40	35
1161		25p. drab, greenish yellow, brt rose-red, ultramarine, grey-brown, grey-black & silver	85	90
		Set of 2	1.25	1.25
		Set of 2 Gutter Pairs	2.50	
		First Day Cover		2.00
		Presentation Pack.........................	1.90	
		Souvenir Book	4.00	
		P.H.Q. Cards (set of 2)	1.10	2.25

The souvenir book is a 12-page illustrated booklet with a set of mint stamps in a sachet attached to the front cover.

1981 (12 Aug). **25th Anniv of Duke of Edinburgh Award Scheme.** *Phosphorised paper.* P 14.

1162	**637**	14p. greenish yellow, magenta, pale new blue, black, emerald & silver	35	35
1163	**638**	18p. greenish yellow, magenta, pale new blue, black, cobalt & gold	50	50
1164	**639**	22p. greenish yellow, magenta, pale new blue, black, red-orange & gold	60	60
1165	**640**	25p. brt orange, mauve, pale new blue, black, flesh & bronze	70	70
		Set of 4	1.90	1.90
		Set of 4 Gutter Pairs	4.00	
		First Day Cover		1.90
		Presentation Pack.........................	2.50	
		P.H.Q. Cards (set of 4)	1.75	2.25

Special First Day of Issue Postmarks

Philatelic Bureau, Edinburgh 2.25
London W2.. 2.00

Special First Day of Issue Postmarks

Philatelic Bureau, Edinburgh 2.25
Hull 2.00

645 Father Christmas

646 Jesus Christ

641 Cockle-dredging

642 Hauling in Trawl Net

647 Flying Angel

648 Joseph and Mary arriving
at Bethlehem

643 Lobster Potting

644 Hoisting Seine Net

649 Three Kings approaching
Bethlehem

(Des B. Sanders)

1981 (23 Sept). **Fishing Industry.** *Phosphorised paper. P 15 × 14.*

1166	**641**	14p.	slate, greenish yellow, magenta, new blue, orange-brown, olive-grey & bronze-green	35	35
1167	**642**	18p.	slate, greenish yellow, brt crimson, ultramarine, black & greenish slate...	50	50
1168	**643**	22p.	grey, greenish yellow, brt rose, dull ultramarine, reddish lilac & black	60	60
1169	**644**	25p.	grey, greenish yellow, brt rose, cobalt & black	70	65
			Set of 4	1.90	1.90
			Set of 4 Gutter Pairs	4.00	
			First Day Cover		1.90
			Presentation Pack........................	2.50	
			P.H.Q. Cards (set of 4)	2.00	2.00

Nos. 1166/9 were issued on the occasion of the centenary of the Royal National Mission to Deep Sea Fishermen.

(Des Samantha Brown (11½p.), Tracy Jenkins (14p.), Lucinda Blackmore (18p.), Stephen Moore (22p.), Sophie Sharp (25p.))

1981 (18 Nov). **Christmas.** *Children's Pictures. One phosphor band (11½p.) or phosphorised paper (others). P 15 × 14.*

1170	**645**	11½p.	ultramarine, black, red, olive-bistre, brt green & gold	25	30
1171	**646**	14p.	bistre-yellow, brt magenta, blue, greenish blue, brt green, black & gold	35	40
1172	**647**	18p.	pale blue-green, bistre-yellow, brt magenta, ultramarine, black & gold ..	45	50
1173	**648**	22p.	dp turquoise-blue, lemon, magenta, black & gold	55	60

111

1174 **649**	25p. royal blue, lemon, brt magenta, black & gold	65	70
	Set of 5	2.10	2.25
	Set of 5 Gutter Pairs	4.50	
	First Day Cover		2.40
	Presentation Pack	2.75	
	P.H.Q. Cards (set of 5)	2.00	2.25

Special First Day of Issue Postmarks

Philatelic Bureau, Edinburgh	2.50
Bethlehem, Llandeilo, Dyfed	2.50

Collectors Pack 1981

1981 (18 Nov). *Comprises Nos. 1143/74.*
CP1174a Collectors Pack 22.00

650 Charles Darwin and Giant Tortoises

651 Darwin and Marine Iguanas

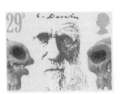

652 Darwin, Cactus Ground Finch and Large Ground Finch

653 Darwin and Prehistoric Skulls

(Des D. Gentleman)

1982 (10 Feb). **Death Centenary of Charles Darwin.** *Phosphorised paper. P 15 × 14.*

1175 **650**	15½p. dull purple, drab, bistre, black & grey-black	35	35
1176 **651**	19½p. violet-grey, bistre-yellow, slate-black, red-brown, grey-black & black	55	60
1177 **652**	26p. sage green, bistre-yellow, orange, chalky blue, grey-black, red-brown & black	65	70

1178 **653**	29p. grey-brown, yellow-brown, brown-ochre, black & grey-black	70	75
	Set of 4	2.10	2.25
	Set of 4 Gutter Pairs	4.50	
	First Day Cover		2.25
	Presentation Pack	2.75	
	P.H.Q. Cards (set of 4)	2.50	4.00

Special First Day of Issue Postmarks

Philatelic Bureau, Edinburgh	2.50
Shrewsbury	2.50

654 Boys' Brigade

655 Girls' Brigade

656 Boy Scout Movement

657 Girl Guide Movement

(Des B. Sanders)

1982 (24 Mar). **Youth Organizations.** *Phosphorised paper. P 15 × 14.*

1179 **654**	15½p. gold, greenish yellow, pale orange, mauve, dull blue & grey-black	35	35
1180 **655**	19½p. gold, greenish yellow, pale orange, brt rose, dp ultramarine, olive-bistre & grey-black	60	65
1181 **656**	26p. gold, greenish yellow, olive-sepia, ro-sine, dp blue, dp dull green & grey black	80	85

1182 **657**	29p. gold, yellow, dull orange, cerise, dull ultramarine, chestnut & grey-black...	85	90
	Set of 4	2.40	2.60
	Set of 4 Gutter Pairs	5.50	
	First Day Cover		2.60
	Presentation Pack	3.25	
	P.H.Q. Cards (set of 4)	2.50	5.00

Nos. 1179/82 were issued on the occasion of the 75th anniversary of the Boy Scout Movement; the 125th birth anniversary of Lord Baden-Powell and the centenary of the Boys' Brigade (1983).

Special First Day of Issue Postmarks

Edinburgh Philatelic Bureau	2.75
Glasgow	3.00
London SW...	2.75

(Des A. George)

1982 (28 Apr). **Europa.** *British Theatre. Phosphorised paper.* P 15 × 14.

1183 **658**	15½p. carmine-lake, greenish blue, greenish yellow, grey-black, bottle green & silver	35	35
1184 **659**	19½p. rosine, new blue, greenish yellow, black, ultramarine & silver	60	70
1185 **660**	26p. carmine-red, brt rose-red, greenish yellow, black, dull ultramarine, lake-brown & silver	85	90
1186 **661**	29p. rose-red, greenish yellow, brt blue, grey-black & silver	90	1.00
	Set of 4	2.40	2.60
	Set of 4 Gutter Pairs	5.50	
	First Day Cover		2.60
	Presentation Pack	3.00	
	P.H.Q. Cards (set of 4)	2.50	4.00

Special First Day of Issue Postmarks

Philatelic Bureau, Edinburgh	2.75
Stratford-upon-Avon	2.75

658 Ballerina

659 "Harlequin"

660 "Hamlet"

661 Opera Singer

662 Henry VIII and *Mary Rose*

663 Admiral Blake and *Triumph*

664 Lord Nelson and H.M.S. *Victory*

665 Lord Fisher and H.M.S. *Dreadnought*

666 Viscount Cunningham and H.M.S. *Warspite*

(Des Marjorie Saynor. Eng C. Slania. Recess and photo)

1982 (16 June). **Maritime Heritage.** *Phosphorised paper. P* 15 × 14.

1187	662	15½p. black, lemon, bright rose, pale orange, ultramarine & grey	35	35
1188	663	19½p. black, greenish yellow, brt rose-red, pale orange, ultramarine & grey.......	50	60
1189	664	24p. black, orange-yellow, brt rose-red, lake-brown, dp ultramarine & grey ...	55	60
1190	665	26p. black, orange-yellow, brt rose, lemon, ultramarine & grey.................	65	70
		a. Imperf (pair)		
1191	666	29p. black, olive-yellow, brt rose, orange-yellow, ultramarine & grey	70	80
		Set of 5	2.60	2.90
		Set of 5 Gutter Pairs	5.50	
		First Day Cover		3.00
		Presentation Pack.........................	3.25	
		P.H.Q. Cards (set of 5)	3.00	5.00

Nos. 1187/91 were issued on the occasion of Maritime England Year, the Bicentenary of the Livery Grant by City of London to Worshipful Company of Shipwrights and the raising of *Mary Rose* from Portsmouth Harbour.

Special First Day of Issue Postmarks

Philatelic Bureau, Edinburgh	3.50
Portsmouth	3.25

667 "Strawberry Thief" (William Morris)	**668** Untitled (Steiner and Co)
669 "Cherry Orchard" (Paul Nash)	**670** "Chevron" (Andrew Foster)

(Des Peter Hatch Partnership)

1982 (23 July). **British Textiles.** *Phosphorised paper. P* 14 × 15.

1192	667	15½p. blue, olive-yellow, rosine, dp blue-green, bistre & Prussian blue...........	35	35
		a. Imperf (horiz pair)		
1193	668	19½p. olive-grey, greenish yellow, brt magenta, dull green, yellow-brown & black	60	65
		a. Imperf (vert pair)		
1194	669	26p. brt scarlet, dull mauve, dull ultramarine & brt carmine.........................	70	65
1195	670	29p. bronze-green, orange-yellow, turquoise-green, stone, chestnut & sage-green	80	75
		Set of 4	2.40	2.25
		Set of 4 Gutter Pairs	5.00	
		First Day Cover		2.25
		Presentation Pack	3.00	
		P.H.Q. Cards (set of 4)	2.50	4.00

Nos. 1192/5 were issued on the occasion of the 250th birth anniversary of Sir Richard Arkwright (inventor of spinning machine).

Special First Day of Issue Postmarks

Philatelic Bureau, Edinburgh	3.00
Rochdale	3.00

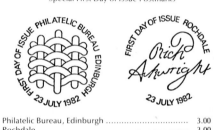

671 Development of Communications

672 Modern Technological Aids

(Des Delaney and Ireland)

1982 (8 Sept). **Information Technology.** *Phosphorised paper. P* 14 × 15.

1196	671	15½p. black, greenish yellow, brt rose-red, bistre-brown, new blue & lt ochre	40	40
		a. Imperf (pair)	£250	
1197	672	26p. black, greenish yellow, brt rose-red, olive-bistre, new blue & lt olive-grey	80	80
		a. Imperf (pair)		
		Set of 2	1.10	1.10
		Set of 2 Gutter Pairs	2.40	
		First Day Cover		1.50
		Presentation Pack	1.75	
		P.H.Q. Cards (set of 2)	1.50	3.00

Special First Day of Issue Postmarks

Philatelic Bureau, Edinburgh 4.00
Birmingham 4.00
Crewe 4.00

Philatelic Bureau, Edinburgh 1.75
London WC 1.75

673 Austin "Seven" and "Metro"   **674** Ford "Model T" and "Escort"   **677** "While Shepherds Watched"   **678** "The Holly and the Ivy"

675 Jaguar "SS 1" and "XJ6"   **676** Rolls-Royce "Silver Ghost" and "Silver Spirit"

679 "I Saw Three Ships"   **680** "We Three Kings"

(Des S. Paine. Litho Questa)

1982 (13 Oct). **British Motor Cars.** *Phosphorised paper.* P 14½ × 14.
1198	673	15½p. slate, orange-vermilion, brt orange, drab, yellow-green, olive-yellow, bluish grey & black	50	50
1199	674	19½p. slate, brt orange, olive-grey, rose-red, dull vermilion, grey & black	90	1.00
1200	675	26p. slate, red-brown, brt orange, turquoise-green, myrtle-green, dull blue-green, grey & olive	1.00	1.10
1201	676	29p. slate, brt orange, carmine-red, reddish purple, grey & black	1.25	1.25
		Set of 4	3.25	3.50
		Set of 4 Gutter Pairs	7.00	
		First Day Cover		3.50
		Presentation Pack..........................	4.00	
		P.H.Q. Cards (set of 4)	2.50	4.00

Special First Day of Issue Postmarks

681 "Good King Wenceslas"

(Des Barbara Brown)

1982 (17 Nov). **Christmas.** *Carols.* One phosphor band (12½p.) or *phosphorised paper* (others). P 15 × 14.
1202	677	12½p. black, greenish, yellow, brt scarlet, steel blue, red-brown & gold..........	30	30
1203	678	15½p. black, bistre-yellow, brt rose-red, brt blue, brt green & gold....................	40	45
1204	679	19½p. black, bistre-yellow, brt rose-red, dull blue, dp brown & gold	60	65
1205	680	26p. black, bistre-yellow, brt magenta, brt blue, chocolate, gold & orange-red ..	60	65
1206	681	29p. black, bistre-yellow, magenta, brt blue, chestnut, gold & brt magenta ..	70	75
		Set of 5	2.40	2.40
		Set of 5 Gutter Pairs	5.25	
		First Day Cover		2.50
		Presentation Pack..........................	3.25	
		P.H.Q. Cards (set of 5)	3.00	4.00

Special First Day of Issue Postmarks

Special First Day of Issue Postmarks

Philatelic Bureau, Edinburgh 3.00
Bethlehem, Llandeilo, Dyfed 3.00

Philatelic Bureau, Edinburgh 2.75
Peterborough 2.75

Collectors Pack 1982

1982 (17 Nov). *Comprises Nos. 1175/1206.*
CP1206a Collectors Pack 26.00

686 Tropical Island   **687** Desert

682 Salmon   **683** Pike

688 Temperate Farmland   **689** Mountain Range

684 Trout   **685** Perch

(Des D. Fraser)

1983 (9 Mar). **Commonwealth Day.** *Geographical Regions. Phosphorised paper. P 14 × 15.*

1211	**686**	15½p. greenish blue, greenish yellow, brt rose, lt brown, grey-black, dp claret & silver	35	35
1212	**687**	19½p. brt lilac, greenish yellow, magenta, dull blue, grey-black, dp dull blue & silver	65	65
1213	**688**	26p. lt blue, greenish yellow, brt magenta, new blue. grey-black, violet & silver .	60	65
1214	**689**	29p. dull violet-blue, reddish violet, slate-lilac, new blue, myrtle-green, black & silver	75	75
		Set of 4	2.25	2.25
		Set of 4 Gutter Pairs	4.75	
		First Day Cover		2.50
		Presentation Pack.........................	3.00	
		P.H.Q. Cards (set of 4)	2.50	4.00

(Des A. Jardine)

1983 (26 Jan). **British River Fishes.** *Phosphorised paper. P 15 × 14.*

1207	**682**	15½p. grey-black, bistre-yellow, brt purple, new blue & silver..........................	35	35
1208	**683**	19½p. black, bistre-yellow, olive-bistre, dp claret, silver & dp bluish green	65	65
1209	**684**	26p. grey-black, bistre-yellow, chrome-yellow, magenta, silver & pale blue ..	60	65
1210	**685**	29p. black, greenish yellow, brt carmine, new blue & silver..........................	75	75
		Set of 4	2.25	2.25
		Set of 4 Gutter Pairs	4.75	
		First Day Cover		2.50
		Presentation Pack.........................	3.00	
		P.H.Q. Cards (set of 4)	2.50	4.50

Special First Day of Issue Postmarks

693 Musketeer and Pikeman, The Royal Scots (1633)

694 Fusilier and Ensign, The Royal Welch Fusiliers (mid-18th century)

Philatelic Bureau, Edinburgh 2.75
London SW... 2.75

690 Humber Bridge

691 Thames Flood Barrier

695 Riflemen, 95th Rifles (The Royal Green Jackets) (1805)

696 Sergeant (khaki service) and Guardsman (full dress), The Irish Guards (1900)

692 *Iolair* (oilfield emergency support vessel)

(Des M. Taylor)

1983 (25 May). **Europa.** *Engineering Achievements. Phosphorised paper.* P 15 × 14.

1215	**690**	16p. silver, orange-yellow, ultramarine, black & grey	50	45
1216	**691**	20½p. silver, greenish yellow, brt purple, blue, grey-black & grey..................	1.40	1.10
1217	**692**	28p. silver, lemon, brt rose-red, chestnut, dull ultramarine, black & grey..........	1.40	1.10
		Set of 3	3.00	2.50
		Set of 3 Gutter Pairs	6.50	
		First Day Cover		2.50
		Presentation Pack..........................	3.25	
		P.H.Q. Cards (set of 3)	2.50	3.75

Special First Day of Issue Postmarks

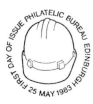

Philatelic Bureau, Edinburgh 2.75
Hull 2.75

697 Paratroopers, The Parachute Regiment (1983)

(Des E. Stemp)

1983 (6 July). **British Army Uniforms.** *Phosphorised paper.* P 14 × 15.

1218	**693**	16p. black, buff, dp brown, slate-black, rose-red, gold & new blue	40	40
1219	**694**	20½p. black, buff, greenish yellow, slate-black, brown-rose, gold & brt blue...	60	65
1220	**695**	26p. black, buff, slate-purple, green, bistre & gold...............................	80	85
1221	**696**	28p. black, buff, lt brown, grey, dull rose, gold & new blue	85	90
1222	**697**	31p. black, buff, olive-yellow, grey, dp magenta, gold & new blue	90	95
		Set of 5	3.25	3.25
		Set of 5 Gutter Pairs	7.00	
		First Day Cover		3.25
		Presentation Pack..........................	4.25	
		P.H.Q. Cards (set of 5)	3.75	5.00

Nos. 1218/22 were issued on the occasion of the 350th anniversary of the Royal Scots, the senior line regiment of the British Army.

Special First Day of Issue Postmarks

Philatelic Bureau, Edinburgh 4.00
Aldershot 4.00

Special First Day of Issue Postmarks

Philatelic Bureau, Edinburgh 3.25
Oxford 3.25

698 20th-century Garden, Sissinghurst   **699** 19th-century Garden, Biddulph Grange

702 Merry-go-round   **703** Big Wheel, Helter-Skelter and Performing Animals

704 Side Shows   **705** Early Produce Fair

(Des A. Restall)

700 18th-century Garden, Blenheim   **701** 17th-century Garden, Pitmedden

1983 (5 Oct).   **British Fairs.** *Phosphorised paper. P 15 × 14.*
1227	**702**	16p.	grey-black, greenish yellow, orange-red, ochre & turquoise-blue	40	40
1228	**703**	20½p.	grey-black, yellow-ochre, yellow-orange, brt magenta, violet & black ..	50	55
1229	**704**	28p.	grey-black, bistre-yellow, orange-red, violet & yellow-brown	80	90
1230	**705**	31p.	grey-black, greenish yellow, red, dp turquoise-green, slate-violet & brown	90	90
			Set of 4	2.40	2.40
			Set of 4 Gutter Pairs	5.00	
			First Day Cover		2.75
			Presentation Pack	3.25	
			P.H.Q. Cards (set of 4)	2.50	4.00

Special First Day of Issue Postmarks

Philatelic Bureau, Edinburgh 3.00
Nottingham 3.00

(Des Liz Butler, Litho J.W.)

1983 (24 Aug).   **British Gardens.** *Phosphorised paper. P 14.*
1223	**698**	16p.	greenish yellow, brt purple, new blue, black, brt green & silver..........	40	40
1224	**699**	20½p.	greenish yellow, brt purple, new blue, black, brt green & silver..........	50	55
1225	**700**	28p.	greenish yellow, brt purple, new blue, black, brt green & silver..........	80	90
1226	**701**	31p.	greenish yellow, brt purple, new blue, black, brt green & silver..........	90	90
			Set of 4	2.40	2.40
			Set of 4 Gutter Pairs	5.00	
			First Day Cover		2.75
			Presentation Pack	3.25	
			P.H.Q. Cards (set of 4)	2.50	4.00

Nos. 1223/6 were issued on the occasion of the death bicentenary of "Capability" Brown (landscape gardener)

706 "Christmas Post" (pillar-box)

707 "The Three Kings" (chimney-pots)

708 "World at Peace" (Dove and Blackbird)

709 "Light of Christmas" (street lamp)

710 "Christmas Dove" (hedge sculpture) (Des T. Meeuwissen)

1983 (16 Nov). **Christmas.** *One phosphor band (12½p.) or phosphorised paper (others). P 15 × 14.*

1231 706	12½p.	black, greenish yellow, brt rose-red, brt blue, gold & grey-black..............	30	30
	a.	Imperf (horiz pair)	£750	
1232 707	16p.	black, greenish yellow, brt rose, pale new blue, gold & brown-purple	45	40
	a.	Imperf (pair)		
1233 708	20½p.	black, greenish yellow, brt rose, new blue, gold & blue..........................	55	60
1234 709	28p.	black, lemon, brt carmine, bluish violet, gold, dp turquoise-green & purple	85	90
1235 710	31p.	black, greenish yellow, brt rose, new blue, gold, green & brown-olive	90	90
		Set of 5	2.90	2.75
		Set of 5 Gutter Pairs	6.00	
		First Day Cover		2.75
		Presentation Pack..........................	3.50	
		P.H.Q. Cards (set of 5)	3.00	4.50

Special First Day of Issue Postmarks

Philatelic Bureau, Edinburgh	3.25
Bethlehem, Llandeilo, Dyfed	3.50

Collectors Pack 1983

1983 (16 Nov). *Comprises Nos. 1207/35.*
CP1235a Collectors Pack 38.00

711 Arms of the College of Arms

712 Arms of King Richard III (founder)

713 Arms of the Earl Marshal of England

714 Arms of the City of London

(Des J. Matthews)

1984 (17 Jan). **500th Anniv of College of Arms.** *Phosphorised paper. P 14½.*

1236 711	16p.	black, chrome-yellow, reddish brown, scarlet-vermilion, brt blue & grey-black	40	40
1237 712	20½p.	black, chrome-yellow, rosine, brt blue & grey-black	60	70
1238 713	28p.	black, chrome-yellow, rosine, brt blue, dull green & grey-black	80	90
1239 714	31p.	black, chrome-yellow, rosine, brt blue & grey-black	85	90
		Set of 4	2.40	2.50
		Set of 4 Gutter Pairs	5.00	
		First Day Cover		2.75
		Presentation Pack	3.25	
		P.H.Q. Cards (set of 4)	2.50	5.00

Special First Day of Issue Postmarks

Philatelic Bureau, Edinburgh	3.25
London EC	3.75

715 Highland Cow

716 Chillingham Wild Bull

720 Garden Festival Hall, Liverpool

721 Milburngate Centre, Durham

717 Hereford Bull

718 Welsh Black Bull

722 Bush House, Bristol

723 Commercial Street Development, Perth

719 Irish Moiled Cow

(Des B. Driscoll)

(Des R. Maddox and Trickett and Webb Ltd)

1984 (6 Mar). **British Cattle.** *Phosphorised paper. P* 15 × 14.

1240	**715**	16p.	grey-black, bistre-yellow, rosine, yellow-orange, new blue & pale drab....	40	40
1241	**716**	20½p.	grey-black, greenish yellow, magenta, bistre, dull blue-green, pale drab & lt green	65	65
1242	**717**	26p.	black, chrome-yellow, rosine, reddish brown, new blue & pale drab	65	65
1243	**718**	28p.	black, greenish yellow, brt carmine, orange-brown, dp dull blue & pale drab	85	85
1244	**719**	31p.	grey-black, bistre-yellow, rosine, red-brown, lt blue & pale drab	85	90
			Set of 5	3.25	3.00
			Set of 5 Gutter Pairs	6.50	
			First Day Cover		3.25
			Presentation Pack	3.75	
			P.H.Q. Cards (set of 5)	3.00	4.75

Nos. 1240/4 were issued on the occasion of the centenary of the Highland Cattle Society and the bicentenary of the Royal Highland and Agricultural Society of Scotland.

1984 (10 Apr). **Urban Renewal.** *Phosphorised paper. P* 15 × 14.

1245	**720**	16p.	brt emerald, greenish yellow, cerise, steel-blue, black, silver & flesh	40	40
1246	**721**	20½p.	brt orange, greenish yellow, dp dull blue, yellowish green, azure, black & silver	65	60
			a. Imperf (horiz pair)	£1000	
1247	**722**	28p.	rosine, greenish yellow, Prussian blue, pale blue-green, black & silver.	85	85
1248	**723**	31p.	blue, greenish yellow, cerise, grey-blue, brt green, black & silver	85	90
			a. Imperf (vert pair)		
			Set of 4	2.50	2.50
			Set of 4 Gutter Pairs	5.50	
			First Day Cover		3.00
			Presentation Pack	3.00	
			P.H.Q. Cards (set of 4)	2.50	4.25

Nos. 1245/8 were issued on the occasion of 150th anniversaries of the Royal Institute of British Architects and the Chartered Institute of Building, and to commemorate the first International Gardens Festival, Liverpool.

Special First Day of Issue Postmarks

Philatelic Bureau, Edinburgh 3.50
Oban, Argyll.. 4.00

Special First Day of Issue Postmarks

Philatelic Bureau, Edinburgh 3.25
Liverpool 3.50

724 C.E.P.T. 25th Anniversary Logo   725 Abduction of Europa

726 Lancaster House

(Des J. Larrivière (*T* 724), F. Wegner (*T* 725))

1984 (15 May).   **25th Anniv of C.E.P.T. ("Europa")** (*T* 724) **and Second Elections to European Parliament** (*T* 725). *Phosphorised paper.* P 15 × 14.

1249	**724**	16p. greenish slate, dp blue & gold	40	40
		a. Horiz pair. Nos. 1249/50	90	1.00
1250	**725**	16p. greenish slate, dp blue, black & gold	40	40
1251	**724**	20½p. Venetian red, dp magenta & gold	55	55
		a. Horiz pair. Nos. 1251/2	1.25	1.40
1252	**725**	20½p. Venetian red, dp magenta, black & gold	55	55
		Set of 4	2.00	1.75
		Set of 4 Gutter Pairs	4.00	
		First Day Cover		2.25
		Presentation Pack	2.75	
		P.H.Q. Cards (set of 4)	2.50	4.25

Nos. 1249/50 and 1251/2 were each printed together, *se-tenant*, in horizontal pairs throughout the sheets.

Special First Day of Issue Postmarks

Philatelic Bureau, Edinburgh 2.50
London SW... 2.50

(Des P. Hogarth)

1984 (5 June).   **London Economic Summit Conference.** *Phosphorised paper.* P 14 × 15.

1253	**726**	31p. silver, bistre-yellow, brown-ochre, black, rosine, brt blue & reddish lilac	80	85
		Gutter Pair	1.60	
		First Day Cover		2.00
		P.H.Q. Card	50	1.50

Special First Day of Issue Postmarks

Philatelic Bureau, Edinburgh 2.25
London SW... 2.25

727 View of Earth from "Apollo 11"

728 Navigational Chart of English Channel

729 Greenwich Observatory

730 Sir George Airy's Transit Telescope

(Des H. Waller. Litho Questa)

1984 (26 June). **Centenary of the Greenwich Meridian.** *Phosphorised paper.* P 14 × 14½.

1254 **727**	16p.	new blue, greenish yellow, magenta, black, scarlet and blue-black	40	40
1255 **728**	20½p.	olive-sepia, lt brown, pale buff, black & scarlet..............................	60	55
1256 **729**	28p.	new blue, greenish yellow, scarlet, black & brt purple.........................	85	80
1257 **730**	31p.	dp blue, cobalt, scarlet & black	85	80
		Set of 4	2.60	2.40
		Set of 4 Gutter Pairs	5.50	
		First Day Cover		2.50
		Presentation Pack.........................	3.00	
		P.H.Q. Cards (set of 4)	2.50	5.00

On Nos. 1254/7 the Meridian is represented by a scarlet line.

Special First Day of Issue Postmarks

Philatelic Bureau, Edinburgh	2.75
London SE10	3.00

(Des K. Bassford and S. Paine. Eng C. Slania. Recess and photo)

1984 (31 July). **Bicentenary of First Mail Coach Run, Bath and Bristol to London.** *Phosphorised paper.* P 15 × 14.

1258 **731**	16p.	pale stone, black, grey-black & brt scarlet	40	40
	a.	Horiz strip of 5. Nos. 1258/62	2.25	2.10
1259 **732**	16p.	pale stone, black, grey-black & brt scarlet	40	40
1260 **733**	16p.	pale stone, black, grey-black & brt scarlet	40	40
1261 **734**	16p.	pale stone, black, grey-black & brt scarlet	40	40
1262 **735**	16p.	pale stone, black, grey-black & brt scarlet	40	40
		Set of 5	2.25	1.75
		Gutter Strip of 10	4.50	
		First Day Cover		2.25
		Presentation Pack.........................	3.00	
		Souvenir Book	5.50	
		P.H.Q. Cards (set of 5)	3.00	4.00

Nos. 1258/62 were printed together, *se-tenant*, in horizontal strips of 5 throughout the sheet.

The souvenir book is a 24-page illustrated booklet with a set of mint stamps in a sachet attached to the front cover.

Special First Day of Issue Postmarks

Philatelic Bureau, Edinburgh	2.40
Bristol	2.75

731 Bath Mail Coach, 1784   **732** Attack on Exeter Mail, 1816

733 Norwich Mail in Thunderstorm, 1827   **734** Holyhead and Liverpool Mails leaving London, 1828

736 Nigerian Clinic

737 Violinist and Acropolis, Athens

738 Building Project, Sri Lanka

739 British Council Library, Middle East

735 Edinburgh Mail Snowbound, 1831

(Des F. Newell and J. Sorrell)

1984 (25 Sept). **50th Anniv of the British Council.** *Phosphorised paper.* P 15 × 14.

1263 **736**	17p.	grey-green, greenish yellow, brt purple, dull blue, black, pale green & yellow-green	40	40
1264 **737**	22p.	crimson, greenish yellow, brt rose-red, dull green, black, pale drab & slate-purple	60	65
1265 **738**	31p.	sepia, olive-bistre, red, black, pale stone & olive-brown	90	95
1266 **739**	34p.	steel blue, yellow, rose-red, new blue, black, azure & pale blue	90	95
		Set of 4	2.50	2.60
		Set of 4 Gutter Pairs	5.50	
		First Day Cover		2.60
		Presentation Pack	3.25	
		P.H.Q. Cards (set of 4)	2.40	4.00

Special First Day of Issue Postmarks

Philatelic Bureau, Edinburgh	3.00
London SW	2.75

(Des Yvonne Gilbert)

1984 (20 Nov). **Christmas.** *One phosphor band (13p.) or phosphorised paper (others).* P 15 × 14.

1267 **740**	13p.	pale cream, grey-black, bistre-yellow, magenta, red-brown & lake-brown	30	30
		Eu. Underprint Type 4	50	
1268 **741**	17p.	pale cream, grey-black, yellow, magenta, dull blue & dp dull blue	40	45
1269 **742**	22p.	pale cream, grey-black, olive-yellow, brt magenta, brt blue & brownish grey	55	55
1270 **743**	31p.	pale cream, grey-black, bistre-yellow, magenta, dull blue & lt brown	95	95
1271 **744**	34p.	pale cream, olive-grey, bistre-yellow, magenta, turquoise-green & brown-olive	95	95
		Set of 5	3.00	3.00
		Set of 5 Gutter Pairs	6.00	
		First Day Cover		3.00
		Presentation Pack	3.50	
		P.H.Q. Cards (set of 5)	3.00	4.25

Examples of No. 1267Eu from the 1984 Christmas booklet (No. FX7) show a random pattern of blue double-lined stars printed on the reverse over the gum.

Special First Day of Issue Postmarks

Philatelic Bureau, Edinburgh	3.75
Bethlehem, Llandeilo, Dyfed	3.75

Collectors Pack 1984

1984 (20 Nov). *Comprises Nos. 1236/71.*
CP1271a Collectors Pack ... 35.00

Post Office Yearbook

1984. *Comprises Nos. 1236/71 in 24-page hardbound book with slip case, illustrated in colour.* ... 55.00

740 The Holy Family

741 Arrival in Bethlehem

742 Shepherd and Lamb

743 Virgin and Child

745 "The Flying Scotsman"

746 "The Golden Arrow"

744 Offering of Frankincense

747 "The Cheltenham Flyer"

748 "The Royal Scot"

123

749 "The Cornish Riviera"

(Des T. Cuneo)

752 Wart-biter Bush-cricket

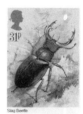

753 Stag Beetle

1985 (22 Jan). **Famous Trains.** *Phosphorised paper. P* 15 × 14.

1272	**745**	17p. black, lemon, magenta, dull blue, grey-black & gold	70	75
		a. Imperf (pair)	£1250	
1273	**746**	22p. black, greenish yellow, brt rose, dp dull blue, grey-black & gold	85	85
1274	**747**	29p. black, greenish yellow, magenta, blue, grey-black & gold	1.10	1.10
1275	**748**	31p. black, bistre-yellow, brt magenta, new blue, slate-black & gold	1.25	1.25
1276	**749**	34p. black, greenish yellow, brt rose, blue, slate-black & gold	1.50	1.50
		Set of 5	5.00	5.00
		Set of 5 Gutter Pairs	11.00	
		First Day Cover		7.50
		Presentation Pack	6.00	
		P.H.Q. Cards (set of 5)	3.25	11.00

Nos. 1272/6 were issued on the occasion of the 150th anniversary of the Great Western Railway Company.

Special First Day of Issue Postmarks

Philatelic Bureau, Edinburgh 8.50
Bristol 8.50

750 Buff-tailed Bumble Bee

751 Seven-spotted Ladybird

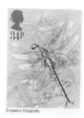

754 Emperor Dragonfly

(Des G. Beningfield)

1985 (12 Mar). **Insects.** *Phosphorised paper. P* 14 × 15.

1277	**750**	17p. black, greenish yellow, magenta, blue, azure, gold & slate-black	50	55
1278	**751**	22p. black, greenish yellow, brt rose-red, dull blue-green, slate-black & gold	65	65
1279	**752**	29p. black, greenish yellow, brt rose, greenish blue, grey-black, gold & bistre-yellow	85	85
1280	**753**	31p. black, greenish yellow, rose, pale new blue & gold	95	1.00
1281	**754**	34p. black, greenish yellow, magenta, greenish blue, grey-black & gold	1.00	1.00
		Set of 5	3.75	3.75
		Set of 5 Gutter Pairs	8.00	
		First Day Cover		4.00
		Presentation Pack	4.50	
		P.H.Q. Cards (set of 5)	2.75	5.50

Nos. 1277/81 were issued on the occasion of the centenaries of the Royal Entomological Society of London's Royal Charter, and of the Selborne Society.

Special First Day of Issue Postmarks

Philatelic Bureau, Edinburgh 4.75
London SW.. 4.75

755 "Water Music" (George Frideric Handel)

756 "The Planets' Suite" (Gustav Holst)

759 R.N.L.I. Lifeboat and Signal Flags

760 Beachy Head Lighthouse and Chart

757 "The First Cuckoo" (Frederick Delius)

758 "Sea Pictures" (Edward Elgar)

761 "Marecs A" Communications Satellite and Dish Aerials

762 Buoys

(Des F. Newell and J. Sorrell. Litho J.W.)

(Des W. McLean)

1985 (14 May). **Europa.** *European Music Year. British Composers. Phosphorised paper. P 14 × 14½.*

1282	755	17p. black, brt yellow-green, dp magenta, new blue, grey-black & gold	40	40
1283	756	22p. black, greenish yellow, brt magenta, new blue, grey-black & gold	60	65
1284	757	31p. black, greenish yellow, magenta, greenish blue, grey-black & gold	90	95
1285	758	34p. black, olive-yellow, bistre, turquoise-blue, slate & gold	1.00	95
		Set of 4	2.75	2.75
		Set of 4 Gutter Pairs	6.00	
		First Day Cover		3.75
		Presentation Pack	3.50	
		P.H.Q. Cards (set of 4)	2.50	5.00

Nos. 1282/5 were issued on the occasion of the 300th birth anniversary of Handel.

1985 (18 June). **Safety at Sea.** *Phosphorised paper. P 14.*

1286	759	17p. black, azure, emerald, ultramarine, orange-yellow, vermilion, brt blue & chrome-yellow	40	40
1287	760	22p. black, azure, emerald, ultramarine, orange-yellow, vermilion, brt blue & chrome-yellow	60	65
1288	761	31p. black, azure, emerald, ultramarine, orange-yellow, vermilion & brt blue	90	95
1289	762	34p. black, azure, emerald, ultramarine, orange-yellow, vermilion, brt blue & chrome-yellow	1.00	95
		Set of 4	2.75	2.60
		Set of 4 Gutter Pairs	6.00	
		First Day Cover		3.75
		Presentation Pack	3.50	
		P.H.Q. Cards (set of 4)	2.50	5.00

Nos. 1286/9 were issued on the occasion of the bicentenary of the unimmersible lifeboat and the 50th anniversary of radar.

Special First Day of Issue Postmarks

Special First Day of Issue Postmarks

Philatelic Bureau, Edinburgh	4.25
Worcester	4.25

Philatelic Bureau, Edinburgh	4.25
Eastbourne	4.25

763 Datapost Motorcyclist, City of London

764 Rural Postbus

767 King Arthur and Merlin

768 Lady of the Lake

769 Queen Guinevere and Sir Lancelot

770 Sir Galahad

(Des Yvonne Gilbert)

765 Parcel Delivery in Winter

766 Town Letter Delivery

(Des P. Hogarth)

1985 (3 Sept). **Arthurian Legends.** *Phosphorised paper.* P 15 × 14.

1294	767	17p. grey-black, lemon, brown-lilac, ultramarine, grey-black & silver.............	40	40
		a. Imperf (pair)		
1295	768	22p. black, lemon, brown-lilac, pale blue, grey-black, silver & grey-black	60	65
1296	769	31p. black, lemon, magenta, turquoise-blue, grey-black, silver & grey-black .	95	95
1297	770	34p. grey, lemon, magenta, new blue, grey-black, silver & grey-black	95	95
		Set of 4	2.75	2.60
		Set of 4 Gutter Pairs	6.00	
		First Day Cover		3.75
		Presentation Pack........................	3.50	
		P.H.Q. Cards (set of 4)	2.50	5.00

Nos. 1294/7 were issued on the occasion of the 500th anniversary of the printing of Sir Thomas Malory's *Morte d'Arthur*.

1985 (30 July). **350 Years of Royal Mail Public Postal Service.** *Phosphorised paper. P* 14 × 15.

1290	763	17p. black, greenish yellow, brt carmine, greenish blue, yellow-brown, grey-black & silver	40	40
		a. Imperf on 3 sides (vert pair)		
		Eu. Underprint Type 5	65	
1291	764	22p. black, greenish yellow, cerise, steel-blue, lt green, grey-black & silver.....	60	65
1292	765	31p. black, greenish yellow, brt carmine, dull blue, drab, grey-black & silver ...	95	95
1293	766	34p. black, greenish yellow, cerise, ultramarine, lt brown, grey-black & silver	95	95
		Set of 4	2.75	2.60
		Set of 4 Gutter Pairs	6.00	
		First Day Cover		3.75
		Presentation Pack........................	3.50	
		P.H.Q. Cards (set of 4)	2.50	5.00

No. 1290a shows perforation indentations at right, but is imperforate at top, bottom and on the left-hand side.

Examples of No. 1290Eu from the 1985 £1.70 booklet (sold at £1.53) (No. FT4) show a blue double-lined D in a random pattern, on the reverse over the gum.

Special First Day of Issue Postmarks

Philatelic Bureau, Edinburgh	4.50
Tintagel, Cornwall	4.50

Special First Day of Issue Postmarks

Philatelic Bureau, Edinburgh	4.25
Bagshot, Surrey..	4.25

HAVE YOU READ THE NOTES AT THE BEGINNING OF THIS CATALOGUE?

These often provide answers to the enquiries we receive.

771 Peter Sellers
(from photo by Bill Brandt)

772 David Niven
(from photo by Cornell Lucas)

773 Charlie Chaplin
(from photo by Lord Snowdon)

774 Vivien Leigh
(from photo by Angus McBean)

775 Alfred Hitchcock
(from photo by Howard Coster)

(Des K. Bassford)

1985 (8 Oct). **British Film Year.** *Phosphorised paper. P 14½.*

1298	**771**	17p. grey-black, olive-grey, gold & silver ..	40	40
1299	**772**	22p. black, brown, gold & silver	70	70
1300	**773**	29p. black, lavender, gold & silver	90	90
1301	**774**	31p. black, pink, gold & silver	80	80
1302	**775**	34p. black, greenish blue, gold & silver ...	90	95
		Set of 5	3.50	3.50
		Set of 5 Gutter Pairs	7.50	
		First Day Cover		5.00
		Presentation Pack	4.00	
		Souvenir Book	6.50	
		P.H.Q. Cards (set of 5)	2.75	6.00

The souvenir book is a 24-page illustrated booklet with a set of mint stamps in a sachet attached to the front cover.

Special First Day of Issue Postmarks

Philatelic Bureau, Edinburgh	5.75
London WC	5.75

776 Principal Boy

777 Genie

778 Dame

779 Good Fairy

780 Pantomine Cat

(Des A. George)

1985 (19 Nov). **Christmas.** *Pantomime Characters. One phosphor band (12p) or phosphorised paper (others). P 15 × 14.*

1303	**776**	12p. new blue, greenish yellow, brt rose, gold, grey-black & silver	35	35
		a. Imperf (pair)		
		Eu. Underprint Type 4	40	
1304	**777**	17p. emerald, greenish yellow, brt rose, new blue, black, gold & silver..........	45	50
		a. Imperf (pair)		
1305	**778**	22p. brt carmine, greenish yellow, pale new blue, grey, gold & silver	60	65
1306	**779**	31p. brt orange, lemon, rose, slate-purple, silver & gold	85	85
1307	**780**	34p. brt reddish violet, brt blue, brt rose, black, grey-brown, gold & silver	95	1.00
		Set of 5	3.00	3.00
		Set of 5 Gutter Pairs	6.50	
		First Day Cover		3.75
		Presentation Pack	3.75	
		P.H.Q. Cards (set of 5)	2.75	5.50
		Christmas Folder (contains No. 1303 × 50)	18.00	

Examples of No. 1303Eu from the 1985 Christmas booklet (No. FX8) show a random pattern of blue double-lined stars printed on the reverse over the gum.

Special First Day of Issue Postmarks

Special First Day of Issue Postmarks

Philatelic Bureau, Edinburgh	4.25
Bethlehem, Llandeilo, Dyfed	4.25

Philatelic Bureau, Edinburgh	5.00
Birmingham	5.00

Collectors Pack 1985

1985 (19 Nov). *Comprises Nos. 1272/1307*
CP1307a Collectors Pack 35.00

Post Office Yearbook

1985. *Comprises Nos. 1272/1307 in 32-page hardbound book with slip case, illustrated in colour* 60.00

781 Light Bulb and North Sea Oil Drilling Rig (Energy)

782 Thermometer and Pharmaceutical Laboratory (Health)

785 Dr. Edmond Halley as Comet

786 *Giotto* Spacecraft approaching Comet

783 Garden Hoe and Steelworks (Steel)

784 Loaf of Bread and Cornfield (Agriculture)

787 "Maybe Twice in a Lifetime"

788 Comet orbiting Sun and Planets

(Des K. Bassford. Litho Questa)

(Des R. Steadman)

1986 (14 Jan). **Industry Year.** *Phosphorised paper. P $14\frac{1}{2}$ × 14.*

1308	**781**	17p. gold, black, magenta, greenish yellow & new blue	45	45
1309	**782**	22p. gold, pale turquoise-green, black, magenta, greenish yellow & blue	65	65
1310	**783**	31p. gold, black, magenta, greenish yellow & new blue	85	85
1311	**784**	34p. gold, black, magenta, greenish yellow & new blue	95	1.00
		Set of 4	₊2.75	2.75
		Set of 4 Gutter Pairs	5.50	
		First Day Cover		4.50
		Presentation Pack	3.25	
		P.H.Q. Cards (set of 4)	2.25	5.50

1986 (18 Feb). **Appearance of Halley's Comet.** *Phosphorised paper. P 15 × 14.*

1312	**785**	17p. black, bistre, rosine, blue, grey-black, gold & dp brown	45	45
1313	**786**	22p. orange-vermilion, greenish yellow, brt purple, new blue, black & gold ...	65	70
1314	**787**	31p. black, greenish yellow, brt purple, dp turquoise-blue, grey-black & gold	85	85
1315	**788**	34p. blue, greenish yellow, magenta, dp turquoise-blue, black & gold	95	1.00
		Set of 4	2.75	2.75
		Set of 4 Gutter Pairs	5.50	
		First Day Cover		5.00
		Presentation Pack	3.25	
		P.H.Q. Cards (set of 4)	2.40	5.00

Special First Day of Issue Postmarks

Special First Day of Issue Postmarks

Philatelic Bureau, Edinburgh 5.50
London SE10 .... 5.50

789 Queen Elizabeth in 1928, 1942 and 1952

790 Queen Elizabeth in 1958, 1973 and 1982

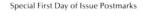

T789/90 were printed horizontally se-tenant within the sheet

(Des J. Matthews)

1986 (21 Apr). **60th Birthday of Queen Elizabeth II.** *Phosphorised paper.* P 15 × 14.

1316	**789**	17p. grey-black, turquoise-green, brt green, green and dull blue	45	45
		a. Pair. Nos. 1316/17	1.25	1.25
1317	**790**	17p. grey-black, dull blue, greenish blue and indigo	45	45
1318	**789**	34p. grey-black, dp dull purple, yellow-orange and red	90	95
		a. Pair. Nos. 1318/19	2.00	2.00
1319	**790**	34p. grey-black, olive-brown, yellow-brown, olive-brown and red	90	95
		Set of 4	2.90	2.50
		Set of 4 Gutter Pairs	6.00	
		First Day Cover		4.50
		Presentation Pack	4.00	
		Souvenir Book	6.50	
		P.H.Q. Cards (set of 4)	2.40	5.25

The souvenir book is a special booklet, fully illustrated and containing a mint set of stamps.

Special First Day of Issue Postmarks

Philatelic Bureau, Edinburgh 5.00
Windsor 5.00

Special First Day of Issue Postmarks

791 Barn Owl   **792** Pine Marten

793 Wild Cat   **794** Natterjack Toad

(Des K. Lilly)

1986 (20 May). **Europa.** *Nature Conservation – Endangered Species.* *Phosphorised paper.* P 14½ × 14.

1320	**791**	17p. gold, greenish yellow, rose, yellow-brown, olive-grey, new blue and black	50	55
1321	**792**	22p. gold, greenish yellow, reddish brown, olive-yellow, turquoise-blue, grey-black and black	60	65
1322	**793**	31p. gold, brt yellow-green, magenta, lt brown, ultramarine, olive-brown and black	1.00	1.00
1323	**794**	34p. gold, greenish yellow, brt rose-red, brt green, grey-black and black	1.00	1.00
		Set of 4	2.90	2.90
		Set of 4 Gutter Pairs	6.00	
		First Day Cover		4.50
		Presentation Pack	3.75	
		PHQ Cards (set of 4)	2.00	5.25

Special First Day of Issue Postmarks

Philatelic Bureau, Edinburgh 5.00
Lincoln 5.00

759 Peasants working
in fields

796 Freemen working
at Town Trades

801 Weightlifting

802 Rifle Shooting

797 Knight and Retainers

798 Lord at Banquet

(Des Tayburn Design Consultancy)

803 Hockey

(Des N. Cudworth)

1986 (17 Jun). **900th Anniv of Domesday Book.** *Phosphorised paper.*
P 15 × 14.

1324	795	17p. yellow-brown, vermilion, lemon, bright emerald, orange-brown, grey & brownish grey	45	50
1325	796	22p. yellow-ochre, red, greenish blue, chestnut, grey-black & brownish grey	55	60
1326	797	31p. yellow-brown, vermilion, green, Indian red, grey-black & brownish grey	85	80
1327	798	34p. yellow-ochre, bright scarlet, grey-brown, new blue, lake-brown, grey-black & grey	90	85
		Set of 4	2.60	2.60
		Set of 4 Gutter Pairs	5.00	
		First Day Cover		3.75
		Presentation Pack	3.25	
		P.H.Q. Cards (set of 4)	2.00	5.00

Special First Day of Issue Postmarks

Philatelic Bureau, Edinburgh	4.00
Gloucester	4.50

799 Athletics

800 Rowing

1986 (15 July). **Thirteenth Commonwealth Games, Edinburgh and
World Hockey Cup for Men, London** (34p.). *Phosphorised paper.*
P 15 × 14.

1328	799	17p. black, greenish yellow, orange-vermilion, ultramarine, chestnut & emerald	45	45
1329	800	22p. black, lemon, scarlet, new blue, royal blue, chestnut & dp ultramarine	60	60
1330	801	29p. grey-black, greenish yellow, scarlet, new blue, ochre, brown-rose & pale chestnut	80	80
1331	802	31p. black, greenish yellow, rose, blue, dull yellow-green, chestnut & yellow-green	85	90
1332	803	34p. black, lemon, scarlet, bright blue, bright emerald, red-brown & vermilion	85	90
		a. Imperf (pair)		
		Set of 5	3.25	3.50
		Set of 5 Gutter Pairs	6.50	
		First Day Cover		5.50
		Presentation Pack	4.00	
		P.H.Q. Cards (set of 5)	2.25	5.75

No. 1332 also commemorates the Centenary of the Hockey Association.

Special First Day of Issue Postmarks

Philatelic Bureau, Edinburgh	6.00
Head Post Office, Edinburgh	6.00

STAMP MONTHLY

Finest and most informative magazine for all collectors.
Obtainable from your newsagent or by postal subscription –
details on request

804   805

Prince Andrew and Miss Sarah Ferguson (from photo by Gene Nocon)

(Des J. Matthews)

1986 (22 July). **Royal Wedding.** *One phosphor band* (12p.) *or phosphorised paper* (17p.). *P* 14 × 15.

1333 **804**	12p. lake, greenish yellow, cerise, ultramarine, black & silver	35	30
1334 **805**	17p. steel blue, greenish yellow, cerise, ultramarine, black & gold	55	55
	a. Imperf (pair)	85	
	Set of 2	85	85
	Set of 2 Gutter Pairs	1.75	
	First Day Cover		2.50
	Presentation Pack	1.50	
	P.H.Q. Cards (set of 2)	1.10	2.75

Special First Day of Issue Postmarks

Philatelic Bureau, Edinburgh 3.00
London, SW1 .... 3.00

806 Stylised Cross on Ballot Paper

(Des J. Gibbs. Litho Questa)

1986 (19 Aug). **32nd Commonwealth Parliamentary Association Conference.** *Phosphorised paper. P* 14 × 14½.

1335 **806**	34p. pale grey-lilac, black, vermilion, yellow & ultramarine	90	90
	Gutter Pair	1.90	
	First Day Cover		1.60
	P.H.Q. Card	50	1.75

Special First Day of Issue Postmarks

Philatelic Bureau, Edinburgh 2.10
London, SW1 .... 2.10

807 Lord Dowding and Hawker "Hurricane"   **808** Lord Tedder and Hawker "Typhoon"

809 Lord Trenchard and De Havilland "DH9A"   **810** Sir Arthur Harris and Avro "Lancaster"

811 Lord Portal and De Havilland "Mosquito"

(Des B. Sanders)

1986 (16 Sept). **History of the Royal Air Force.** *Phosphorised paper. P* 14½.

1336 **807**	17p. pale blue, greenish yellow, brt rose, blue, black & grey-black	40	40
1337 **808**	22p. pale turquoise-green, greenish yellow, magenta, new blue, black & grey-black	60	60
	a. Face value omitted*	£400	
	b. Queen's head omitted*	£400	

131

1338 **809**	29p. pale drab, olive-yellow, magenta, blue, grey-black & black	80	80
1339 **810**	31p. pale flesh, greenish yellow, magenta, ultramarine, black & grey-black	80	80
1340 **811**	34p. buff, greenish yellow, magenta, blue, grey-black & black	85	85
	Set of 5	3.25	3.25
	Set of 5 Gutter Pairs	6.50	
	First Day Cover		4.50
	Presentation Pack	4.00	
	P.H.Q. Cards (set of 5)	2.50	6.00

Nos. 1336/40 were issued to celebrate the 50th anniversary of the first R.A.F. Commands.

*Nos. 1337a/b come from three consecutive sheets on which the stamps in the first vertical row are without the face value and those in the second vertical row the Queen's head.

Special First Day of Issue Postmarks

Philatelic Bureau, Edinburgh	5.00
Farnborough	5.00

812 The Glastonbury Thorn

813 The Tanad Valley Plygain

814 The Hebrides Tribute

815 The Dewsbury Church Knell

816 The Hereford Boy Bishop

(Des Lynda Gray)

1986 (18 Nov–2 Dec). **Christmas.** One phosphor band (12p., 13p.) or phosphorised paper (others). P 15 × 14.

1341 **812**	12p. gold, greenish yellow, vermilion, dp brown, emerald & dp blue (2.12)	40	40
1342	13p. dp blue, greenish yellow, vermilion, dp brown, emerald & gold	35	40
	Eu. Underprint Type 4 (2.12)	50	
1343 **813**	18p. myrtle-green, yellow, vermilion, dp blue, black, reddish brown & gold	45	45
1344 **814**	22p. vermilion, olive-bistre, dull blue, dp brown, dp green & gold	55	60
1345 **815**	31p. dp brown, yellow, vermilion, violet, dp dull green, black & gold	75	80
1346 **816**	34p. violet, lemon, vermilion, dp dull blue, reddish brown & gold	85	90
	Set of 6	3.00	3.25
	Set of 6 Gutter Pairs	6.50	
	First Day Covers (2)		5.00
	Presentation Pack (Nos. 1342/6)	3.25	
	P.H.Q. Cards (Nos. 1342/5) (Set of 5)	2.50	5.25
	Christmas Folder (contains No. 1342Eu × 36)	16.00	

No. 1341 represented a discount of 1p., available between 2 and 24 December 1986, on the current second class postage rate.

Special First Day of Issue Postmarks

Philatelic Bureau, Edinburgh (Nos. 1342/6) (18 Nov)	4.00
Bethlehem, Llandeilo, Dyfed (Nos. 1342/6) (18 Nov)	4.00
Philatelic Bureau, Edinburgh (No. 1341) (2 Dec)	1.50

Collectors Pack 1986

1986 (18 Nov). *Comprises Nos. 1308/40 and 1342/46.*
CP1346a   Collectors Pack 27.00

Post Office Yearbook

1986 (18 Nov). *Comprises Nos. 1308/46 in 32-page hardbound book with slip case, illustrated in colour* 45.00

HAVE YOU READ THE NOTES AT THE BEGINNING OF THIS CATALOGUE?

These often provide answers to the enquiries we receive.

817 North American
Blanket Flower

818 Globe Thistle

821 *The Principia
Mathematica*

822 *Motion of Bodies
in Ellipses*

819 *Echeveria*

820 Autumn Crocus

(Adapted J. Matthews)

823 *Optick Treatise*

824 *The System of the World*

(Des Sarah Godwin)

1987 (20 Jan). **Flower Photographs by Alfred Lammer.** *Phosphorised
paper. P 14½ × 14.*

1347	**817**	18p. silver, greenish yellow, rosine, dp green & black	45	45
1348	**818**	22p. silver, greenish yellow, new blue, greenish blue & black	55	60
1349	**819**	31p. silver, greenish yellow, scarlet, blue-green, dp green & black	75	80
		a. Imperf (pair)		
1350	**820**	34p. silver, greenish yellow, magenta, dull blue, dp green & black	85	90
		Set of 4	2.40	2.50
		Set of 4 Gutters Pairs	5.00	
		First Day Cover		3.75
		Presentation Pack	3.00	
		P.H.Q. Cards (set of 4)	1.90	5.75

1987 (24 Mar). **300th Anniv of *The Principia Mathematica* by Sir Isaac
Newton.** *Phosphorised paper. P 14 × 15.*

1351	**821**	18p. black, greenish yellow, cerise, blue-green, grey-black and silver	45	45
1352	**822**	22p. black, greenish yellow, bright orange, blue, bright emerald, silver & bluish violet	55	60
1353	**823**	31p. black, greenish yellow, scarlet, new blue, bronze-green, silver & slate-green	75	80
1354	**824**	34p. black, greenish yellow, red, bright blue, grey-black & silver	85	90
		Set of 4	2.40	2.50
		Set of 4 Gutter Pairs	5.00	
		First Day Cover		3.75
		Presentation Pack	3.00	
		P.H.Q. Cards (set of 4)	2.00	5.00

Special First Day of Issue Postmarks

Special First Day of Issue Postmarks

Philatelic Bureau, Edinburgh	4.25
Richmond, Surrey	4.25

Philatelic Bureau, Edinburgh	4.25
Woolsthorpe, Lincs	4.25

825 Willis Faber and Dumas Building, Ipswich

826 Pompidou Centre, Paris

829 Brigade Members with Ashford Litter, 1887

830 Bandaging Blitz Victim, 1940

827 Staatsgalerie, Stuttgart

828 European Investment Bank, Luxembourg

831 Volunteer with fainting Girl, 1965

832 Transport of Transplant Organ by Air Wing, 1987

(Des B. Tattersfield)

1987 (12 May). **Europa. British Architects in Europe.** *Phosphorised paper.* P 15 × 14.

1355	**825**	18p.	black, bistre-yellow, cerise, brt blue, dp grey & grey-black......................	45	45
1356	**826**	22p.	black, greenish yellow, carmine, brt blue, dp grey & grey-black	55	60
1357	**827**	31p.	grey-black, bistre-yellow, cerise, brt blue, brt green, black & dull violet ..	75	80
			a. Imperf (horiz pair).........................		
1358	**828**	34p.	black, greenish yellow, cerise, brt blue, grey-black & dp grey	85	90
			Set of 4..	2.40	2.50
			Set of 4 Gutter Pairs	5.00	
			First Day Cover		3.75
			Presentation Pack.........................	3.00	
			P.H.Q. Cards (set of 4)..................	1.90	5.00

(Des Debbie Cook. Litho Questa)

1987 (16 Jun). **Centenary of St. John Ambulance Brigade.** *Phosphorised paper.* P 14 × 14½.

1359	**829**	18p.	new blue, greenish yellow, magenta, black, silver & pink........................	30	35
1360	**830**	22p.	new blue, greenish yellow, magenta, black, silver & cobalt	35	40
1361	**831**	31p.	new blue, greenish yellow, magenta, black, silver & bistre-brown	50	55
1362	**832**	34p.	new blue, greenish yellow, magenta, black, silver & greenish grey..........	55	60
			Set of 4..	1.50	1.75
			Set of 4 Gutter Pairs	3.25	
			First Day Cover		3.50
			Presentation Pack.........................	1.90	
			P.H.Q. Cards (set of 4)..................	85	4.50

Special First Day of Issue Postmarks

Special First Day of Issue Postmarks

Philatelic Bureau, Edinburgh 4.25
Ipswich 4.25

Philatelic Bureau, Edinburgh 4.00
London, EC1 .... 4.00

833 Arms of the Lord Lyon King of Arms

834 Scottish Heraldic Banner of Prince Charles

837 Crystal Palace, "Monarch of the Glen" (Landseer) and Grace Darling

838 *Great Eastern, Beeton's Book of Household Management* and Prince Albert

835 Arms of Royal Scottish Academy of Painting, Sculpture and Architecture

836 Arms of Royal Society of Edinburgh

839 Albert Memorial, Ballot Box and Disraeli

840 Diamond Jubilee Emblem, Newspaper Placard for Relief of Mafeking and Morse Key

(Des J. Matthews)

1987 (21 July). **300th Anniv of Revival of Order of the Thistle.** *Phosphorised paper.* P 14½.

1363 **833**	18p. black, lemon, scarlet, blue, dp green, slate & brown	30	35
1364 **834**	22p. black, greenish yellow, carmine, new blue, dp green, grey & lake-brown ..	35	40
1365 **835**	31p. black, greenish yellow, scarlet, new blue, dull green, grey & grey-black..	50	55
1366 **836**	34p. black, greenish yellow, scarlet, dp ultramarine, dull green, grey and yellow-brown	55	60
	Set of 4	1.50	1.75
	Set of 4 Gutter Pairs	3.25	
	First Day Cover		3.50
	Presentation Pack	1.90	
	P.H.Q. Cards (set of 4)	85	4.50

(Des M. Dempsey. Eng C. Slania. Recess and photo Harrison)

1987 (8 Sept). **150th Anniv of Queen Victoria's Accession.** *Phosphorised paper.* P 15 × 14.

1367 **837**	18p. pale stone, dp blue, lemon, rose, greenish blue, brown-ochre & grey-black	30	35
1368 **838**	22p. pale stone, dp brown, lemon, rose, grey-black & brown-ochre	35	40
1369 **839**	31p. pale stone, dp lilac, lemon, cerise, brown-ochre, greenish blue & grey-black	50	55
1370 **840**	34p. pale stone, myrtle-green, yellow-ochre, reddish brown & brown-ochre	55	60
	Set of 4	1.50	1.75
	Set of 4 Gutter Pairs	3.25	
	First Day Cover		3.50
	Presentation Pack	1.90	
	P.H.Q. Cards (set of 4)	85	4.50

Special First Day of Issue Postmarks

Philatelic Bureau, Edinburgh	4.00
Rothesay, Isle of Bute	4.00

Special First Day of Issue Postmarks

Philatelic Bureau, Edinburgh	4.00
Newport, Isle of Wight	4.00

841 Pot by Bernard Leach

842 Pot by Elizabeth Fritsch

847 Sleeping Child and
Father Christmas in Sleigh

848 Child reading

843 Pot by Lucie Rie

844 Pot by Hans Coper

(Des T. Evans)

849 Child playing Recorder
and Snowman

(Des M. Foreman)

1987 (13 Oct). **Studio Pottery.** *Phosphorised paper. P* 14½ × 14.

1371	**841**	18p. gold, lemon, lt red-brown, chestnut, lt grey & black	30	35
1372	**842**	26p. blue over silver, yellow-orange, brt purple, lavender, bluish violet, grey-brown & black	40	45
1373	**843**	31p. rose-lilac over silver, greenish yellow, cerise, new blue, grey-lilac & black	50	55
1374	**844**	34p. copper, yellow-brown, reddish brown, grey-lilac & black	55	60
		Set of 4	1.60	1.75
		Set of 4 Gutter Pairs	3.50	
		First Day Cover		3.50
		Presentation Pack	2.00	
		P.H.Q. Cards (set of 4)	90	4.50

Special First Day of Issue Postmarks

Philatelic Bureau, Edinburgh 4.00
St. Ives, Cornwall 4.00

845 Decorating the
Christmas Tree

846 Waiting for Father
Christmas

1987 (17 Nov). **Christmas.** *One phosphor band (13p.) or phosphorised paper (others). P* 15 × 14.

1375	**845**	13p. gold, greenish yellow, rose, greenish blue & black	20	25
		Eu. Underprint Type 4	20	
1376	**846**	18p. gold, greenish yellow, brt purple, greenish blue, brt blue & black	30	35
1377	**847**	26p. gold, greenish yellow, brt purple, new blue, brt blue & black	40	45
1378	**848**	31p. gold, greenish yellow, scarlet, brt magenta, dull rose, greenish blue & black	50	55
1379	**849**	34p. gold, greenish yellow, dull rose, greenish blue, brt blue & black	55	60
		Set of 5	1.75	2.00
		Set of 5 Gutter Pairs	3.75	
		First Day Cover		3.25
		Presentation Pack	2.10	
		P.H.Q. Cards (set of 5)	1.10	4.75
		Christmas Folder (contains No. 1375Eu × 36)	7.00	

Special First Day of Issue Postmarks

Philatelic Bureau, Edinburgh 3.75
Bethlehem, Llandeilo, Dyfed 3.75

Collectors Pack 1987

1987 (17 Nov). *Comprises Nos. 1347/79.*
CP1379a Collectors Pack 14.00

Post Office Yearbook

1987 (17 Nov). *Comprises Nos. 1347/79 in 32-page hardbound book with slip case, illustrated in colour* 24.00

850 Bull-rout (Jonathan Couch)

851 Yellow Waterlily (Major Joshua Swatkin)

852 Bewick's Swan (Edward Lear)

853 *Morchella esculenta* (James Sowerby)

(Des E. Hughes)

854 Revd William Morgan (Bible translator, 1588)

855 William Salesbury (New Testament translator, 1567)

856 Bishop Richard Davies (New Testament translator, 1567)

857 Bishop Richard Parry (editor of Revised Welsh Bible, 1620)

(Des K. Bowen)

1988 (19 Jan). **Bicentenary of Linnean Society.** *Archive Illustrations. Phosphorised paper. P 15 × 14.*

1380	**850**	18p. grey-black, stone, orange-yellow, brt purple, olive-bistre & gold..............	30	35
1381	**851**	26p. black, stone, bistre-yellow, dull orange, greenish blue, gold & pale bistre	40	45
1382	**852**	31p. black, stone, greenish yellow, rose-red, dp blue, gold & olive-bistre	50	55
1383	**853**	34p. black, stone, yellow, pale bistre, olive-grey, gold & olive-bistre	55	60
		Set of 4	1.60	1.75
		Set of 4 Gutter Pairs	3.50	
		First Day Cover		3.00
		Presentation Pack........................	2.00	
		P.H.Q. Cards (set of 4)..................	90	4.50

1988 (1 Mar). **400th Anniv of Welsh Bible.** *Phosphorised paper. P 14½ × 14.*

1384	**854**	18p. grey-black, greenish yellow, cerise, blue, black & emerald....................	30	35
1385	**855**	26p. grey-black, yellow, brt rose-red, turquoise-blue, black & orange	40	45
1386	**856**	31p. black, chrome-yellow, carmine, new blue, grey-black & blue	50	55
1387	**857**	34p. grey-black, greenish yellow, cerise, turquoise-green, black & brt violet ..	55	60
		Set of 4	1.60	1.75
		Set of 4 Gutter Pairs	3.50	
		First Day Cover		3.00
		Presentation Pack........................	2.00	
		P.H.Q. Cards (set of 4)..................	90	4.50

Special First Day of Issue Postmarks

Special First Day of Issue Postmarks

Philatelic Bureau, Edinburgh 4.00
London, W1 .... 4.00

Philatelic Bureau, Edinburgh 4.00
Ty Mawr, Wybrnant, Gwynedd 4.00

18p

26p

858 Gymnastics (Centenary of British Amateur Gymnastics Association)

859 Downhill Ski-ing (Ski Club of Great Britain)

31p

34p

860 Tennis (Centenary of Lawn Tennis Association)

861 Football (Centenary of Football League)

(Des J. Sutton)

1988 (22 Mar). **Sports Organizations.** *Phosphor paper.* P 14½.

1388	**858**	18p.	violet-blue, greenish yellow, rosine, brt rose, new blue & silver	30	35
1389	**859**	26p.	violet-blue, greenish yellow, vermilion, carmine, yellow-orange & silver	40	45
1390	**860**	31p.	violet-blue, greenish yellow, rose, blue, pale greenish blue, silver & brt orange..	50	55
1391	**861**	34p.	violet-blue, greenish yellow, vermilion, blue, brt emerald, silver & pink	55	60
			Set of 4	1.60	1.75
			Set of 4 Gutter Pairs	3.50	
			First Day Cover		3.00
			Presentation Pack........................	2.00	
			P.H.Q. Cards (set of 4)..................	90	4.50

Special First Day of Issue Postmarks

Philatelic Bureau, Edinburgh	....	4.00
Wembley	....	4.00

Royal Mail Postage Labels

These imperforate labels were issued as an experiment by the Post Office. Special microprocessor controlled machines were installed at post offices in Cambridge, London, Shirley (Southampton) and Windsor to provide an after-hours sales service to the public. The machines printed and dispensed the labels according to the coins inserted and the buttons operated by the customer. Values were initially available in ½p. steps to 16p. and in addition, the labels were sold at philatelic counters in two packs containing either 3 values (3½., 12½., 16p.) or 32 values (½p. to 16p.).

From 28 August 1984 the machines were adjusted to provide values up to 17p. After 31 December 1984 labels including ½p. values were withdrawn. The machines were taken out of service on 30 April 1985.

Machine postage-paid impression in red on phosphorised paper with grey-green background design. No watermark. Imperforate.

1984 (1 May–28 Aug).

	Set of 32 (½p. to 16p.)	30.00	35.00
	Set of 3 (3½p., 12½p., 16p.)	3.75	4.25
	Set of 3 on First Day Cover (1.5.84)		6.00
	Set of 2 (16½p., 17p.) (28.8.84)	4.50	5.00

REGIONAL ISSUES

I. CHANNEL ISLANDS

C **1** Gathering Vraic   C **2** Islanders gathering Vraic

(Des J. R. R. Stobie (1d.) or from drawing by E. Blampied (2½d.). Photo Harrison)

1948 (10 May). *Third Anniv of Liberation. W* **127** *of Great Britain.
P* 15 × 14.

C1	C **1**	1d. scarlet	8	8
C2	C **2**	2½d. ultramarine	15	15
		First Day Cover		12.00

PRINTERS (£ s. d. stamps of all regions):—Photo Harrison & Sons. Portrait by Dorothy Wilding Ltd.

DATES OF ISSUE. Conflicting dates of issue have been announced for some of the regional issues, partly explained by the stamps being released on different dates by the Philatelic Bureau in Edinburgh or the Philatelic Counter in London and in the regions. We have adopted the practice of giving the earliest known dates, since once released the stamps could have been used anywhere in the U.K.

II. NORTHERN IRELAND

N **1**   N **2**   N **3**

(Des W. Hollywood (3d., 4d., 5d.), L. Pilton (6d., 9d.), T. Collins (1s. 3d., 1s. 6d.))

1958–67. *P* 15 × 14. *W* **179.**

NI1	N **1**	3d. deep lilac (18.8.58)		10	10
		p. One centre phosphor band (9.6.67)		10	15
NI2		4d. ultramarine (7.2.66)		10	10
		p. Two phosphor bands (10.67)		10	15
NI3	N **2**	6d. deep claret (29.9.58)		20	20
NI4		9d. bronze-green (2 phosphor bands)			
		(1.3.67)		30	35
NI5	N **3**	1s. 3d. green (29.9.58)		30	35
NI6		1s. 6d. grey-blue (2 phosphor bands)			
		(1.3.67)		30	35
		Ey. Phosphor omitted		£200	

First Day Covers

18.8.58	3d. (*NI1*)		11.00
29.9.58	6d., 1s. 3d. (*NI3, NI5*)		14.00
7.2.66	4d. (*NI2*)		2.75
1.3.67	9d., 1s. 6d. (*NI4, NI6*)		1.75

For Nos. NI1, 3 and 5 in Presentation Pack, see below Wales No. W6.

1968–69. *No watermark. Chalk-surfaced paper. One centre phosphor band (Nos. NI8/9) or two phosphor bands (others). Gum arabic (No. NI7) or PVA gum (others). P* 15 × 14.

NI 7	N **1**	4d. dp brt blue (27.6.68)		10	12
		Ev. PVA gum* (23.10.68)		8.00	
NI 8		4d. olive-sepia (4.9.68)		10	12
		Ey. Phosphor omitted		£200	
NI 9		4d. brt vermilion (26.2.69)		20	20
		Ey. Phosphor omitted		5.00	
NI10		5d. royal blue (4.9.68)		12	20
		Ey. Phosphor omitted		25.00	
NI11	N **3**	1s. 6d. grey-blue (20.5.69)		2.50	3.00
		Ey. Phosphor omitted			

First Day Cover (NI8, NI10)		75
Presentation Pack (containing Nos.		
NI1p, NI4/6, NI8/10) (9.12.70)*		3.00

*No. NI7Ev was never issued in Northern Ireland. After No. NI7 (gum arabic) had been withdrawn from Northern Ireland whilst still on sale at the philatelic counters elsewhere, about fifty sheets with PVA gum were sold over the London Philatelic counter on 23 October, 1968, and some were also on sale at the British Philatelic Exhibition Post Office.

For full information on all future British issues, collectors should write to the British Post Office Philatelic Bureau, 20 Brandon Street, Edinburgh EH3 5TT

139

N 4

(Des J. Matthews after plaster cast by Arnold Machin)

I   II

Redrawn design of Type N 4 (litho ptgs.)

As originally issued the $11\frac{1}{2}$, $12\frac{1}{2}$, 13, 14, $15\frac{1}{2}$, 16, 17, 18p. (violet), $19\frac{1}{2}$, 22p. (blue) and 28p., showed the emblem on a screened background and 12, $20\frac{1}{2}$, 22p. (yellow-green), 26 and 31p. on a solid background.

Two Types of Crown

Type I:– Crown with all pearls individually drawn. Screened background.

Type II:– Crown with clear outlines, large pearls and strong white line below them. First 3 pearls at left are joined. Solid background.

Values, with narrow figures, were used for the 22p. yellow-green (Type I) and 26p. perf. 15 × 14 (Type II).

1971 (7 July)–**87.** *Decimal Currency. Chalk-surfaced paper. Type N **4**.*

(a) *Photo Harrison. With phosphor bands.* P 15 × 14

NI12	$2\frac{1}{2}$p. brt magenta (1 centre band)	90	12
NI13	3p. ultramarine (2 bands)	40	12
	Ey. Phosphor omitted........................	20.00	
NI14	3p. ultramarine (1 centre band) (23.1.74).	12	15
NI15	$3\frac{1}{2}$p. olive-grey (2 bands)(23.1.74)	20	20
NI16	$3\frac{1}{2}$p. olive-grey (1 centre band) (6.11.74)...	20	20
NI17	$4\frac{1}{2}$p. grey-blue (2 bands) (6.11.74)...........	20	20
NI18	5p. reddish violet (2 bands)	1.50	1.50
NI19	$5\frac{1}{2}$p. violet (2 bands) (23.1.74)	20	20
	Ey. Phosphor omitted........................	£225	
NI20	$5\frac{1}{2}$p. violet (1 centre band) (21.5.75).........	20	20
NI21	$6\frac{1}{2}$p. greenish blue (1 centre band) (14.1.76)	20	20
NI22	7p. purple-brown (1 centre band) (18.1.78)	25	25
NI23	$7\frac{1}{2}$p. chestnut (2 bands)	2.50	2.50
	Ey. Phosphor omitted........................	55.00	
NI24	8p. rosine (2 bands) (23.1.74)	25	30
	Ey. Phosphor omitted........................	45.00	
NI25	$8\frac{1}{2}$p. yellow-green (2 bands) (14.1.76).......	30	30
NI26	9p. dp violet (2 bands) (18.1.78).............	30	30
	Ey. Phosphor omitted........................	30.00	
NI27	10p. orange-brown (2 bands) (20.10.76)....	30	30
NI28	10p. orange-brown (1 centre band) (23.7.80)	30	30
NI29	$10\frac{1}{2}$p. steel-blue (2 bands) (18.1.78)	40	35
NI30	11p. scarlet (2 bands) (20.10.76).............	40	40
	Ey. Phosphor omitted........................	5.00	

(b) *Photo Harrison. On phosphorised paper.* P 15 × 14

NI31	12p. yellowish green (23.7.80)	40	40
NI32	$13\frac{1}{2}$p. purple-brown (23.7.80)	60	70
NI33	15p. ultramarine (23.7.80)	45	50

(c) *Litho Questa. One side phosphor band* ($11\frac{1}{2}$p., 12p., $12\frac{1}{2}$p., 13p.) *or on phosphorised paper* (*others*). P 15 × 14 (12p., 13p., 17p., 18p. (No. NI43), 22p. (No. NI47), 31p.) or $13\frac{1}{2}$ × 14 (*others*)

NI34	$11\frac{1}{2}$p. ochre-brown (8.4.81)......................	60	60
NI35	12p. brt emerald (Type II) (7.1.86)..........	20	30
NI36	$12\frac{1}{2}$p. lt emerald (24.2.82)	40	40
	a. Perf 15 × 14 (28.2.84)	5.00	3.50
NI37	13p. pale chestnut (Type I) (23.10.84)	35	30
	Ea. Type II (11.12.86).......................	20	30
	Ey. Phosphor omitted (Type I)		
NI38	14p. grey-blue (8.4.81)	55	50
NI39	$15\frac{1}{2}$p. pale violet (24.2.82).......................	65	60
NI40	16p. drab (27.4.83).............................	90	75
	a. Perf 15 × 14 (28.2.84)	60	60
NI41	17p. grey-blue (Type I) (23.10.84)	50	25
	Ea. Type II (10.9.86)	15.00	18.00
NI42	18p. dp violet (Type I) (8.4.81)...............	85	75
NI43	18p. olive-grey (Type II) (6.1.87)	35	45
NI44	$19\frac{1}{2}$p. olive-grey (24.2.82)	1.75	2.00
NI45	$20\frac{1}{2}$p. ultramarine (27.4.83)	1.25	1.00
NI46	22p. blue (8.4.81)	90	1.10
NI47	22p. yellow-green (23.10.84)..................	35	50
NI48	26p. rosine (Type I) (24.2.82)	80	90
	a. Perf 15 × 14 (Type II) (27.1.87).......	40	50
NI49	28p. dp violet blue (Type I) (27.4.83)	70	90
	a. Perf 15 × 14 (Type II) (27.1.87).......	45	65
NI50	31p. brt purple (Type I) (23.10.84)	50	50
	Ea. Type II (14.4.87)	50	60

From 1972 printings were made on the fluorescent white paper and from 1973 printings had dextrin added to the PVA gum (see notes after No. X981 of Great Britain).

	First Day Covers	
7.7.71	$2\frac{1}{2}$p., 3p., 5p., $7\frac{1}{2}$p. (NI12/13, NI18, NI23)	4.00
23.1.74	3p., $3\frac{1}{2}$p., $5\frac{1}{2}$p., 8p. (NI14/15, NI19, NI24)	1.50
6.11.74	$4\frac{1}{2}$p. (NI17)	1.00
14.1.76	$6\frac{1}{2}$p., $8\frac{1}{2}$p. (NI21, NI25).......................	80
20.10.76	10p., 11p. (NI27, NI30)	1.00
18.1.78	7p., 9p., $10\frac{1}{2}$p. (NI22, NI26, NI29)	1.00
23.7.80	12p., $13\frac{1}{2}$p., 15p. (NI31/3)	2.25
8.4.81	$11\frac{1}{2}$p., 14p., 18p., 22p. (NI34, NI38, NI42, NI46)	2.50
24.2.82	$12\frac{1}{2}$p., $15\frac{1}{2}$p., $19\frac{1}{2}$p., 26p. (NI36, NI39, NI44, NI48)	2.50
27.4.83	16p., $20\frac{1}{2}$p., 28p. (NI40, NI45, NI49) ..	3.00
23.10.84	13p., 17p., 22p., 31p. (NI37, NI41, NI47, NI50)	4.00
7.1.86	12p. (NI35)	80
6.1.87	18p. (NI43)	1.50

Presentation Packs

7.7.71	2½p., 3p. (2 bands), 5p., 7½p. (Nos. NI12/13, NI18, NI23)	
		4.00
29.5.74	3p. (1 centre band), 3½p. (2 bands) or (1 centre band), 5½p. (2 bands) or (1 centre band), 8p. (Nos. NI14, NI15 or NI16, NI19 or NI20, NI24). The 4½p. (No. NI17) was added later	3.00
20.10.76	6½p., 8½p., 10p. (2 bands), 11p. (Nos. NI21, NI25, NI27, NI30)	1.60
28.10.81	7p., 9p., 10½p., 12p. (photo), 13½p., 15p., 11½p., 14p., 18p. dp violet, 22p. blue (Nos. NI22, NI26, NI29, NI31/4, NI38, NI42, NI46)	6.00
3.8.83	10p. (1 centre band), 12½p., 16p., 20½p., 26p., 28p. (Nos. NI28, NI36, NI40, NI45, NI48/9)	4.00
23.10.84	10p. (1 centre band), 13p., 16p., 17p., 22p. yellow-green, 26p., 28p., 31p. (Nos. NI28, NI37, NI40a, NI41, NI47/50)	6.00
3.3.87	12p. (litho), 13p., 17p., 18p. olive-grey, 22p. yellow-green, 26p., 28p., 31p. (Nos. NI35, NI37, NI41, NI43, NI47, NI48a, NI49a, NI50)	3.00

III. SCOTLAND

S 1   S 2   S 3

(Des. G. Huntly (3d., 4d., 5d.), J. Fleming (6d., 9d.), A. Imrie (1s. 3d., 1s. 6d.))

1958–67. *W 179. P 15 × 14.*

S1	S 1	3d. dp lilac (18.8.58)	10	10
		p. Two phosphor bands (29.1.63)	15.00	1.25
		pa. One side phosphor band (30.4.65)	15	25
		pb. One centre phosphor band (9.11.67)	10	10
S2		4d. ultramarine (7.2.66)	10	10
		p. Two phosphor bands	10	20
S3	S 2	6d. dp claret (29.9.58)	10	10
		p. Two phosphor bands (29.1.63)	15	20
S4		9d. bronze-green (2 phosphor bands) (1.3.67)	25	30
S5	S 3	1s. 3d. green (29.9.58)	25	30
		p. Two phosphor bands (29.1.63)	25	30
S6		1s. 6d. grey-blue (2 phosphor bands) (1.3.67)	30	30

First Day Covers

18.8.58	3d. (S1)	7.00
29.9.58	6d., 1s. 3d. (S3, S5)	12.00
7.2.66	4d. (S2)	2.75
1.3.67	9d., 1s. 6d. (S4, S6)	1.75

The one phosphor band on No. S1pa was produced by printing broad phosphor bands across alternate vertical perforations. Individual stamps show the band at right or left (same prices either way).

For Nos. S1, 3 and 5 in Presentation Pack, see below Wales No. W6.

1967–70. *No watermark. Chalk-surfaced paper. One centre phosphor band (S7, S9/10) or two phosphor bands (others). Gum arabic (Nos. S7, S8) or PVA gum (others). P 15 × 14.*

S 7	S 1	3d. dp lilac (16.5.68)	10	10
		Ey. Phosphor omitted	5.50	
		Ev. PVA gum	10	
		Eya. Phosphor omitted (No. S7Ev)	2.50	
S 8		4d. dp brt blue (28.11.67)	10	10
		Ey. Phosphor omitted	7.00	
		Ev. PVA gum (25.7.68)	10	
S 9		4d. olive-sepia (4.9.68)	10	10
		Ey. Phosphor omitted	1.75	
S10		4d. brt vermilion (26.2.69)	10	10
		Ey. Phosphor omitted	2.00	
S11		5d. royal blue (4.9.68)	20	10
		Ey. Phosphor omitted	40.00	
S12	S 2	9d. bronze-green (28.9.70)	5.50	5.50
		Ey. Phosphor omitted	£140	
S13	S 3	1s. 6d. grey-blue (12.12.68)	1.25	1.00
		Ey. Phosphor omitted	£110	

	First Day Cover (S9, S11)	75
	Presentation Pack (containing Nos. S3, S5p, S7, S9/13) (9.12.70)	14.00

STAMP MONTHLY

Finest and most informative magazine for all collectors. Obtainable from your newsagent or by postal subscription – details on request

S 4

(Des J. Matthews after plaster cast by Arnold Machin)

I   II

Redrawn design of Type S 4 (litho ptgs.)

The introduction of the redrawn lion took place when Waddington's had the contract and therefore the 13, 17, 22 and 31p. exist in both types and perforated 13½ × 14. The Questa printings, perforated 15 × 14, are all Type II.

The Types of Lion

Type I:– The eye and jaw appear larger and there is no line across the bridge of the nose.

Type II:– The tongue is thick at the point of entry to the mouth and the eye is linked to the background by a solid line.

Values, with narrow figures, were used for the 18p. olive-grey, 22p. yellow-green and 26p. perf 15 × 14, all Type II.

1971 (7 July)–**87.** *Decimal Currency. Chalk-surfaced paper. Type* S 4.
(a) *Photo Harrison. With phosphor bands.* P 15 × 14

S14	2½p. brt magenta (1 centre band)	20	12
	Ey. Phosphor omitted..........................	5.00	
	Eg. Gum arabic (22.9.72)	20	
S15	3p. ultramarine (2 bands)	30	15
	Ey. Phosphor omitted..........................	4.50	
	Eg. Gum arabic (14.12.72)....................	35	
	Ega. Imperf (pair)	£400	
S16	3p. ultramarine (1 centre band) (23.1.74).	12	12
S17	3½p. olive-grey (2 bands) (23.1.74)	20	20
	Ey. Phosphor omitted.........................	20.00	
S18	3½p. olive-grey (1 centre band) (6.11.74) ...	20	20
S19	4½p. grey-blue (2 bands) (6.11.74)............	20	20
S20	5p. reddish violet (2 bands)	1.50	1.50
S21	5½p. violet (2 bands) (23.1.74)	20	20
S22	5½p. violet (1 centre band) (21.5.75)........	20	20
	a. Imperf (pair)	£350	
S23	6½p. greenish blue (1 centre band) (14.1.76)	20	20
S24	7p. purple-brown (1 centre band) (18.1.78)...................................	25	25
S25	7½p. chestnut (2 bands)	1.75	2.00
	Ey. Phosphor omitted..........................	4.50	
S26	8p. rosine (2 bands) (23.1.74)	30	40
S27	8½p. yellow-green (2 bands) (14.1.76)	30	30
S28	9p. dp violet (2 bands) (18.1.78)............	30	30
S29	10p. orange-brown (2 bands) (20.10.76)....	30	30
S30	10p. orange-brown (1 centre band) (23.7.80)	30	35

S31	10½p. steel-blue (2 bands) (18.1.78)	40	35
S32	11p. scarlet (2 bands) (20.10.76)	35	35
	Ey. Phosphor omitted..........................	1.50	

(b) *Photo Harrison. On phosphorised paper.* P 15 × 14

S33	12p. yellowish green (23.7.80)	40	30
S34	13½p. purple-brown (23.7.80)	60	60
S35	15p. ultramarine (23.7.80)	45	45

(c) *Litho J.W.* (11½p., 12p. (No. S37), 12½p., 13p. (Nos. S39/Ea), 14p., 15½p., 16p., 17p. (No. S43/Ea), 18p. (No. S44), 19½p., 20½p., 22p. (Nos. S48/9Ea), 26p. (No. S50), 28p. (No. S51), 31p. (No. S52/Ea), Questa (others). One side phosphor band (11½p., 12p., 12½p., 13p.) or on phosphorised paper (others). P 15 × 14 (18p. (No. S45)) or 13½ × 14 (others)

S36	11½p. ochre-brown (8.4.81)......................	60	60
	Ey. Phosphor omitted..........................	£850	
S37	12p. brt emerald (7.1.86)	40	35
	a. Perf 15 × 14 (29.4.86)	35	35
S38	12½p. lt emerald (24.2.82)	40	40
S39	13p. pale chestnut (Type 1) (23.10.84)......	40	40
	Ea. Type II (1.85)	40	45
	b. Perf 15 × 14 (Type II) (4.11.86)........	20	30
S40	14p. grey-blue (8.4.81)	55	50
S41	15½p. pale violet (24.2.82)	60	60
S42	16p. drab (27.4.83)	45	45
S43	17p. grey-blue (Type I) (23.10.84)	75	80
	Ea. Type II (1.85)	70	75
	b. Perf 15 × 14 (Type II) (29.4.86)........	40	55
S44	18p. dp violet (Type I) (8.4.81)...............	75	65
S45	18p. olive-grey (Type II) (6.1.87)	35	45
S46	19½p. olive-grey (24.2.82)	1.75	2.00
S47	20½p. ultramarine (27.4.83)	1.25	1.00
S48	22p. blue (8.4.81)	90	1.10
S49	22p. yellow-green (Type I) (23.10.84)	70	75
	Ea. Type II (1.86)	70	90
	b. Perf 15 × 14 (Type II) (27.1.87)........	35	50
S50	26p. rosine (Type I) (24.2.82)	80	90
	a. Perf 15 × 14 (Type II) (27.1.87)........	40	50
S51	28p. dp violet-blue (Type I) (27.4.83)	80	90
	a. Perf 15 × 14 (Type II) (27.1.87)........	45	65
S52	31p. brt purple (Type I) (23.10.84)	80	1.00
	Ea. Type II (1.86)	35.00	20.00
	b. Perf 15 × 14 (Type II) (29.4.86)........	50	65

From 1972 printings were on fluorescent white paper. From 1973 printings had dextrin added (see notes after No. X981 of Great Britain).

First Day Covers

7.7.71	2½p., 3p., 5p., 7½p. (S14/15, S20, S25) .	4.00
23.1.74	3p., 3½p., 5½p., 8p. (S16/17, S21, S26) .	1.50
6.11.74	4½p. (S19)...................................	1.00
14.1.76	6½p., 8½p. (S23, S27)......................	80
20.10.76	10p., 11p. (S29, S32)	1.00
18.1.78	7p., 9p., 10½p. (S24, S28, S31)	1.00
23.7.80	12p., 13½p., 15p. (S33/5)..................	2.25
8.4.81	11½p., 14p., 18p., 22p. (S36, S40, S44, S48)	2.50
24.2.82	12½p., 15½p., 19½p., 26p. (S38, S41, S46, S50)	2.50
27.4.83	16p., 20½p., 28p. (S42, S47, S51)	3.90
23.10.84	13p., 17p., 22p., 31p. (S39, S43, S49, S52)....................................	4.00
7.1.86	12p. (S37)	1.25
6.1.87	18p. (S45)	1.50

Presentation Packs

7.7.71	2½p., 3p. (2 bands), 5p., 7½p. (Nos. S14/15, S20, S25)	4.00
29.5.74*	3p. (1 centre band), 3½p. (2 bands) or (1 centre band), 5½p. (2 bands) or (1 centre band), 8p. (Nos. S16, S17 or S18, S21 or S22, S26). The 4½p. (No. S19) was added later	3.00
20.10.76	6½p., 8½p., 10p. (2 bands), 11p. (Nos. S23, S27, S29, S32)	1.60
28.10.81	7p., 9p., 10½p. (photo), 13½p., 15p., 11½p., 14p., 18p. dp violet, 22p. blue (Nos. S24, S28, S31, S33/6, S40, S44, S48)	6.00
3.8.83	10p. (1 centre band), 12½p., 16p., 20½p., 26p., 28p. (Nos. S30, S38, S42, S47, S50/1)	4.00
23.10.84	10p. (1 centre band), 13p., 16p., 17p., 22p. yellow-green, 26p., 28p., 31p. (Nos. S30, S39, S42/3, S49/52)	6.00
3.3.87	12p. (litho), 13p., 17p., 18p. olive-grey, 22p. yellow-green, 26p., 28p., 31p. (Nos. S37a, S39b, S43b, S45, S49b, S50a, S51a, S52b)	3.00

1977–78. EXPERIMENTAL MACHINE PACKETS. These are small cartons containing loose stamps for sale in vending machines. The experiment was confined to the Scottish Postal Board area, where six vending machines were installed, the first becoming operational in Dundee about February 1977.

The cartons carry labels inscribed "ROYAL MAIL STAMPS", their total face value (30p. or 60p.) and their contents.

At first the 30p. packet contained two 6½p. and two 8½p. Scottish Regional stamps and the 60p. packet had four of each. The stamps could be in pairs or blocks, but also in strips or singles.

With the change in postal rates on 13 June 1977 these packets were withdrawn on 11 June and on the 13 June the contents were changed, giving three 7p. and one 9p. for the 30p. packet and double this for the 60p. packet. However, this time ordinary British Machin stamps were used. Moreover, the Edinburgh machine, situated in an automatic sorting area, was supplied with 7p. stamps with two phosphor bands instead of the new centre band 7p. stamps, despite instructions having been given to withdraw the two band stamps. However, the demand for these packets was too great to be filled and by 27 June the machine was closed down. It was brought back into use on 16 August 1977, supplying 7p. stamps with the centre band.

The 6½p. and 8½p. Scottish Regional packets were put on sale at the Edinburgh Philatelic Bureau in June 1977 and withdrawn in April 1978. The packets with the 7p. and 9p. Machin stamps were put on sale at the Bureau in June 1977 and withdrawn in December 1978.

Such machine packets are outside the scope of this catalogue.

IV. WALES

From the inception of the Regional stamps, the Welsh versions were tendered to members of the public at all Post Offices within the former County of Monmouthshire but the English alternatives were available on request. Offices with a Monmouthshire postal address but situated outside the County, namely Beachley, Brockweir, Redbrook, Sedbury, Tutshill, Welsh Newton and Woodcroft, were not supplied with the Welsh Regional stamps.

With the re-formation of Counties, Monmouthshire became known as Gwent and was also declared to be part of Wales. From 1 July 1974, therefore, except for the offices mentioned above, only Welsh Regional stamps were available at the offices under the jurisdiction of Newport, Gwent.

W 1    W 2    W 3

(Des R. Stone)

1958–67. W **179.** P 15 × 14.

W1	W **1**	3d. dp lilac (18.8.58)	10	10
		p. One centre phosphor band (16.5.67)	10	12
W2		4d. ultramarine (7.2.66)	10	10
		p. Two phosphor bands (10.67)	10	10
W3	W **2**	6d. dp claret (29.9.58)	40	20
W4		9d. bronze-green (2 phosphor bands) (1.3.67)	25	30
		Ey. Phosphor omitted	£300	
W5	W **3**	1s. 3d. green (29.9.58)	25	30
W6		1s. 6d. grey-blue (2 phosphor bands) (1.3.67)	30	30
		Ey. Phosphor omitted	40.00	

First Day Covers

18.8.58	3d. (W1)	7.00
29.9.58	6d., 1s. 3d. (W3, W5)	10.00
7.2.66	4d. (W2)	2.75
1.3.67	9d., 1s. 6d. (W4, W6)	1.75
	Presentation Pack*	90.00

*This was issued in 1960 and comprises Guernsey No. 7, Jersey No. 10, Isle of Man No. 2, Northern Ireland Nos. NI1, 3 and 5, Scotland Nos. S1, 3 and 5 and Wales and Monmouthshire Nos. W1, 3 and 5 together with 6-page printed leaflet describing the stamps. There exist two forms: (a) inscribed "7s.3d." for sale in U.K.; and (b) inscribed "$1.20" for sale in the U.S.A.

1967–69. No wmk. Chalk-surfaced paper. One centre phosphor band (W7, W9/10) or two phosphor bands (others). Gum arabic (3d.) or PVA gum (others). P 15 × 14.

W7	W **1**	3d. dp lilac (6.12.67)	10	10
		Ey. Phosphor omitted	40.00	
W8		4d. dp brt blue (21.6.68)	10	10
W9		4d. olive-sepia (4.9.68)	10	10
W10		4d. brt vermilion (26.2.69)	15	20
		Ey. Phosphor omitted	2.00	
W11		5d. royal blue (4.9.68)	15	10
		Ey. Phosphor omitted	2.25	
W12	W **3**	1s. 6d. grey-blue (1.8.69)	3.00	3.00

	First Day Cover (W9, W11)	75
	Presentation Pack (containing Nos. W4, W6/7, W9/11) (9.12.70)	3.00

W 4

(Des J. Matthews after plaster cast by Arnold Machin)

I   II

Redrawn design of Type W 4 (litho ptgs.)

As originally issued the 11½, 12½, 13, 14, 15½, 16, 17, 18p. (violet), 19½, 22p. (blue) and 28p., showed the emblem on a screened background and the 12, 20½, 22p. (yellow-green), 26 and 31p. on a solid background.

Two Types of Dragon

Type I:– The eye is complete with white dot in the centre. Wing-tips, tail and tongue are thin.

Type II:– The eye is joined to the nose by a solid line. Tail, wing-tips, claws and tongue are wider than in Type I.

With the introduction of the re-drawn dragon (Type II) the background of the 17p. was changed to solid. Values, with narrow figures, were used for the 22p. yellow-green (Type I) and 26p. perf. 15 × 14 (Type II).

1971 (7 July)–**87.** *Decimal Currency. Chalk-surfaced paper. Type W 4.*

(a) Photo Harrison. With phosphor bands. P 15 × 14

W13	2½p. brt magenta (1 centre band)	12	12
	Ey. Phosphor omitted..........................	6.00	
	Eg. Gum arabic (22.9.72)	20	
	Ega. Imperf (pair)	£350	
W14	3p. ultramarine (2 bands)	25	12
	Ey. Phosphor omitted........................	15.00	
	Eg. Gum arabic (6.6.73)......................	35	
	Eya. Phosphor omitted (No. W14Eg.).......	3.50	
W15	3p. ultramarine (1 centre band) (23.1.74).	12	20
W16	3½p. olive-grey (2 bands) (23.1.74)	20	20
W17	3½p. olive-grey (1 centre band) (6.11.74) ...	20	25
W18	4½p. grey-blue (6.11.74)...............	20	20
W19	5p. reddish violet (2 bands)	1.50	1.50
	Ey. Phosphor omitted........................	11.00	
W20	5½p. violet (2 bands) (23.1.74)	20	20
	Ey. Phosphor omitted........................	£160	
W21	5½p. violet (1 centre band) (21.5.75)........	20	25
	a. Imperf (pair)	£400	
W22	6½p. greenish blue (1 centre band) (14.1.76)	20	20
W23	7p. purple-brown (1 centre band) (18.1.78)	25	25
W24	7½p. chestnut (2 bands)	2.00	2.25
	Ey. Phosphor omitted........................	75.00	
W25	8p. rosine (2 bands) (23.1.74)	25	30
	Ey. Phosphor omitted	£450	
W26	8½p. yellow-green (2 bands) (14.1.76).......	30	30
W27	9p. dp violet (2 bands) (18.1.78)	30	30
W28	10p. orange-brown (2 bands) (20.10.76)....	30	30

W29	10p. orange-brown (1 centre band) (23.7.80).......................................	30	30
W30	10½p. steel-blue (2 bands) (18.1.78)	40	35
W31	11p. scarlet (2 bands) (20.10.76)	40	40

(b) Photo Harrison. On phosphorised paper. P 15 × 14

W32	12p. yellow green (23.7.80)	40	35
W33	13½p. purple-brown (23.7.80)	60	70
W34	15p. ultramarine (23.7.80)	45	50

(c) Litho Questa. One side phosphor band (11½p., 12p., 12½p., 13p.) *or on phosphorised paper* (others). *P* 15 × 14 (12p., 13p., 17p., 18p. (No. W44), 22p. (No. W48), 31p.) *or* 13½ × 14 (others).

W35	11½p. ochre-brown (8.4.81)......................	60	60
W36	12p. brt emerald (Type II) (7.1.86)...........	35	40
W37	12½p. lt emerald (24.2.82)	40	45
	a. Perf 15 × 14 (10.1.84)	5.00	2.50
W38	13p. pale chestnut (Type I) (23.10.84)	35	30
	Ea. Type II (1.87)	20	30
W39	14p. grey-blue (8.4.81).........................	50	50
W40	15½p. pale violet (24.2.82)	65	60
W41	16p. drab (27.4.83)	1.00	90
	a. Perf 15 × 14 (10.1.84)	70	75
W42	17p. grey-blue (Type I) (23.10.84)	50	50
	Ea. Type II (18.8.86)	8.00	9.00
W43	18p. dp violet (Type I) (8.4.81)	75	65
W44	18p. olive-grey (Type II) (6.1.87)	35	45
W45	19½p. olive-grey (24.2.82)	1.75	2.00
W46	20½p. ultramarine (27.4.83)	1.25	1.00
W47	22p. blue (8.4.81)	90	1.00
W48	22p. yellow-green (23.10.84)	35	50
W49	26p. rosine (Type I) (24.2.82)	80	90
	a. Perf. 15 × 14 (Type II) (27.1.87)........	40	50
W50	28p. dp violet-blue (Type I) (27.4.83)	80	90
	a. Perf 15 × 14 (Type II) (27.1.87)........	45	65
W51	31p. brt purple (23.10.84)	50	70

From 1972 printings were on fluorescent white paper. From 1973 printings had dextrin added (see notes after No. X981 of Great Britain).

	First Day Covers		
7.7.71	2½p., 3p., 5p., 7½p. (W13/14, W19, W24)...................................		4.00
23.1.74	3p., 3½p., 5½p., 8p. (W15/16, W20, W25)		1.50
6.11.74	4½p. (W18)		1.00
14.1.76	6½p., 8½p. (W22, W26)		80
20.10.76	10p., 11p. (W28, W31).....................		1.00
18.1.78	7p., 9p., 10½p. (W23, W27, W30)		1.00
23.7.80	12p., 13½p., 15p. (W32/4)		2.25
8.4.81	11½p., 14p., 18p., 22p. (W35, W39, W43, W47)................................		2.50
24.2.82	12½p., 15½p., 19½p., 26p. (W37, W40, W45, W49)................................		2.50
27.4.85	16p., 20½p., 28p. (W41, W46, W50) ...		3.00
23.10.84	13p., 17p., 22p., 31p. (W38, W42, W48, W50)................................		4.00
7.1.86	12p. (W36)..................................		1.25
6.1.87	18p. (W44)..................................		1.50

Presentation Packs

7.7.71	2½p., 3p. (2 bands), 5p., 7½p. (*Nos.* W13/14, W19, W24)	4.00
29.5.74	3p. (1 centre band), 3½p. (2 bands) *or* (1 centre band), 5½p. (2 bands) *or* (1 centre band), 8p. (*Nos.* W15, W16 *or* W17, W20 *or* W21, W25). The 4½p. (No. W18) was added later..............	3.00
20.10.76	6½p., 8½p., 10p. (2 bands), 11p. (*Nos.* W22, W26, W28, W31)	1.60
28.10.81	7p., 9p., 10½p., 12p. (photo), 13½p., 15p., 11½p., 14p., 18p. dp violet, 22p. blue (*Nos.* W23, W27, W30, W32/5, W39, W43, W47)	6.00
3.8.83	10p. (1 centre band), 12½p., 16p., 20½p., 26p., 28p. (*Nos.* W29, W37, W41, W46, W49/50)	4.00
23.10.84	10p. (1 centre band), 13p., 16p., 17p., 22p. yellow-green, 26p., 28p., 31p. (*Nos.* W29, W38, W41a, W42, W48/51)	6.00
3.3.87	12p. (litho), 13p., 17p., 18p. olive-grey, 22p. yellow-green, 26p., 28p., 31p. (*Nos.* W36, W38, W42, W44, W48, W49a, W50a, W51)	3.00

V. GUERNSEY

War Occupation Issues

BISECTS. On 24 December 1940 authority was given, by Post Office notice, that prepayment of penny postage could be effected by using half a British 2d. stamp, diagonally bisected. Such stamps were first used on 27 December 1940.

The 2d. stamps generally available were those of the Postal Centenary issue, 1940 (S.G. 482) and the first colour of the King George VI issue (S.G. 465). These are listed under Nos. 482a and 465b. A number of the 2d. King George V, 1912–22, and of the King George V photogravure stamp (S.G. 442) which were in the hands of philatelists, were also bisected and used.

1

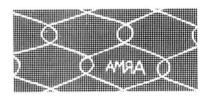

1a Loops (*half actual size*)

(Des E. W. Vaudin. Typo Guernsey Press Co Ltd)

1941–44. *Rouletted.* (a) *White paper. No wmk.*

1	1	½d. light green (7.4.41)	2.50	2.00
		a. *Emerald-green* (6.41)	2.50	2.00
		b. *Bluish green* (11.41)	42.00	28.00
		c. *Bright green* (2.42)	24.00	12.00
		d. *Dull green* (9.42)	4.00	3.00
		e. *Olive-green* (2.43)	18.00	22.00
		f. *Pale yellowish green* (7.43 and later) (*shades*)	2.50	2.00
		g. Imperf (pair)	£125	
		h. Imperf between (horiz pair)	£500	
		i. Imperf between (vert pair)	£600	
2		1d. scarlet (18.2.41)	1.50	1.00
		a. *Pale vermilion* (7.43) (etc.)	3.50	2.50
		b. *Carmine* (1943)	3.75	3.50
		c. Imperf. (pair)	£125	75.00
		d. Imperf between (horiz pair)	£500	
		da. Imperf vert (centre stamp of horiz strip of 3)	£600	
		e. Imperf between (vert pair)	£600	
		f. Printed double (scarlet shade)	60.00	
3		2½d. ultramarine (12.4.44)	4.50	5.50
		a. *Deep ultramarine* (7.44)	4.50	5.50
		b. Imperf (pair)	£300	
		c. Imperf between (horiz pair)	£700	
		Set of 3	8.00	8.00

First Day Covers

7.4.41	½d.		5.00
18.2.41	1d.		5.00
12.4.44	2½d.		6.00

(b) Bluish French bank-note paper. W **1**a *(sideways)*

4	**1**	½d. bright green (11.3.42)		12.00	22.00
5		1d. scarlet (9.4.42)		8.00	22.00
		Set of 2		19.00	40.00

First Day Covers

11.3.42	½d.		70.00
9.4.42	1d.		38.00

The dates given for the shades of Nos. 1 and 2 are the months in which they were printed as indicated on the printer's imprints. Others are issue dates.

Regional Issues

2   **3**

(Des E. A. Piprell. Portrait by Dorothy Wilding Ltd. Photo Harrison & Sons)

1958 (18 Aug)–**67.** *W* **179** *of Great Britain.* P 15 × 14.

6	**2**	2½d. rose-red (8.6.64)		30	40
7	**3**	3d. dp lilac		30	30
		p. One centre phosphor band (24.5.67)		10	20
8		4d. ultramarine (7.2.66)		25	30
		p. Two phosphor bands (24.10.67)		10	20
		Set of 3 (cheapest)		40	75

First Day Covers

18.8.58	3d.		9.00
8.6.64	2½d.		12.00
7.2.66	4d.		8.00

For No. 7 in Presentation Pack, see Regional Issues below Wales No. W6.

1968–69. *No wmk. Chalk-surfaced paper. PVA gum*. One centre phosphor band (Nos. 10/11) or two phosphor bands (others).* P 15 × 14.

9	**3**	4d. pale ultramarine (16.4.68)		10	25
		Ey. Phosphor omitted		40.00	
10		4d. olive-sepia (4.9.68)		12	20
		Ey. Phosphor omitted		40.00	
11		4d. brt vermilion (26.2.69)		12	30
12		5d. royal blue (4.9.68)		12	30
		Set of 4		40	95

First Day Cover

4.9.68	4d., 5d.		1.00

No. 9 was not issued in Guernsey until 22 April.
*PVA Gum. See note after No. 722 of Great Britain.
Further detailed information on the stamps of Guernsey will be found in the Stanley Gibbons *Channel Islands Specialised Catalogue.*

VI. ISLE OF MAN

Although specifically issued for use in the Isle of Man, these issues were also valid for use throughout Great Britain.

DATES OF ISSUE. The note at the beginning of Northern Ireland also applies here.

Nos. 8/11 and current stamps of Great Britain were withdrawn from sale on the island from 5 July 1973 when the independent postal administration was established but remained valid for use there for a time. They also remained on sale at the Philatelic Sales counters in the United Kingdom until 4 July 1974.

1   **2**

(Des J. Nicholson. Portrait by Dorothy Wilding Ltd. Photo Harrison)

1958 (18 Aug)–**68.** *W* **179**. P 15 × 14.

1	**1**	2½d. carmine-red (8.6.64)		40	80
2	**2**	3d. dp lilac		10	10
		a. Chalk-surfaced paper (17.5.63)		20.00	12.00
		p. One centre phosphor band (27.6.68)		10	20
3		4d. ultramarine (7.2.66)		1.25	1.00
		p. Two phosphor bands (5.7.67)		10	10
		Set of 3 (cheapest)		55	90

First Day Covers

18.8.58	3d.		13.00
8.6.64	2½d.		13.00
7.2.66	4d.		11.00

No. 2a was released in London sometime after 17 May 1963, this being the date of issue in Douglas.
For No. 2 in Presentation Pack, see Regional Issues below Wales No. W6.

1968–69. *No wmk. Chalk-surfaced paper. PVA gum. One centre phosphor band (Nos. 5/6) or two phosphor bands (others).* P 15 × 14.

4	**2**	4d. blue (24.6.68)		10	25
5		4d. olive-sepia (4.9.68)		10	30
		Ey. Phosphor omitted		20.00	
6		4d. brt vermilion (26.2.69)		45	60
7		5d. royal blue (4.9.68)		45	60
		Ey. Phosphor omitted		£150	
		Set of 4		1.00	1.60

First Day Cover

4.9.68	4d., 5d.		1.60

3

(Des J. Matthews. Portrait after plaster cast by Arnold Machin. Photo Harrison)

1971 (7 July). *Decimal Currency. Chalk-surfaced paper. One centre phosphor band (2½p.) or two phosphor bands (others).* P 15 × 14.

8	**3**	2½p. brt magenta		10	15
		Ey. Phosphor omitted		£800	
9		3p. ultramarine		12	15

10	**3**	5p. reddish violet	60	60
		Ey. Phosphor omitted.........................	£200	
11		7½p. chestnut	60	85
		Set of 4	1.25	1.60
		Presentation Pack.........................	2.00	

First Day Cover

7.7.71 2½p., 3p., 5p., 7½p.	4.00

All values exist with PVA gum on ordinary cream paper and the 2½p. and 3p. also on fluorescent white paper.

VII. JERSEY

War Occupation Issues

(Des Major N. V. L. Rybot. Typo *Evening Post*, Jersey)

1941–42. *White paper (thin to thick). No wmk. P 11.*

1	**1**	½d. bright green (29.1.42)..................	4.50	3.00
		a. Imperf between (vert pair)..............	£600	
		b. Imperf. between (horiz pair)	£500	
		c. Imperf (pair)	£150	
		d. On greyish paper	5.50	5.50
2		1d. scarlet (1.4.41)...........................	3.50	2.75
		a. Imperf between (vert pair)..............	£600	
		b. Imperf between (horiz pair)	£500	
		c. Imperf (pair)	£175	
		d. On chalk-surfaced paper	38.00	40.00
		e. On greyish paper	4.25	5.50

First Day Covers

29.1.42 ½d.	4.50
1.4.41 1d.	4.50

2 Old Jersey Farm

3 Portelet Bay

4 Corbière Lighthouse

5 Elizabeth Castle

6 Mont Orgueil Castle

7 Gathering Vraic (seaweed)

(Des E. Blampied. Eng H. Cortot. Typo French Govt Works, Paris)

1943–44. *No wmk. P 13½.*

3	**2**	½d. green (1 June).............................	7.00	3.75
		a. Rough, grey paper (6.10.43)	8.50	10.00
4	**3**	1d. scarlet (1 June)............................	75	50
		a. On newsprint (28.2.44)...................	2.75	2.00
5	**4**	1½d. brown (8 June)............................	1.50	3.00
6	**5**	2d. orange-yellow (8 June)	2.50	2.25
7	**6**	2½d. blue (8 June)	1.50	2.25
		a. On newsprint (25.2.44)...................	60	1.75
		ba. Thin paper*	£175	
8	**7**	3d. violet (29 June)............................	80	4.50
		Set of 6	12.00	14.00
		First Day Covers (3)		15.00

*On No. 7ba the design shows clearly through the back of the stamp.

Regional Issues

8   **9**

(Des E. Blampied (T **8**), W. Gardner (T **9**). Portrait by Dorothy Wilding Ltd. Photo Harrison & Sons)

1958 (18 Aug)–**67.** *W 179 of Great Britain. P 15 × 14.*

9	**8**	2½d. carmine-red (8.6.64)	30	45
		a. Imperf three sides (pair)	£650	
10	**9**	3d. dp lilac	30	30
		p. One centre phosphor band (9.6.67)..	10	20
11		4d. ultramarine (7.2.66)	25	30
		p. Two phosphor bands (5.9.67)...........	10	20
		Set of 3 (cheapest)	40	80

First Day Covers

18.8.58	3d.	10.00	
8.6.64	2½d.	12.00	
7.2.66	4d.	8.00	

For No. 10 in Presentation Pack, see Regional Issues below Wales No. W6.

1968–69. *No wmk. Chalk-surfaced paper. PVA gum*. One centre phosphor band (4d. values) or two phosphor bands (5d.). P 15 × 14*

12	**9**	4d. olive-sepia (4.9.68)	12	20
		Ey. Phosphor omitted	£750	
13		4d. brt vermilion (26.2.69)	12	30
14		5d. royal blue (4.9.68)	12	30
		Set of 3	30	75

First Day Cover

4.9.68 4d., 5d.	1.10

*PVA Gum. See note after No. 722 of Great Britain.

Further detailed information on the stamps of Jersey will be found in the Stanley Gibbons *Channel Islands Specialised Catalogue*.

POSTAGE DUE STAMPS

PERFORATIONS. All postage due stamps are perf 14 × 15.

WATERMARK. The watermark always appears sideways and this is the "normal" listed in this Catalogue for Nos. D1/D68. Varieties occur as follows. The point of identification is which way the top of the crown points, but (where they occur) the disposition of the letters needs to be noted also.

The meaning of the terms is given below: (1) as described and illustrated in the Catalogue, i.e. as read through the front of the stamp, and (2) what is seen during watermark detection when the stamp is face down and the back is under examination.

(1) As described

Watermark	Crown pointing	Letters reading
Sideways	left	upwards
Sideways-inverted	right	downwards
Sideways and reversed	left	downwards, back to front
Sideways-inverted and reversed	right	upwards, back to front

(2) As detected (stamp face down)

Watermark		
Sideways	right	upwards, back to front
Sideways-inverted	left	downwards, back to front
Sideways and reversed	right	downwards
Sideways-inverted and reversed	left	upwards

D 1

D 2

(Typo by Somerset House (early trial printings of ½d., 1d., 2d. and 5d.; all printings of 1s.) and by Harrison (later printings of all values except 1s.). Not easily distinguishable except by the control)

1914 (20 Apr)–**23.** W **100** (*Simple Cypher*) *sideways-inverted on* 1½d., 4d. *and* 1s. *and sideways on others.*

D1	D **1**	½d. emerald	40	40
		Wi. Watermark sideways-inverted	1.25	1.00
		Wj. Watermark sideways and reversed....	12.00	
		Wk. Watermark sideways-inverted and reversed		
D2		1d. carmine	40	40
		a. Pale carmine	75	40
		Wi. Watermark sideways-inverted	80	40
		Wj. Watermark sideways-inverted and reversed	10.00	
D3		1½d. chestnut (1923)	35.00	14.00
		Wi. Watermark sideways	35.00	18.00
D4		2d. agate	40	40
		Wi. Watermark sideways-inverted	2.25	1.50
		Wj. Watermark sideways-inverted and reversed	5.00	
D5		3d. violet (1918)	2.00	1.25
		a. Bluish violet	3.00	2.75
		Wi. Watermark sideways-inverted	11.00	2.00

D6	D **1**	4d. dull grey-green (1921)	10.00	1.75
		Wi. Watermark sideways		
D7		5d. brownish cinnamon	2.50	1.25
		Wi. Watermark sideways-inverted	25.00	15.00
D8		1s. brt blue (1915)	20.00	2.25
		a. Dp brt blue	22.00	2.25
		Wi. Watermark sideways	55.00	20.00
		Set of 8	65.00	20.00

The 1d. is known bisected and used to make up a 1½d. rate on understamped letters from Ceylon (1921) and the 2d. bisected and used as 1d. at West Kensington and at Streatham both in the same year.

1924. *As 1914–23, but on thick chalk-surfaced paper.*

D9	D **1**	1d. carmine	2.25	3.00

(Typo Waterlow and (from 1934) Harrison)

1924–31. W **111** (*Block Cypher*) *sideways.*

D10	D **1**	½d. emerald (6.25)	25	30
		Wi. Watermark sideways-inverted	5.00	1.25
D11		1d. carmine (4.25)	50	30
		Wi. Watermark sideways-inverted		
D12		1½d. chestnut (10.24)	25.00	14.00
		Wi. Watermark sideways-inverted		
D13		2d. agate (7.24)	1.50	50
		Wi. Watermark sideways-inverted		
D14		3d. dull violet (10.24)	2.00	50
		a. Printed on gummed side	55.00	†
		b. Experimental paper W **111**a	40.00	35.00
		Wi. Watermark sideways-inverted	7.50	
D15		4d. dull grey-green (10.24)	12.00	2.40
		Wi. Watermark sideways-inverted	25.00	
D16		5d. brownish cinnamon (1.31)	20.00	25.00
D17		1s. dp blue (9.24)	5.00	1.00
		Wi. Watermark sideways-inverted		
D18	D **2**	2s. 6d. purple/*yellow* (10.24)	38.00	2.00
		Wi. Watermark sideways-inverted		
		Set of 9	£200	42.00

1936–37. W **125** (E 8 R) *sideways.*

D19	D **1**	½d. emerald (6.37)	6.00	5.00
D20		1d. carmine (5.37)	1.00	1.60
D21		2d. agate (5.37)	6.50	5.00
D22		3d. dull violet (3.37)	1.60	1.50
D23		4d. dull grey-green (12.36)	11.00	15.00
D24		5d. brownish cinnamon (11.36)	38.00	20.00
		a. Yellow-brown (1937)	11.00	15.00
D25		1s. dp blue (12.36)	7.00	4.50
D26	D **2**	2s. 6d. purple/*yellow* (5.37)	£160	12.00
		Set of 8	£200	55.00

The 1d. is known bisected (Solihull, 3 July 1937).

1937–38. W **127** (G VI R) *sideways.*

D27	D **1**	½d. emerald (1938)	7.00	3.00
D28		1d. carmine (1938)	1.75	40
		Wi. Watermark sideways-inverted		
D29		2d. agate (1938)	1.75	40
		Wi. Watermark sideways-inverted	10.00	
D30		3d. violet (1938)	8.00	40
		Wi. Watermark sideways-inverted	25.00	
D31		4d. dull grey-green (1937)	45.00	8.00
		Wi. Watermark sideways-inverted		
D32		5d. yellow-brown (1938)	7.00	1.50
		Wi. Watermark sideways-inverted	35.00	
D33		1s. dp blue (1937)	45.00	1.00
		Wi. Watermark sideways-inverted	50.00	

D34	D **2**	2s. 6d. purple/yellow (1938)..................	55.00	2.00
		Set of 8	£150	14.00

The 2d. is known bisected in June 1951 (Harpenden and St. Albans) and on 30 October 1954 (Harpenden).

DATES OF ISSUE. The dates for Nos. D35/68 are those on which stamps were first issued by the Supplies Department to postmasters.

1951–52. *Colours changed and new value (1½d.). W* **127** *(G VI R) sideways.*

D35	D **1**	½d. orange (18.9.51)............................	1.75	2.00
D36		1d. violet-blue (6.6.51)........................	1.10	70
		Wi. Watermark sideways-inverted..........		
D37		1½d. green (11.2.52)	1.75	1.75
		Wi. Watermark sideways-inverted..........	8.50	
D38		4d. blue (14.8.51)	20.00	9.00
D39		1s. ochre (6.12.51)	25.00	3.50
		Set of 5	45.00	15.00

The 1d. is known bisected (Dorking, 1952, and Camberley, 6 April 1954).

1954–55. *W* **153** *(Mult Tudor Crown and* E 2 R*) sideways.*

D40	D **1**	½d. orange (8.6.55)	3.00	2.50
		Wi. Watermark sideways-inverted..........	10.00	
D41		2d. agate (28.7.55)	1.90	2.00
D42		3d. violet (4.5.55)	40.00	25.00
D43		4d. blue (14.7.55)	16.00	15.00
		a. Imperf (pair)	£225	
D44		5d. yellow-brown (19.5.55)	15.00	10.00
D45	D **2**	2s. 6d. purple/yellow (11.54)................	£110	6.00
		Set of 6	£160	55.00

1955–57. *W* **165** *(Mult St. Edward's Crown and* E 2 R*) sideways.*

D46	D **1**	½d. orange (16.7.56)............................	1.40	2.50
		Wi. Watermark sideways-inverted..........	10.00	
D47		1d. violet-blue (7.6.56)	4.00	2.00
D48		1½d. green (13.2.56)	3.75	3.00
		Wi. Watermark sideways-inverted..........	12.00	
D49		2d. agate (22.5.56)	35.00	2.50
D50		3d. violet (5.3.56)	4.50	1.25
		Wi. Watermark sideways-inverted..........	25.00	
D51		4d. blue (24.4.56)	20.00	2.75
		Wi. Watermark sideways-inverted..........	30.00	
D52		5d. brown-ochre (23.3.56)	28.00	2.00
D53		1s. ochre (22.11.55)	70.00	1.50
		Wi. Watermark sideways-inverted..........		
D54	D **2**	2s. 6d. purple/yellow (28.6.57)	£150	8.00
		Wi. Watermark sideways-inverted..........		
D55		5s. scarlet/yellow (25.11.55)	80.00	20.00
		Wi. Watermark sideways-inverted..........		
		Set of 10......................................	£350	40.00

The 2d. is known bisected (June 1956), and also the 4d. (Poplar, London, April 1959).

1959–63. *W* **179** *(Mult St. Edward's Crown) sideways.*

D56	D **1**	½d. orange (18.10.61)	10	60
		Wi. Watermark sideways-inverted..........	1.00	
D57		1d. violet-blue (9.5.60)	10	15
		Wi. Watermark sideways-inverted..........	5.00	
D58		1½d. green (5.10.60)	80	1.50
D59		2d. agate (14.9.59)	1.25	25
		Wi. Watermark sideways-inverted..........	15.00	
D60		3d. violet (24.3.59)..............................	40	15
		Wi. Watermark sideways-inverted..........	2.00	
D61		4d. blue (17.12.59)	40	20
		Wi. Watermark sideways-inverted..........	10.00	

D62	D **1**	5d. yellow-brown (6.11.61)	40	45
		Wi. Watermark sideways-inverted..........	3.00	
D63		6d. purple (29.3.62)	60	30
		Wi. Watermark sideways-inverted..........	12.00	
D64		1s. ochre (11.4.60)	1.40	25
		Wi. Watermark sideways-inverted..........	3.00	
D65	D **2**	2s. 6d. purple/yellow (11.5.61)	4.00	45
		Wi. Watermark sideways-inverted..........	6.00	
D66		5s. scarlet/yellow (8.5.61)	7.00	75
		Wi. Watermark sideways-inverted..........	9.00	
D67		10s. blue/yellow (2.9.63)	9.00	3.50
		Wi. Watermark sideways-inverted..........	28.00	
D68		£1 purple/yellow (2.9.63)......................	45.00	6.00
		Set of 13	60.00	13.00

Whiter paper. The note after No. 586 also applies to Postage Due stamps.

The 1d. is known bisected (Newbury, Dec. 1962).

1968–69. *Typo. No wmk. Chalk-surfaced paper.*

D69	D **1**	2d. agate (11.4.68)	40	40
		Ev. PVA gum (26.11.68)	1.25	
D70		3d. violet (9.9.68)................................	25	40
D71		4d. blue (6.5.68)	25	40
		Ev. PVA gum		
D72		5d. orange-brown (31.1.69)	5.00	5.00
D73		6d. purple (9.9.68)...............................	80	60
D74		1s. ochre (19.11.68)	80	1.00
		Set of 6	7.00	7.00

The 2d. and 4d. exist with gum arabic and PVA gum; remainder with PVA gum only.

1968–69. *Photo. No wmk. Chalk-surfaced paper.* PVA gum. P 14 × 15.

D75	D **1**	4d. blue (12.6.69)	5.50	6.00
D76		8d. red (3.10.68).................................	1.25	75

Nos. D75/6 are smaller, 21½ × 17½mm.

D **3**   D **4**

(Des J. Matthews. Photo Harrison)

1970 (17 June)**–75.** *Decimal Currency. Chalk-surfaced paper.* P 14 × 15.

D77	D **3**	½p. turquoise-blue (15.2.71).................	5	15
D78		1p. dp reddish purple (15.2.71)	5	10
D79		2p. myrtle-green (15.2.71)	8	10
D80		3p. ultramarine (15.2.71)......................	10	10
D81		4p. yellow-brown (15.2.71)	12	12
D82		5p. violet (15.2.71)..............................	15	20
D83		7p. red-brown (21.8.74)........................	30	40
D84	D **4**	10p. carmine	25	25
D85		11p. slate-green (18.6.75)	40	50
D86		20p. olive-brown	55	30
D87		50p. ultramarine	1.25	45
D88		£1 black	2.40	60

Postage Due

D89　D **4**　　£5 orange-yellow and black (2.4.73)...... 12.00 　2.00
　　　　　　Set of 13 .... 17.00 　4.75
　　　　　　Presentation Pack (Nos. D77/82, D84,
　　　　　　D86/8) (3.11.71)............................. 　8.00
　　　　　　Presentation Pack (Nos. D77/88)
　　　　　　(30.3.77) .... 　5.00

Later printings were on fluorescent white paper, some with dextrin added to the PVA gum (see notes after X980I of Great Britain).

D **5**　　　　　　　　　D **6**
(Des Sedley Place Design Ltd. Photo Harrison)

1982 (9 June).　*Chalk-surfaced paper. P* 14 × 15.

D90	D **5**	1p.	lake...	5	5
D91		2p.	bright blue	5	8
D92		3p.	dp mauve	5	20
D93		4p.	dp blue	8	15
D94		5p.	sepia	8	20
D95	D **6**	10p.	lt brown......................................	15	25
D96		20p.	olive-green	30	40
D97		25p.	dp greenish blue	40	60
D98		50p.	grey-black	75	90
D99		£1	red...	1.50	1.25
D100		£2	turquoise-blue	3.00	2.40
D101		£5	dull orange..................................	7.50	1.40
			Set of 12......................................	12.50	5.00
			Set of 12 Gutter Pairs....................	30.00	
			Presentation Pack........................	14.00	

OFFICIAL STAMPS

In 1840 the 1d. black (Type **1**), with "V R" in the upper corners, was prepared for official use, but never issued for postal purposes. Obliterated specimens are those which were used for experimental trials of obliterating inks, or those that passed through the post by oversight.

V **1**

1840. *Prepared for use but not issued; "V" "R" in upper corners. Imperf.*

			Un	Used	Used on cover
V1	V **1**	1d. black	£5500	£4000	£12000

The Official stamps would be more correctly termed Departmental stamps as they were exclusively for the use of certain government departments. Unitl 1882 official mail used ordinary postage stamps purchased at post offices, the cash being refunded once a quarter. Later the government departments obtained Official stamps by requisition.

Official stamps were on sale to the public for a short time at Somerset House but they were not sold from post offices. The system of only supplying the Government departments with stamps was open to abuse so that all official stamps were withdrawn on 14 May 1904.

OVERPRINTS, PERFORATIONS, WATERMARKS. All Official stamps were overprinted by Thomas De La Rue & Co. and are perf 14. They are on Crown watermarked paper unless otherwise stated.

INLAND REVENUE

These stamps were used by revenue officials in the provinces, mail to and from Head Office passing without a stamp. The London Office used these stamps only for foreign mail.

I.R.   I. R.

OFFICIAL OFFICIAL
(O **1**)   (O **2**)

*Optd with Types O **1** (½d. to 1s.) or O **2** (others)*

1882–1901. *Stamps of Queen Victoria. (a) Issues of 1880–81.*

			Un	★ Used	Used on cover
O1		½d. green (1.11.82)	10.00	3.00	20.00
O3		1d. lilac (Die II) (1.10.82)	1.00	65	15.00
	a.	Optd in blue-black	£100	18.00	
	b.	"OFFICIAL" omitted	—	£2250	
	Wi.	Watermark inverted			
O4		6d. grey (3.11.82)	75.00	20.00	

No. O3 with the lines of the overprint transposed is an essay.

(b) Issues of 1884–88

O5	½d. slate-blue (8.5.85)	25.00	8.00
O6	2½d. lilac (12.3.85)	95.00	35.00
O7	1s. green (12.3.85)	£2500	£450
O8	5s. rose (*blued paper*) (12.3.85)	£2750	£475
O9	5s. rose (3.90)	£1300	£400
	a. Raised stop after "R"	£1600	£325
	b. Optd in blue-black	£2000	£450
O9c	10s. cobalt (12.3.85)	£5000	£700
O10	10s. ultramarine (3.90)	£2250	£475
	a. Raised stop after "R"	£3000	£500
	b. Optd in blue-black	£3500	£700
O10c	10s. ultramarine (*blued paper*) (12.3.85)	£5000	£1400
O11	£1 brown-lilac (watermark Crowns) (12.3.85)	£18000	
	a. Frame broken	£20000	
O12	£1 brown-lilac (watermark Orbs) (3.90)	£22000	
	a. Frame broken	£25000	

(c) Issues of 1887–92

O13	½d. vermilion (5.88)	1.10	40	12.00
	a. Without "I.R."	£1500		
	b. Imperf	£850		
	c. Opt double (imperf)	£1000		
O14	2½d. purple/*blue* (2.92)	50.00	5.00	
O15	1s. green (9.89)	£200	20.00	
O16	£1 green (6.92)	£3500	£450	
	a. No stop after "R"	—	£700	
	b. Frame broken	£5500	£900	

Nos. O3, O13, O15 and O16 may be found with two varieties of overprint, namely, 1887 printings, *thin* letters, and 1894 printings, *thicker* letters.

(d) Issues of 1887 and 1900

O17	½d. blue-green (4.01)	3.00	85	15.00
O18	6d. purple/*rose-red* (1.7.01)	£100	20.00	
O19	1s. green and carmine (12.01)	£600	£100	
★O1/19	**For well-centred, lightly used**		+**35%**	

1902–4. *Stamps of King Edward VII.*

O20	½d. blue-green, O (4.2.02)	15.00	2.00	80.00
O21	1d. scarlet, O (4.2.02)	10.00	70	40.00
O22	2½d. ultramarine, O (19.2.02)	£400	70.00	
O23	6d. dull purple, O (14.3.04)	£50000	£30000	
O24	1s. green & carmine, O (29.4.02)	£400	65.00	
O25	5s. carmine, O (29.4.02)	£4000	£1300	
	a. Raised stop after "R"	£4500	£1500	
O26	10s. ultramarine, O (29.4.02)	£15000	£9500	
	a. Raised stop after "R"	£17000	£11000	
O27	£1 dull blue-green, O (29.4.02)	£12000	£6000	

OFFICE OF WORKS

These were for use on official correspondence from the London Head Office and from departments in Birmingham, Bristol, Edinburgh, Glasgow, Leeds, Liverpool, Manchester and Southampton. They were also issued to the Clerks of Works at various embassies abroad.

O. W.

OFFICIAL
(O **3**)

Optd with Type O 3

1896 (24 Mar)–**02.** *Stamps of Queen Victoria*

			Un	Used	★ Used on cover
O31	½d. vermilion		90.00	40.00	£180
O32	½d. blue-green (5.11.01)		£150	75.00	
O33	1d. lilac (Die II)		£150	40.00	£200
O34	5d. dull purple & blue (II) (29.4.02)		£750	£150	
O35	10d. dull purple & carmine (28.5.02)		£950	£225	

1902 (11 Feb)–**03.** *Stamps of King Edward VII.*

			Un	Used
O36	½d. blue-green, **O**		£350	80.00
O37	1d. scarlet, **O**		£350	80.00
O38	2d. green & carmine, **O** (29.3.02)		£600	75.00
O39	2½d. ultramarine, **O** (20.3.02)		£700	£100
O40	10d. purple & carmine, **O** (18.5.03)		£3500	£1500
★O31/40	**For well-centred, lightly used**			+25%

ARMY

Letters to and from the War Office in London passed without postage. The overprinted stamps were distributed to District and Station Paymasters for local correspondence.

ARMY **ARMY** **ARMY**

OFFICIAL **OFFICIAL** **OFFICIAL**

(O **4**) (O **5**) (O **6**)

Optd with Type O 4 (½d., 1d.) or O 5 (2½d., 6d.)

1896 (1 Sept)–**01.** *Stamps of Queen Victoria.*

			Un	Used	
O41	½d. vermilion		1.10	50	20.00
	a. "OFFICIAL"		35.00	16.00	
	b. Lines of opt transposed		£1000		
	Wi. Watermark inverted		£170	60.00	
O42	½d. blue-green (4.00)		1.75	3.00	
	Wi. Watermark inverted		£130	40.00	
O43	1d. lilac (Die II)		1.00	50	30.00
	a. "OFFICIAL"		35.00	16.00	
O44	2½d. purple/*blue*		4.00	2.00	
O45	6d. purple/*rose-red* (8.01)		13.00	8.00	

1902. *Stamps of King Edward VII optd with Type O 4.*

			Un	Used	
O48	½d. blue-green, **O** (11.2.02)		1.75	65	50.00
O49	1d. scarlet, **O** (11.2.02)		1.25	55	50.00
	a. "ARMY" omitted				
O50	6d. dull purple, **O** (23.8.02)		60.00	30.00	

1903 (Sept). *Optd with Type O 6.*

			Un	Used
O52	6d. dull purple, **O**		£850	£275

GOVERNMENT PARCELS

These stamps were issued to all departments, including the Head Office, for use on parcels weighing over 3 lb. Below this weight government parcels were sent by letter post to avoid the 55% of the postage paid from accruing to the railway companies, as laid down by parcel-post regulations. Most government parcels stamps suffered heavy postmarks in use.

GOVT PARCELS

(O **7**)

Optd as Type O 7

1883 (1 July)–**86.** *Stamps of Queen Victoria*

			Un	★ Used
O61	1½d. lilac (30.4.86)		£100	25.00
	a. No dot under "T"		£130	28.00
	b. Dot to left of "T"		£100	28.00
O62	6d. dull green (30.4.86)		£500	£200
O63	9d. dull green (1.8.83)		£625	£175
O64	1s. brown (watermark Crown, Pl 13)		£425	70.00
	a. No dot under "T"		£475	80.00
	b. Dot to left of "T"		£475	80.00
O64c	1s. brown (Pl 14)		£725	£110
	ca. No dot under "T"		£825	£100
	cb. Dot to left of "T"			

1887–90. *Stamps of Queen Victoria*

			Un	Used
O65	1½d. dull purple & pale green (29.10.87) ..		12.00	2.00
	a. No dot under "T"		18.00	2.75
	b. Dot to right of "T"		16.00	1.75
	c. Dot to left of "T"		16.00	1.75
O66	6d. purple/*rose-red* (19.12.87)		25.00	10.00
	a. No dot under "T"		30.00	12.00
	b. Dot to right of "T"		30.00	12.00
	c. Dot to left of "T"		30.00	11.00
O67	9d. dull purple & blue (21.8.88)		55.00	15.00
O68	1s. dull green (25.3.90)		£120	70.00
	a. No dot under "T"		£140	75.00
	b. Dot to right of "T"		£140	75.00
	c. Dot to left of "T"		£160	80.00
	d. Optd in blue-black			

1891–1900. *Stamps of Queen Victoria*

			Un	Used
O69	1d. lilac (Die II) (6.97)		5.00	1.00
	a. No dot under "T"		15.00	8.00
	b. Dot to left of "T"		15.00	8.00
	c. Opt inverted		£800	£450
	d. Ditto. Dot to left of "T"		£900	£500
	Wi. Watermark inverted		—	40.00
O70	2d. grey-green & carmine (24.10.91) ...		45.00	3.75
	a. No dot under "T"		50.00	4.25
	b. Dot to left of "T"		50.00	5.00
O71	4½d. green & carmine (9.92)		£100	75.00
	b. Dot to right of "T"			
	Wi. Watermark inverted			
O72	1s. green & carmine (11.00)		£160	50.00
	a. Opt inverted		—	£3750
★O61/72	**For well-centred lightly used**			+**100%**

1902. *Stamps of King Edward VII.*

			Un	Used
O74	1d. scarlet, **O** (30.10.02)		15.00	5.00
O75	2d. green & carmine, **O** (29.4.02)		65.00	15.00
O76	6d. dull purple, **O** (19.2.02)		£100	15.00
O77	9d. purple & ultramarine (28.8.02)		£225	50.00
O78	1s. green & carmine, **O** (17.12.02)		£350	85.00

BOARD OF EDUCATION

BOARD OF EDUCATION

(O **8**)

Optd with Type O 8

1902 (19 Feb). *Stamps of Queen Victoria.*

			Un	Used
O81	5d. dull purple & blue (II)		£500	£100
O82	1s. green & carmine		£950	£375

1902–4. *Stamps of King Edward VII.*

O83	½d. blue-green, **O** (19.2.02)	16.00	5.00
O84	1d. scarlet, **O** (19.2.02)	16.00	5.00
O85	2½d. ultramarine, **O** (19.2.02)	£500	50.00
O86	5d. purple & blue, **O** (6.2.04)	£2000	£950
O87	1s. green & carmine, **O** (23.2.02)	£25000	£15000

ROYAL HOUSEHOLD

R.H.

OFFICIAL

(O **9**)

1902. *Stamps of King Edward VII optd with Type O* **9**.

		Un	Used	Used on cover
O91	½d. blue-green, **O** (29.4.02)	£150	95.00	£400
O92	1d. scarlet, **O** (19.2.02)	£130	85.00	£300

ADMIRALTY

ADMIRALTY   ADMIRALTY

OFFICIAL   OFFICIAL

(O **10**)   (O **11**)

1903 (3 Mar). *Stamps of King Edward VII optd with Type O* **10**.

O101	½d. blue-green, **O**	9.00	3.00	£225
O102	1d. scarlet, **O**	5.00	2.50	50.00
O103	1½d. purple & green, **O**	60.00	40.00	
O104	2d. green & carmine, **O**	80.00	50.00	
O105	2½d. ultramarine, **O**	£100	38.00	
O106	3d. purple/yellow, **O**	£100	35.00	

1903–4. *Stamps of King Edward VII optd with Type O* **11**.

O107	½d. blue-green, **O** (9.03)	7.00	4.00	£250
O108	1d. scarlet, **O** (11.03)	6.50	3.50	50.00
O109	1½d. purple & green, **O** (2.04)	£175	50.00	
O110	2d. green & carmine, **O** (3.04)	£400	£100	
O111	2½d. ultramarine, **O** (3.04)	£450	£225	
O112	3d. purple/yellow, **O** (2.04)	£350	85.00	

Stamps of various issues perforated with a Crown and initials ("H.M.O.W.", "O.W.", "B.T." or "S.O.") or with initials only ("H.M.S.O." or "D.S.I.R.") have also been used for official purposes, but these are outside the scope of the catalogue.

STAMP MONTHLY

Finest and most informative magazine for all collectors. Obtainable from your newsagent or by postal subscription – details on request

POSTAL FISCAL STAMPS

PRICES. Prices in the used column are for stamps with genuine postal cancellations dated from the time when they were authorised for use as postage stamps. Beware of stamps with fiscal cancellations removed and fraudulent postmarks applied.

VALIDITY. The 1d. Surface-printed stamps were authorised for postal use from 1 June 1881 and the 3d. and 6d. values, together with the Embossed issues, from 1 January 1883.

SURFACE-PRINTED ISSUES

(Typo Thomas De La Rue & Co.)

F 1
Rectangular Buckle

F 2

F 3
Octagonal Buckle

F 4

F 5
Double-lined Anchor

F 6
Single-lined Anchor

1853–57. P 15½ × 15. (a) Wmk F **5** (inverted) (1853–55).

			Un	Used	Used on cover
F1	F **1**	1d. lt blue (10.10.53)	8.50	11.00	£100
F2	F **2**	1d. ochre (10.53)	45.00	30.00	£130
		a. Tête-bêche (in block of four)	£8000		
F3	F **3**	1d. pale turquoise-blue (1854)	10.00	10.00	£100
		Wi. Watermark upright	30.00	22.00	
F4		1d. lt blue/blue (1854)	28.00	19.00	£120
		Wi. Watermark upright	50.00	50.00	

F5	F **4**	1d. reddish lilac/blue glazed paper (25.3.55)....................	45.00	11.00	£100
		Wi. Watermark upright	85.00	25.00	

Only one example is known of No. F2a outside the National Postal Museum and the Royal Collection.

(b) Wmk F **6** (1856–57)

F6	F **4**	1d. reddish lilac (shades)	5.50	4.00	80.00
F7		1d. reddish lilac/bluish (shades) (1857)	5.50	4.00	80.00

(F 7)

1860 (3 Apr). No. F7 optd with Type F **7**, in red.

F8	F **4**	1d. dull reddish lilac/blue	£325	£275	£450

BLUE PAPER. In the following issues we no longer distinguish between bluish and white paper. There is a range of papers from white or greyish to bluish.

F 8

F 9

F 10

1860–67. Bluish to white paper. P 15½ × 15. (a) Wmk F **6** (1860).

F9	F **8**	1d. reddish lilac (May)	4.75	4.75	65.00
F10	F **9**	3d. reddish lilac (June)	£190	60.00	£120
F11	F **10**	6d. reddish lilac (Oct)	70.00	50.00	£150
		Wi. Watermark inverted............	£120	70.00	
		Wj. Watermark reversed	£110	70.00	

(b) W **40**. (Anchor 16mm high) (1864)

F12	F **8**	1d. pale reddish lilac (Nov)	4.75	4.75	65.00
F13	F **9**	3d. pale reddish lilac................	60.00	45.00	
F14	F **10**	6d. pale reddish lilac...............	70.00	45.00	£150
		Wi. Watermark inverted............	£150		

(c) W **40** (Anchor 18mm high) (1867)

F15	F **8**	1d. reddish lilac	13.00	6.00	£130
F16	F **9**	3d. reddish lilac	38.00	38.00	£110
F17	F **10**	6d. reddish lilac	70.00	35.00	£150

For stamps perf 14, see Nos. F24/7.

F 11   F 12

Four Dies of Type F 12

Die 1.   Corner ornaments small and either joined or broken; heavy
shading under chin

Die 2.   Ornaments small and always broken; clear line of shading
under chin

Die 3.   Ornaments larger and joined; line of shading under chin
extended half way down neck

Die 4.   Ornaments much larger; straight line of shading continued to
bottom of neck

1867–81.   *White to bluish paper. P 14. (a) W 47 (Small Anchor).*

F18	F **11**	1d. purple (1.9.67)	6.00	4.00	50.00
		Wi. Watermark inverted.............			
F19	F **12**	1d. purple (Die I) (6.68)	1.75	1.50	40.00
		Wi. Watermark inverted.............	50.00		
F20		1d. purple (Die 2) (6.76).............	2.50	2.75	40.00
F21		1d. purple (Die 3) (3.77).............	2.50	2.50	40.00
F22		1d. purple (Die 4) (7.78).............	2.25	1.75	40.00

*(b) W **48** (Orb)*

F23	F **12**	1d. purple (Die 4) (1.81).............	2.00	1.50	40.00
		Wi. Watermark inverted.............	50.00		

1881.   *White to bluish paper. P 14.*

*(a) W **40** (Anchor 18mm high) (Jan)*

F24	F **9**	3d. reddish lilac	£325	£200	£325
F25	F **10**	6d. reddish lilac	£170	50.00	£150

*(b) W **40** (Anchor 20 mm high) (May)*

F26	F **9**	3d. reddish lilac	£190	42.00	£110
F27	F **10**	6d. reddish lilac	90.00	60.00	£170

ISSUES EMBOSSED IN COLOUR

(Made at Somerset House)

The embossed stamps were struck from dies not appropriated to any
special purpose on paper which had the words "INLAND REVENUE"
previously printed, and thus became available for payment of any
duties for which no special stamps had been provided.

The die letters are included in the embossed designs and holes were
drilled for the insertion of plugs showing figures indicating dates of
striking.

F 13   F 14

INLAND   INLAND
REVENUE   REVENUE
(F **15**)   (F **16**)

1860 (3 Apr)–**71.**   *Types F **13/14** and similar types embossed on bluish
paper. Underprint Type F **15**. No wmk. Imperf.*

		Un	*Used*
F28	2d. pink (Die A) (1.1.71)	90.00	90.00
F29	3d. pink (Die C)................................	60.00	55.00
	a. *Tête-bêche* (vert pair).....................	£900	
F30	3d. pink (Die D)................................	£250	
F31	6d. pink (Die T)	£650	
F32	6d. pink (Die U)................................	70.00	55.00
	a. *Tête-bêche* (vert pair)	£1000	

F33	9d. pink (Die C) (1.1.71)	£225		
F34	1s. pink (Die E) (28.6.61)	£325	£130	
F35	1s. pink (Die F) (28.6.61)	85.00	65.00	
	a. Tête-bêche (vert pair)	£400		
F36	2s. pink (Die K) (6.8.61)	£250	£150	
F37	2s. 6d. pink (Die N) (28.6.61)	£500		
F38	2s. 6d. pink (Die O) (28.6.61)	60.00	50.00	

1861–71. *As last but perf* 12½.
F39	2d. pink (Die A) (8.71)	£225	£110
F40	3d. pink (Die C)		
F41	3d. pink (Die D)		
F42	9d. pink (Die C) (8.71)	£250	£120
F43	1s. pink (Die E) (8.71)	£190	£110
F44	1s. pink (Die F) (8.71)	£170	85.00
F45	2s. 6d. pink (Die O) (8.71)	£100	50.00

1874 (Nov). *Types as before embossed on white paper. Underprint Type F* **16**, *in green. W* **47** (*Small Anchor*). *P* 12½.
F46	2d. pink (Die A)	—	£150
F47	9d. pink (Die C)		
F48	1s. pink (Die F)	£170	90.00
F49	2s. 6d. pink (Die O)	—	£130

1875 (Nov)–**80.** *As last but colour changed and on white or bluish paper.*
F50	2d. vermilion (Die A) (1880)	£250	85.00
F51	9d. vermilion (Die C) (1876)	£250	£120
F52	1s. vermilion (Die E)	£150	55.00
F53	1s. vermilion (Die F)	£150	55.00
F54	2s. 6d. vermilion (Die O) (1878)	£190	85.00

1882 (Oct). *As last but W* **48** (*Orbs*).
F55	2d. vermilion (Die A)		
F56	9d. vermilion (Die C)		
F57	1s. vermilion (Die E)		
F58	2s. 6d. vermilion (Die O)	£400	£190

The sale of Inland Revenue stamps up to the 2s. value ceased from 30 December 1882 and stocks were called in and destroyed. The 2s. 6d. value remained on sale until 2 July 1883 when it was replaced by the 2s. 6d. "Postage & Revenue" stamp. Inland Revenue stamps still in the hands of the public continued to be accepted for revenue and postal purposes.

POSTMASTER AND U.P.U. SPECIMEN OVERPRINTS

At various times since 1847 the British Post Office, or its printers, has applied "SPECIMEN" or "CANCELLED" overprints to certain stamp issues.

Many of these overprints were purely intended for internal record purposes, but some had a wider use connected to the postal service. Between 1847 and 1873 the G.P.O. circulated examples of new stamps overprinted "SPECIMEN" to its postmasters and from 1879 similar overprints were applied to samples forwarded to the Universal Postal Union for distribution to member administrations. After 1892 such U.P.U. overprints were restricted to stamps with a face value of 1 shilling or above and they were discontinued altogether after March 1948.

In the listings below Types P **1** to P **6** are postmaster specimens and the remainder for the U.P.U.

For a complete listing of all other "SPECIMEN" overprints see the *Great Britain Specialised Catalogue*.

SPECIMEN

SPECIMEN   SPECIMEN

P 1   P 3   P 4

SPECIMEN   **SPECIMEN**   SPECIMEN

P 5   P 6   P 9

SPECIMEN   SPECIMEN   SPECIMEN

P 16   P 23   P 26

SPECIMEN

P 32

1847–54. *Embossed issues.*
No.	Type No.		Specimen	Unused Price
SP1	P 1	1s. pale green (No. 54) (red opt)		£325
		a. Black opt		£450
SP2		10d. brown (No. 57)		£275
SP3		6d. mauve (No. 58)		£550

1855–57. *Surface-printed issues. No corner letters.*

			Unused
	Specimen		Price
No.	Type No.		
SP4	P **3**	4d. carmine/*blued* (No. 62)	£160
SP5	P **4**	4d. rose/*white* (No. 65)	
SP6		6d. dp lilac/*white* (No. 69)	£100
		a. On azure paper	£140
SP7		1s. dp green (No. 71)	£100

1858–70. *Line-engraved issues.*

SP8	P **9**	½d. rose-red (pl 10) (No. 48)	90.00
SP9		1d. rose-red (pl 146) (No. 43)	£100
SP10		1½d. rose-red (pl 3) (No. 51)	£110
SP11		2d. blue (pl 15) (No. 46)	£110

1862–64. *Surface-printed issue. Small uncoloured corner letters.*

SP12	P **5**	3d. dp carmine-rose (No. 75)	80.00
SP13		4d. brt red (No. 79)	60.00
SP14	P **6**	9d. bistre (No. 86)	£100

1867–80. *Large uncoloured corner letters. Wmk Spray of Rose.*

SP15	P **5**	10d. red-brown (No. 112)	80.00
SP16		2s. dull blue (pl 1) (No. 118)	70.00
SP17	P **9**	2s. dull blue (pl 1) (No. 118)	70.00
SP18		2s. brown (No. 121)	£500

1867–83. *Wmk Maltese Cross or Anchor (£5).*

SP19	P **6**	5s. rose (pl 1) (No. 126)	£225
SP20	P **9**	5s. pale rose (pl 2) (No. 127)	£450
SP21		10s. greenish grey (No. 128)	£550
SP22		£1 brown-lilac (No. 129)	£900
SP23		£5 orange/*blued* (No. 133)	£700

1872–73. *Uncoloured letters in corner. Wmk Spray of Rose.*

SP24	P **6**	6d. chestnut (pl 11) (No. 123)	60.00
SP25		6d. grey (pl 12) (No. 125)	70.00

1873–80. *Large coloured corner letters.*

SP26	P **9**	2½d. rosy-mauve (pl 6) (No. 141)	50.00
SP27		2½d. blue (pl 17) (No. 142)	45.00
SP28		3d. rose (pl 18) (No. 143)	60.00
SP29		4d. sage-green (pl 15) (No. 153)	70.00
SP30		4d. grey-brown (pl 17) (No. 154)	50.00
SP31		6d. grey (pl 16) (No. 147)	60.00
SP32		8d. orange (pl 1) (No. 156)	60.00
SP33		1s. green (pl 12) (No. 150)	60.00
SP34		1s. orange-brown (pl 13) (No. 151)	60.00

1880–83. *Wmk Imperial Crown.*

SP35	P **9**	3d. on 3d. lilac (No. 159)	90.00
SP36		6d. on 6d. lilac (No. 162)	90.00

1880–81. *Wmk Imperial Crown.*

SP37	P **9**	½d. dp green (No. 164)	18.00
SP38		1d. Venetian red (No. 166)	18.00
SP39		1½d. Venetian red (No. 167)	18.00
SP40		2d. pale rose (No. 168)	25.00
SP41		5d. indigo (No. 169)	25.00

1881. *Wmk Imperial Crown.*

SP42	P **9**	1d. lilac (14 dots) (No. 170)	25.00
SP43		1d. lilac (16 dots) (No. 172)	18.00

1883–84. *Wmk Anchor or Three Imperial Crowns (£1).*

SP44	P **9**	2s.6d. lilac/*blued* (No. 175)	£150
SP45		5s. crimson (No. 181)	£150
SP46		10s. ultramarine (No. 183)	£160
SP47		£1 brown-lilac (No. 185)	£325

1883–84. *Wmk Imperial Crown.*

SP48	P **9**	½d. slate-blue (No. 187)	18.00
SP49		1½d. lilac (No. 188)	45.00
SP50		2d. lilac (No. 189)	45.00

			Unused
No.	Specimen Type No.		Price
SP51	P **9**	2½d. lilac (No. 190)	45.00
SP52		3d. lilac (No. 191)	45.00
SP53		4d. dull green (No. 192)	70.00
SP54		5d. dull green (No. 193)	70.00
SP55		6d. dull green (No. 194)	£130
SP56		9d. dull green (No. 195)	70.00
SP57		1s. dull green (No. 196)	70.00

1887–91. *"Jubilee" issue.*

SP58	P **9**	½d. vermilion (No. 197)	20.00
SP59		1½d. dull purple & pale green (No. 198)	35.00
SP60		2d. green & scarlet (No. 199)	35.00
SP61		2½d. purple/*blue* (No. 201)	30.00
SP62		3d. purple/*yellow* (No. 202)	30.00
SP63		4d. green & purple-brown (No. 205)	30.00
SP64		5d. dull purple & blue (Die I) (No. 207)	40.00
SP65		6d. purple/*rose-red* (No. 208)	20.00
SP66		9d. dull purple & blue (No. 209)	30.00
SP67		10d. dull purple & carmine (No. 210)	55.00
SP68		1s. dull green (No. 211)	30.00

1902–10. *King Edward VII. De La Rue printings.*

SP69	P **16**	2s.6d. lilac (No. 260)	£120
SP70		5s. brt carmine (No. 263)	£130
SP71		10s. ultramarine (No. 265)	£200
SP72		£1 dull blue-green (No. 266)	£300

1913. *King George V. Wmk Royal Cypher.*

SP73	P **26**	1s. bistre-brown (No. 395)	90.00

1913. *"Seahorse" high values. Printed by Waterlow.*

SP74	P **26**	2s.6d. dp sepia-brown (No. 399)	£200
SP75		5s. rose-carmine (No. 401)	£175
SP76		10s. indigo-blue (No. 402)	£400
SP77		£1 green (No. 403)	£1000

1929. *Ninth U.P.U. Congress.*

SP78	P **32**	£1 black (No. 438) (opt in red)	£950

1936. *Photogravure.*

SP79	P **32**	1s. bistre-brown (No. 449)	40.00

1939. *King George VI.*

SP80	P **23**	1s. bistre-brown (No. 475)	28.00
SP81		2s.6d. brown (No. 476)	£200
SP82		2s.6d. yellow-green (No. 476a)	£200
SP83		5s. red (No. 477)	£200
SP84		10s. dark blue (No. 478)	£350
SP85		10s. ultramarine (No. 478a)	£300

POSTAGE DUE STAMPS

1915. *Wmk Simple Cypher.*

SP86	P **23**	1s. brt blue (No. D8)	15.00

1924. *Wmk Block Cypher.*

SP87	P **23**	2s.6d. purple/*yellow* (No. D18)	

OFFICIAL STAMPS

1887–91. *Optd "GOVT PARCELS".*

SP88	P **9**	1½d. dull purple & pale green (No. O65)	65.00
SP89		2d. grey-green & carmine (No. O70)	50.00
SP90		6d. purple/*rose-red* (No. O66)	65.00
SP91		9d. dull purple & blue (No. O67)	50.00
SP92		1s. dull green (No. O68)	65.00

POST OFFICE STAMP BOOKLETS

The following listing covers all booklets sold by post offices from 1904 until February 1988.

All major variations of contents and cover are included, but minor changes to the covers and differences on the interleaves have been ignored.

From 1913 each booklet carried an edition number, linked to an internal Post Office system of identification which divided the various booklets into series. In 1943 these edition numbers were replaced by edition dates. No attempt has been made to list separately edition numbers for booklets issued prior to 1943, although notes giving their extent are provided for each booklet. Edition dates from August 1943 are listed separately and exist for all £.s.d. and most Decimal Stitched booklets (except for the 1s. booklets, the 2s. booklets (N1/3), the 5s. "Philympia" booklet (No. HP34), the £1 "Stamps for Cooks" booklet (No. ZP1) and the Decimal Sponsored booklets). They are those found printed upon the booklets, either on the outer back cover or on the white leaves.

ERRORS OF MAKE-UP of booklets exist but we do not list them here. More detailed listings can be found in the 2nd, 3rd and 4th volumes of the *Great Britain Specialised Catalogue*.

ILLUSTRATIONS. The illustrations of the covers are ¾ size except where otherwise stated.

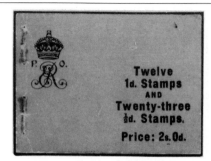

Type BA2

> **PRICES** quoted are for complete booklets containing stamps with "average" perforations (ie. full perforations on two edges of the pane only). Booklets containing panes with complete perforations are worth more.

1906 (June).   *Red cover printed in black as Type BA2. As before but make-up changed to include 12 × 1d. and 23 × ½d. and label showing one green cross (Nos. 217 and 219).*
BA2 .... £300

1907 (Aug).   *Red cover printed in black as Type BA2. Make-up changed to include 18 × 1d. and 11 × ½d. and label showing one green cross (Nos. 217 and 219).*
BA3 .... £275

1911.   *Red cover printed in black as Type BA2 but showing a larger Post Office cypher on cover. As before, but containing stamps by Harrison & Sons (Nos. 267 and 272).*
BA6 .... £350

KING EDWARD VII

2s. Booklets

Type BA1

1904 (Mar).   *Red cover printed in black as Type BA1. Pages of six stamps: 24 × 1d. Wmk Imperial Crown (No. 219)*
BA1 .... £130

KING GEORGE V

2s. Booklets

1911 (Aug).   *Red cover printed in black as Type BA2 showing King George V cypher. Pages of six stamps: 18 × 1d. and 12 × ½d. Wmk Crown (Nos. 325, 329) Die 1B.*
BB1 .... £200

Type BB2

1912 (April).   *As before, but red cover printed in black as Type BB2.*
BB2 .... £225

1912 (Sept).   *As before, but Wmk Simple Cypher (Nos. 334, 336) Die 1B.*
BB3 .... £300

HAVE YOU READ THE NOTES AT THE BEGINNING OF THIS CATALOGUE?

These often provide answers to the enquiries we receive.

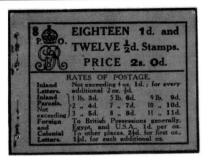

Type BB5

1913 (Jan). *As before, but red cover printed in black as Type BB5.*
BB5 No Edition number or 8 or 9 .... £300

1913 (April). *As before, but 1912–22 Wmk Simple Cypher (Nos. 351, 357).*
BB6 Edition numbers 10 to 45 .... 70.00

1916 (July). *As before, but orange cover printed in black as Type BB5.*
BB9 Edition numbers 46 to 64 .... 70.00

Type BB10

1917 (Sept). *As before, but orange cover printed in black as Type BB10.*
BB10 Edition numbers 65 to 81 .... £100

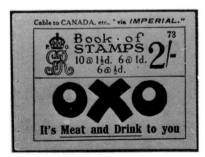

Type BB11

1924 (Feb). *Blue cover printed in black as Type BB11. Pages of six stamps: 10 × 1½d. (first completed by two perforated labels), 6 × 1d. and 6 × ½d. 1912–22 Wmk Simple Cypher (Nos. 351, 357, 362).*
BB11 Edition Nos. 1 or 2 .... £300

1933 (Oct). *As before, but 1924–26 Wmk Block Cypher (Nos. 418/20).*
BB12 Edition numbers 3 to 102 & 108 to 254 .... £100

Type BB13

1929 (May). *Postal Union Congress issue. Cover of special design as Type BB13 printed in blue on buff as before but containing stamps of the P.U.C. issue (Nos. 434/6).*
BB13 Edition numbers 103 to 107 .... £250

1934 (Feb). *Blue cover printed in black as Type BB11, but containing stamps with Block Cypher wmk printed by Harrison & Sons. (Nos. 418/20)*
BB14 Edition numbers 255 to 287 .... 75.00

1935 (Jan). *As before, but containing stamps of the photogravure issue with the se-tenant advertisements printed in brown (Nos. 439/41).*
BB15 Edition numbers 288 to 297 .... £160

Type BB16

1935 (May). *Silver Jubilee issue. Larger size cover printed in blue on buff as Type BB16 and containing pages of four stamps with no se-tenant advertisements: 12 × 1½d., 4 × 1d. and 4 × ½d. (Nos. 453/5).*
BB16 Edition numbers 298 to 304 .... 35.00

1935 (July). *As No. BB15, but containing stamps of the photogravure issue with se-tenant advertisements printed in black (Nos. 439/41).*
BB17 Edition numbers 305 to 353 .... 45.00

3s. Booklets

Type BB18

1918 (Oct). *Orange cover printed in black as Type BB18. Pages of six stamps:* 12 × 1½d., 12 × 1d. *and* 12 × ½d. *1912–22 Wmk Simple Cypher (Nos. 351, 357, 362).*
BB18   Edition numbers 1 to 11 .... £110

1919 (July). *As before, but make-up altered to contain* 18 × 1½d., 6 × 1d. *and* 6 × ½d.
BB19   Edition numbers 12 to 26 .... £110

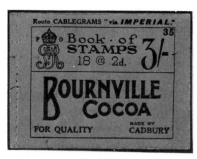

Type BB20

1921 (April). *Experimental booklet bound in blue covers as Type BB20, containing pages of six stamps:* 18 × 2d. (Die I) *(No. 368).*
BB20   Edition numbers 35 and part 37 .... £120

1921 (Dec). *As before, but containing* 2d. (Die II) *(No. 370).*
BB21   Edition numbers 12, 13 and part 37 .... £150

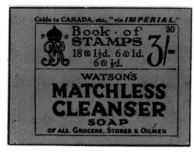

Type BB22

1922 (May). *Scarlet cover printed in black as Type BB22. Pages of six stamps:* 18 × 1½d., 6 × 1d. *and* 6 × ½d. *(Nos. 351, 357, 362).*
BB22   Edition numbers 19, 20, 22, 23 and 25 to 54 .... £130

1922 (June). *Experimental booklet as Edition numbers 12 and 13 bound in blue covers as Type BB22, containing pages of six stamps:* 24 × 1½d. *(No. 362).*
BB23   Edition numbers 21 or 24 .... £190

1924 (Feb). *Scarlet cover printed in black as Type BB22, but containing stamps with Block Cypher wmk, printed by Waterlow & Sons. (Nos. 418/20).*
BB24   Edition numbers 55 to 167 & 173 to 273 .... 45.00

1929 (May). *Postal Union Congress issue. Cover of special design as Type BB13 printed in red on buff as before but containing stamps of the P.U.C. issue (Nos. 434/6).*
BB25   Edition numbers 168 to 172 .... £200

1934 (March). *Scarlet cover printed in black as Type BB22, but containing stamps with the Block Cypher wmk printed by Harrison & Sons. (Nos. 418/20).*
BB26   Edition numbers 274 to 288 .... 65.00

1935 (May). *Silver Jubilee issue. Larger size cover printed in red on buff and containing pages of four stamps:* 20 × 1½d., 4 × 1d. *and* 4 × ½d. *(Nos. 453/5).*
BB28   Edition numbers 294 to 297 .... 35.00

1935 (July). *As No. BB26, but containing stamps of the photogravure issue. (Nos. 439/41).*
BB29   Edition numbers 289 to 293 & 298 to 319 .... 50.00

3s. 6d. Booklets

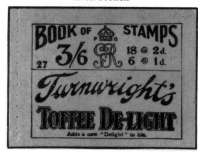

Type BB30

1920 (July). *Orange cover printed in black as Type BB30, containing pages of six stamps:* 18 × 2d. *and* 6 × 1d. *(Nos. 357, 368).*
BB30   Edition numbers 27 to 32 .... £150

Type BB31

1921 (April).   *Orange-red cover printed in black as Type BB31, as before but make-up changed to include stamps of 1912–22 issue with the Simple Cypher wmk: 12 × 2d., 6 × 1½d., 6 × 1d. and 6 × ½d. (Nos. 351, 357, 362, 368 or 370).*
BB31   Edition numbers 1 to 11, 14 to 18, 33, 34, 36 & 38 .... £130

5s. Booklets

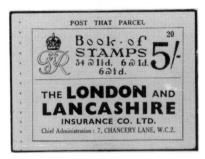

Type BB33

1931 (Aug).   *Green cover printed in black as Type BB33. Pages of six stamps: 34 × 1½d., 6 × 1d. and 6 × ½d. The first 1½d. pane completed by two se-tenant advertisements. Printed by Waterlow & Son on paper with Block Cypher wmk. (Nos. 418/20).*
BB33   Edition number 1 .... £325

1932 (June).   *As before, but buff cover printed in black.*
BB34   Edition numbers 2 to 6 .... £110

1934 (July).   *As before, but containing stamps with Block Cypher wmk printed by Harrison & Sons. (Nos. 418/20).*
BB35   Edition numbers 7 or 8 .... £130

1935 (Feb).   *As before, but containing stamps of the photogravure issue with se-tenant advertisements printed in brown. (Nos. 439/41).*
BB36   Edition number 9 .... £200

1935 (July).   *As before, but containing stamps of the photogravure issue with se-tenant advertisements printed in black. (Nos. 439/41).*
BB37   Edition numbers 10 to 15 .... 75.00

KING EDWARD VIII

6d. Booklet

1936.   *Buff unglazed cover without inscription containing 4 × 1½d. stamps, in panes of two (No. 459).*
BC1 .... 18.00

2s. Booklet

1936 (Oct).   *As No. BB17, except for the K.E.VIII cypher on the cover and containing Nos. 457/9.*
BC2   Edition numbers 354 to 385 .... 30.00

3s. Booklet

1936 (Nov).   *As No. BB29, except for the K.E.VIII cypher on the cover but without "P" and "O" on either side of the crown, and containing Nos. 457/9.*
BC3   Edition numbers 320 to 332 .... 32.00

5s. Booklet

1937 (Mar).   *As No. BB37, but with the K.E.VIII cypher on the cover and containing Nos. 457/9.*
BC4   Edition numbers 16 or 17 .... 85.00

KING GEORGE VI

6d. Booklets

1938 (Jan).   *As No. BC1, but containing stamps in the original dark colours. Buff cover without inscription (No. 464).*
BD1 .... 18.00

1938 (Feb).   *As before, but pink unprinted cover and make-up changed to contain 2 × 1½d., 2 × 1d. and 2 × ½d. in the original dark colours (Nos. 462/4).*
BD2 .... 55.00

1940 (June).   *Pale green unprinted cover and make-up changed to include two panes of stamps with wmk sideways. Stamps in original dark colours with binding margin either at the top or bottom of the pane: 4 × 1d., 4 × ½d. (Nos. 462a/3a).*
BD3 .... 55.00

1s. Booklets

1947 (Dec.).   *Cream cover, unglazed and without inscription containing panes of two stamps in pale shades, all with wmk normal. Panes of two stamps: 4 × ½d., 4 × 1d. and 4 × 1½d. (Nos. 485/7).*
BD4 .... 14.00

1951 (May).   *As before, but containing stamps in changed colours (Nos. 503/5).*
BD5 .... 14.00

1948.   *Cream cover as before, but make-up changed to contain 4 × ½d., 4 × 1d. and 4 × 1½d. in panes of four of the pale shades with wmk normal (Nos. 485/7).*
BD6 .... —

1951 (May).   *As before, but stamps in new colours all wmk normal, margin at either top or at the bottom. (Nos. 503/5).*
BD7 .... 12.00

Type BD8

1952 (Dec).   *Cream cover printed in black as Type BD8. Make-up as before but with wmk either upright or inverted and margins only at the top. (Nos. 503/5).*
BD8 .... 14.00

Type BD10

1954. *As before but cover showing GPO emblem with St. Edward's crown and oval frame as Type BD10 (Nos. 503/5).*
BD10 .... 12.00

2s. 6d. Booklets

Type BD13

1940 (June). *Scarlet cover printed in black as Type BD13, containing panes of six stamps in original dark colours: 6 × 2½d., 6 × 2d. and 6 × ½d. (Nos. 462, 465/6).*
BD13 Edition numbers 1 to 7 .... £200

1940 (Sept). *As before, but blue cover printed in black as Type BD13.*
BD14 Edition numbers 8 to 13 .... £200

2s. Booklets

1937 (Aug). *Blue cover printed in black as Type BB11, but with K.G.VI cypher on the cover and containing stamps in the original dark colours. Panes of six stamps: 10 × 1½d., 6 × 1d. and 6 × ½d. The first 1½d. pane completed by two se-tenant advertisements. (Nos. 462/4).*
BD11 Edition numbers 386 to 412 .... £110

Type BD12

1938 (April). *Blue cover printed in black as Type BD12 (Nos. 462/4).*
BD12 Edition numbers 413 to 508 .... £110

Type BD15

1940 (Oct). *As before, but with green cover printed in black as Type BD15 (Nos. 462, 465/6).*
BD15 Edition numbers 14 to 94 .... £140

1942 (Mar). *As before, but containing stamps in pale shades (Nos. 485, 488/9).*
BD16 Edition numbers 95 to 214 .... £140

Type A
Circular GPO Cypher

1943 (Aug). *As before, but green cover printed in black as Type A* (*Nos. 485, 488/9*).
BD18   Edition dates August 1943 to February 1951 .... 14.00

1951 (May). *As before, but containing stamps in the new colours* (*Nos. 503, 506/7*).
BD19   Edition dates May 1951 to February 1952 .... 16.00

(1) MAY 1951 .... 16.00		(6) OCT 1951 .... 16.00
(2) JUNE 1951 .... 16.00		(7) NOV 1951 .... 16.00
(3) JULY 1951 .... 16.00		(8) DEC 1951 .... 16.00
(4) AUG 1951 .... 16.00		(9) JAN 1952 .... 16.00
(5) SEPT 1951 .... 16.00		(10) FEB 1952 .... 16.00

1952 (March). *As before, but make-up changed to contain:* $6 \times 2\frac{1}{2}d.$, $6 \times 1\frac{1}{2}d.$, $3 \times 1d.$ *and* $6 \times \frac{1}{2}d.$ *The* $1d.$ *pane was completed by three perforated labels in the lower row inscribed "MINIMUM INLAND PRINTED PAPER RATE* $1\frac{1}{2}d.$" (*Nos. 503/5, 507*).
BD20   Edition dates March 1952 to May 1953 ....16.00

(1) MAR 1952 .... 16.00		(9) NOV 1952 .... 16.00
(2) APR 1952 .... 16.00		(10) DEC 1952 .... 16.00
(3) MAY 1952 .... 16.00		(11) JAN 1953 .... 16.00
(4) JUNE 1952 .... 16.00		(12) FEB 1953 .... 16.00
(5) JULY 1952 .... 16.00		(13) MAR 1953 .... 16.00
(6) AUG 1952 .... 16.00		(14) APR 1953 .... 16.00
(7) SEPT 1952 .... 16.00		(15) MAY 1953 .... 16.00
(8) OCT 1952 .... 16.00			

3s. Booklets

1937 (Aug). *Scarlet cover Type BB22 printed in black as No. BC3, except for K.G.VI cypher on the cover and containing stamps in the original dark colours* (*Nos. 462/4*).
BD21   Edition numbers 333 to 343 .... £160

1938 (April). *As before, but scarlet cover printed in black as Type BD12* (*Nos. 462/4*).
BD22   Edition numbers 344 to 377 .... £160

5s. Booklets

1937 (Aug). *Buff cover printed in black as Type BB33, containing stamps of the new reign in the original dark colours. Pages of six stamps:* $34 \times 1\frac{1}{2}d.$, $6 \times 1d.$ *and* $6 \times \frac{1}{2}d.$ *The first* $1\frac{1}{2}d.$ *pane completed by two se-tenant advertisements.* (*Nos. 462/4*).
BD23   Edition numbers 18 to 20 .... £160

Type BD24

1938 (May). *As before, but with redesigned front cover showing GPO emblem as Type BD24 instead of royal cypher.*
BD24   Edition numbers 21 to 29 .... £160

(1) AUG 1943 .... 14.00	(46) MAY 1947 .... 14.00
(2) SEPT 1943 .... 14.00	(47) JUNE 1947 .... 14.00
(3) OCT 1943 .... 14.00	(48) JULY 1947 .... 14.00
(4) NOV 1943 .... 14.00	(49) AUG 1947 .... 14.00
(5) DEC 1943 .... 14.00	(50) SEPT 1947 .... 14.00
(6) JAN 1944 .... 14.00	(51) OCT 1947 .... 14.00
(7) FEB 1944 .... 14.00	(52) NOV 1947 .... 14.00
(8) MAR 1944 .... 14.00	(53) DEC 1947 .... 14.00
(9) APR 1944 .... 14.00	(54) JAN 1948 .... 14.00
(10) MAY 1944 .... 14.00	(55) FEB 1948 .... 14.00
(11) JUNE 1944 .... 14.00	(56) MAR 1948 .... 14.00
(12) JULY 1944 .... 14.00	(57) APR 1948 .... 14.00
(13) AUG 1944 .... 14.00	(58) MAY 1948 .... 14.00
(14) SEPT 1944 .... 14.00	(59) JUNE 1948 .... 14.00
(15) OCT 1944 .... 14.00	(60) JULY 1948 .... 14.00
(16) NOV 1944 .... 14.00	(61) AUG 1948 .... 14.00
(17) DEC 1944 .... 14.00	(62) SEPT 1948 .... 14.00
(18) JAN 1945 .... 14.00	(63) OCT 1948 .... 14.00
(19) FEB 1945 .... 14.00	(64) NOV 1948 .... 14.00
(20) MAR 1945 .... 14.00	(65) DEC 1948 .... 14.00
(21) APR 1945 .... 14.00	(66) JAN 1949 .... 14.00
(22) MAY 1945 .... 14.00	(67) FEB 1949 .... 14.00
(23) JUNE 1945 .... 14.00	(68) MAR 1949 .... 14.00
(24) JULY 1945 .... 14.00	(69) APR 1949 .... 14.00
(25) AUG 1945 .... 14.00	(70) MAY 1949 .... 14.00
(26) SEPT 1945 .... 14.00	(71) JUNE 1949 .... 14.00
(27) OCT 1945 .... 14.00	(72) JULY 1949 .... 14.00
(28) NOV 1945 .... 14.00	(73) AUG 1949 .... 14.00
(29) DEC 1945 .... 14.00	(74) OCT 1949 .... 14.00
(30) JAN 1946 .... 14.00	(75) NOV 1949 .... 14.00
(31) FEB 1946 .... 14.00	(76) DEC 1949 .... 14.00
(32) MAR 1946 .... 14.00	(77) JAN 1950 .... 15.00
(33) APR 1946 .... 14.00	(78) FEB 1950 .... 15.00
(34) MAY 1946 .... 14.00	(79) MAR 1950 .... 15.00
(35) JUNE 1946 .... 14.00	(80) APR 1950 .... 15.00
(36) JULY 1946 .... 14.00	(81) MAY 1950 .... 15.00
(37) AUG 1946 .... 14.00	(82) JUNE 1950 .... 15.00
(38) SEPT 1946 .... 14.00	(83) JULY 1950 .... 15.00
(39) OCT 1946 .... 14.00	(84) AUG 1950 .... 15.00
(40) NOV 1946 .... 14.00	(85) SEPT 1950 .... 15.00
(41) DEC 1946 .... 14.00	(86) OCT 1950 .... 15.00
(42) JAN 1947 .... 14.00	(87) NOV 1950 .... 15.00
(43) FEB 1947 .... 14.00	(88) DEC 1950 .... 14.00
(44) MAR 1947 .... 14.00	(89) JAN 1951 .... 14.00
(45) APR 1947 .... 14.00	(90) FEB 1951 .... 14.00

1940 (July). *As before, but make-up changed to contain:* 18 × 2½d., 6 × 2d. and 6 × ½d. in the original dark colours (Nos. 462, 465/6).
BD25 Edition numbers 1 to 16 (part) £160

1942 (Mar). *As before, but containing stamps in pale shades* (Nos. 485, 488/9).
BD26 Edition numbers 16 (part) to 36 .... £140

1943 (Sept). *As before, but buff cover printed in black as Type* A (see No. BD18, 2s. 6d.) (Nos. 485, 488/9).
BD28 Edition dates September 1943 to December 1950 .... 35.00

(1) SEPT 1943 .... 35.00	(26) JUNE 1947 .... 35.00
(2) OCT 1943 .... 35.00	(27) AUG 1947 .... 35.00
(3) NOV 1943 .... 35.00	(28) OCT 1947 .... 35.00
(4) DEC 1943 .... 35.00	(29) DEC 1947 .... 35.00
(5) FEB 1944 .... 35.00	(30) FEB 1948 .... 35.00
(6) MAR 1944 .... 35.00	(31) APR 1948 .... 35.00
(7) AUG 1944 .... 35.00	(32) JUNE 1948 .... 35.00
(8) OCT 1944 .... 35.00	(33) JULY 1948 .... 35.00
(9) NOV 1944 .... 35.00	(34) AUG 1948 .... 35.00
(10) JAN 1945 .... 35.00	(35) OCT 1948 .... 35.00
(11) FEB 1945 .... 35.00	(36) DEC 1948 .... 35.00
(12) APR 1945 .... 35.00	(37) FEB 1949 .... 35.00
(13) JUNE 1945 .... 35.00	(38) APR 1949 .... 35.00
(14) AUG 1945 .... 35.00	(39) JUNE 1949 .... 35.00
(15) OCT 1945 .... 35.00	(40) AUG 1949 .... 35.00
(16) DEC 1945 .... 35.00	(41) SEPT 1949 .... 35.00
(17) JAN 1946 .... 35.00	(42) OCT 1949 .... 35.00
(18) MAR 1946 .... 35.00	(43) DEC 1949 .... 35.00
(19) MAY 1946 .... 35.00	(44) FEB 1950 .... 35.00
(20) JUNE 1946 .... 35.00	(45) APR 1950 .... 35.00
(21) AUG 1946 .... 35.00	(46) JUNE 1950 .... 35.00
(22) OCT 1946 .... 35.00	(47) AUG 1950 .... 35.00
(23) DEC 1946 .... 35.00	(48) OCT 1950 .... 35.00
(24) FEB 1947 .... 35.00	(49) DEC 1950 .... 35.00
(25) APR 1947 .... 35.00	

Type BD29

1944 (April). *As before, but buff cover printed in black as Type* BD29 (Nos. 485, 488/9).
BD29 Edition dates April or June 1944 ....25.00

(1) APR 1944 ....25.00   (2) JUNE 1944 .... 25.00

1951 (May). *As before, but buff cover changed back to Type* A (see No. BD18, 2s. 6d.) and containing stamps in the new colours. (Nos. 503, 506/7).
BD30 Edition dates May 1951 to January 1952 ....15.00

(1) MAY 1951 .... 15.00   (4) NOV 1951 .... 17.00
(2) JULY 1951 .... 15.00   (5) JAN 1952 .... 17.00
(3) SEPT 1951 .... 17.00

1952 (Mar). *As before, make-up changed to contain:* 18 × 2½d., 6 × 1½d., 3 × 1d. and 6 × ½d. The 1d. pane was completed by three perforated labels in the lower row inscribed "MINIMUM INLAND PRINTED PAPER RATE 1½d." (Nos. 503/5, 507).
BD31 Edition dates March to November 1952 .... 14.00

(1) MAR 1952 .... 14.00   (4) SEPT 1952 .... 16.00
(2) MAY 1952 .... 16.00   (5) NOV 1952 .... 16.00
(3) JULY 1952 .... 14.00

1953 (Jan). *As before, but make-up changed again to include the* 2d. value and containing: 12 × 2½d., 6 × 2d., 6 × 1½d., 6 × 1d. and 6 × ½d. (Nos. 503/7).
BD32 Edition dates January or March 1953 .... 24.00

(1) JAN 1953 .... 24.00   (2) MAR 1953 .... 24.00

QUEEN ELIZABETH II

l.£.s.d. Booklets, 1953–70.

TYPES OF BOOKLET COVER WITH GPO CYPHER

Type A
Circular GPO Cypher
(See illustration above No. BD18)

Type B
Oval Type GPO Cypher

Type C
New GPO Cypher (small)

Type D
New GPO Cypher (large)

1s. Booklets

1953 (2 Sept)–**59.** *I. White unprinted cover. Pages of two stamps: 4 × 1½d., 4 × 1d., 4 × ½d. For use in experimental "D" machines.*

A. *Wmk Tudor Crown (Nos. 515/17)*
E1   No date.. 2.75

B. *Wmk St. Edward's Crown (Nos. 540/2)*
E2   No date (11.57) 5.50

II. White printed cover as Type B. Pages of four stamps: 4 × 1½d., 4 × 1d., 4 × ½d. For use in "E" machines.

A. *Wmk Tudor Crown (Nos. 515/17)*
K1   No date (22.7.54) 4.00

B. *Wmk St. Edward's Crown (Nos. 540/2)*
K2   No date (5.7.56)...................................... 2.90

C. *Wmk Crowns (Nos. 570/2)*
K3   No date (13.8.59) 4.00

2s. Booklets

1959 (22 Apr)–**65.** *Pages of four stamps: 4 × 3d., 4 × 1½d., 4 × ½d.*

I. Salmon cover as Type B. Wmk. St. Edward's Crown (Nos. 540/2 and 545).
N1   No date... 5.50

II. Salmon cover as Type C. Wmk Crowns (Nos. 570/2 and 575).
N2   No date (2.11.60) 4.00

III. Lemon cover as Type C. Wmk Crowns (Nos. 570/2 and 575).
N3   No date (2.61) 4.00

IV. Lemon cover as Type C. Wmk Crowns (sideways) (Nos. 570a, 571a, 572b, 575a) or phosphor (Nos. 610a, 611a, 612a, 615b).
N 4   APR 1961 .... 18.00
      p. With phosphor bands................................... 50.00
N 5   SEPT 1961 .... 28.00
N 6   JAN 1962 .... 26.00
N 7   APR 1962 .... 28.00
N 8   JULY 1962 .... 26.00
      p. With phosphor bands................................... 48.00
N 9   NOV 1962 .... 26.00
      p. With phosphor bands................................... 48.00
N10   JAN 1963 .... 26.00
      p. With phosphor bands................................... 50.00
N11   MAR 1963 .... 28.00

N12   JUNE 1963.. 26.00
      p. With phosphor bands................................... 48.00
N13   AUG 1963 .... 26.00
      p. With phosphor bands................................... 48.00
N14   OCT 1963 .... 26.00
      p.With phosphor bands 60.00
N15   FEB 1964 .... 26.00
      p. With phosphor bands................................... 45.00
N16   JUNE 1964.. 26.00
      p. With phosphor bands................................... 45.00
N17   AUG 1964 .... 28.00
      p.With phosphor bands 45.00
N18   OCT 1964 .... 28.00
      p. With phosphor bands................................... 40.00
N19   DEC 1964... 26.00
      p. With phosphor bands................................... 40.00
N20   APR 1965... 26.00
      p. With phosphor bands................................... 45.00

1965 (16 Aug)–**67.** *New Composition. Pages of four stamps: 4 × 4d. and pane of 2 × 1d. and 2 × 3d. arranged se-tenant horiz.*

Orange-yellow cover as Type C printed in black. Wmk Crowns (sideways) (Nos. 571a, 575a and 576ab) or phosphor (Nos. 611a, 615d (one side phosphor band) and 616ab).
N21   JULY 1965 .... 1.75
      p. With phosphor bands................................... 14.00
N22   OCT 1965 .... 1.75
      p. With phosphor bands................................... 6.00
N23   JAN 1966 .... 2.60
      p. With phosphor bands................................... 6.50
N24   APR 1966 .... 2.60
      p. With phosphor bands................................... 6.50
N25   JULY 1966 .... 2.00
      p. With phosphor bands................................... 6.00
N26   OCT 1966 .... 2.00
      p. With phosphor bands................................... 6.00
N27   JAN 1967 .... 2.50
      p. With phosphor bands................................... 5.00
N28p   APR 1967. With phosphor bands............................. 5.00
N29p   JULY 1967. With phosphor bands 5.00
N30p   OCT 1967. With phosphor bands........................... 5.00

In the *se-tenant* pane the 3d. appears at left or right to facilitate the application of phosphor bands.

The following illustration shows how the *se-tenant* stamps with one phosphor band on 3d. are printed and the arrows indicate where the guillotine falls. The result gives 1d. stamps with two bands and the 3d. stamps with one band either at left or right.

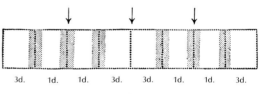

3d.   1d.   1d.   3d.   3d.   1d.   1d.   3d.

1967 (Nov)–**68.** *Composition and cover as Nos. N21/30. Wmk Crowns (sideways) (Nos. 611a, 615b (two phosphor bands) and 616ab).*
N31p   JAN 1968 .... 2.00
N32p   MAR 1968 .... 2.00

2s. Booklets with Machin type stamps

1968 (6 Apr–Aug). *Orange-yellow cover as Type C. Pages of four stamps: 4 × 4d. and pane of 2 × 1d. and 2 × 3d. arranged se-tenant horiz. PVA gum (Nos. 724, 730, 731Ev).*
NP27   MAY 1968 70
NP28   JULY 1968 60
NP29   AUG 1968 60

1968 (16 Sept)–**70.** *Grey cover as Type C. New composition. 4d. stamps only comprising page of 4 × 4d. with two phosphor bands (No. 731Ev) and page of 2 × 4d. with one centre phosphor band (No. 732) se-tenant with two printed labels.*

NP30	SEPT 1968	50
NP31	JAN 1969	90.00

Same composition but all six 4d. stamps have one centre phosphor band (No. 732).

NP31a	SEPT 1968	£450
NP32	NOV 1968	50
NP33	JAN 1969	50

Same composition but change to 4d. bright vermilion with one centre phosphor band (No. 733).

NP34	MAR 1969	80
NP35	MAY 1969	1.00
NP36	JULY 1969	1.40
NP37	SEPT 1969	1.10
NP38	NOV 1969	1.10
NP39	JAN 1970	1.10
NP40	MAR 1970	1.10
NP41	MAY 1970	1.10
NP42	JULY 1970	1.10
NP43	AUG 1970	1.10
NP44	OCT 1970	1.10
NP45	DEC 1970	1.10

2s. Booklets for Holiday Resorts

1963 (15 July)–**64.** *I. Lemon cover as Type C and printed in red. New composition. Pages of four stamps: two of 4 × 2½d. and one of 3 × ½d., and 1 × 2½d. arranged se-tenant. Chalky paper. Wmk Crowns (Nos. 570k and 574k).*

NR1	No date, black stitching	2.25
	a. White stitching (3.9.63)	2.75

II. Lemon cover as Type C and printed in red. Composition changed again. Pages of four stamps 2 × ½d. and 2 × 2½d. arranged sideways, vertically se-tenant. Wmk Crowns (sideways) (No. 570m × 4).

NR2	1964 (1.7.64)	1.10

2s. Booklet for Christmas Cards

1965 (6 Dec). *Orange-yellow cover as Type C printed in red. Two panes of 4 × 3d. arranged sideways. Wmk Crowns (sideways) (No. 575a).*

NX1	1965	55

2s. 6d. Booklets

Green cover. Pages of six stamps: 6 × 2½d., 6 × 1½d., 3 × 1d. (page completed by three perforated labels), 6 × ½d.

LABELS. The wording printed on the labels differs as follows:

"PPR" = "MINIMUM INLAND PRINTED PAPER RATE 1½d." Two types exist:
A. Printed in photogravure 17 mm high.
B. Typographed, 15 mm high.
"Shorthand" = "SHORTHAND IN 1 WEEK" (covering all three labels).
"Post Early" = "PLEASE POST EARLY IN THE DAY".
"PAP" = "PACK YOUR PARCELS SECURELY" (1st label) "ADDRESS YOUR LETTERS CORRECTLY" (2nd label), "AND POST EARLY IN THE DAY" (3rd label).

1953–54. *Composite booklets containing stamps of George VI and Queen Elizabeth II.*

A. *K.G.VI ½d. and 1d. (Nos. 503/4) and Q.E.II 1½d. and 2½d. (Nos. 517 and 519b). Cover as Type A. No interleaving pages.*

F 1	MAY 1953 (PPR 17 mm)	14.00
F 2	JUNE 1953 (PPR 17 mm)	15.00
F 3	JULY 1953 (PPR 17 mm)	15.00
F 4	AUG 1953 (PPR 17 mm)	15.00

B. *Same composition but with addition of two interleaving pages, one at each end. Cover as Type A.*

F 5	SEPT 1953 (PPR 17 mm)	45.00
F 6	SEPT 1953 (PPR 15 mm)	18.00

C. *Same composition and with interleaving pages but cover as Type B.*

F 7	OCT 1953 (PPR 17 mm)	15.00
F 8	OCT 1953 (PPR 17 mm)	15.00
F 9	NOV 1953 (PPR 17 mm)	15.00
F10	NOV 1953 (PPR 15 mm)	40.00
F11	DEC 1953 (PPR 17 mm)	15.00
F12	JAN 1954 (Shorthand)	15.00
F13	FEB 1954 (Shorthand)	15.00

D. *New composition: K.G.VI 1d. (No. 504) and Q.E.II ½d., 1½d. and 2½d. (Nos. 515, 517 and 519b).*

F14	MAR 1954 (PPR 17 mm)	£200

1954–57. *Booklets containing only Queen Elizabeth II stamps. All covers as Type B.*

A. *Wmk Tudor Crown (Nos. 515/17 and 519b).*

F15	MAR 1954 (PPR 15 mm)	£175
F16	APR 1954 (Post Early)	15.00
F17	MAY 1954 (Post Early)	15.00
F18	JUNE 1954 (Post Early)	15.00
F19	JULY 1954 (Post Early)	15.00
F20	AUG 1954 (Post Early)	15.00
F21	SEPT 1954 (Post Early)	15.00
F22	OCT 1954 (Post Early)	15.00
F23	NOV 1954 (Post Early)	15.00
F24	DEC 1954 (Post Early)	17.00

B. *Same composition but with interleaving pages between each pane of stamps.*

F25	JAN 1955 (Post Early)	18.00
F26	JAN 1955 (PAP)	28.00
F27	FEB 1955 (PAP)	16.00
F28	MAR 1955 (PAP)	17.00
F29	APR 1955 (PAP)	16.00
F30	MAY 1955 (PAP)	16.00
F31	JUNE 1955 (PAP)	16.00
F32	JULY 1955 (PAP)	16.00
F33	AUG 1955 (PAP)	16.00

C *Mixed watermarks. Wmk Tudor Crown (Nos. 515/17 and 519b) and wmk St. Edward's Crown (Nos. 540/2 and 544b) in various combinations.*

F34	SEPT 1955 (PAP) .... *From*	16.00

2s. 6d. booklets dated AUGUST, OCTOBER, NOVEMBER and DECEMBER 1955, JANUARY, MAY and JUNE 1956 exist both as listed and with the two watermarks mixed. There are so many different combinations that we do not list them separately, but when in stock selections can be submitted. The SEPTEMBER 1955 booklet (No. F34) only exists in composite form.

D. *Wmk St. Edward's Crown (Nos. 540/2 and 544b).*

F35	OCT 1955 (PAP)	16.00
F36	NOV 1955 (PAP)	16.00
F37	DEC 1955 (PAP)	16.00

F38	JAN 1956 (PAP)	15.00
F39	FEB 1956 (PAP)	15.00
F40	MAR 1956 (PAP)	15.00
F41	APR 1956 (PAP)	15.00
F42	MAY 1956 (PAP)	15.00
F43	JUNE 1956 (PAP)	15.00
F44	JULY 1956 (PAP)	15.00
F45	AUG 1956 (PAP)	15.00
F46	SEPT 1956 (PAP)	15.00
F47	OCT 1956 (PAP)	15.00
F48	NOV 1956 (PAP)	14.00
F49	DEC 1956 (PAP)	14.00
F50	JAN 1957 (PAP)	15.00
F51	FEB 1957 (PAP)	14.00
F52	MAR 1957 (PAP)	14.00

E. *Same wmk but new composition. Pages of six stamps: 6 × 2½d. (No. 544b), 6 × 2d. (No. 543b) and 6 × ½d. (No. 540).*

F53	APR 1957	11.00
F54	MAY 1957	11.00
F55	JUNE 1957	11.00
F56	JULY 1957	11.00
F57	AUG 1957	11.00
F58	SEPT 1957	10.00
F59	OCT 1957	10.00
F60	NOV 1957	10.00
F61	DEC 1957	14.00

3s. Booklets

1958–65. *Pages of six stamps: 6 × 3d., 6 × 1½d., 6 × 1d., 6 × ½d.*

I. Red cover as Type B.
A. *Wmk St. Edward's Crown (Nos. 540/2 and 545).*

M1	JAN 1958	12.00
M2	FEB 1958	13.00
M3	MAR 1958	13.00
M4	APR 1958	13.00
M5	MAY 1958	13.00
M6	JUNE 1958	13.00
M7	JULY 1958	13.00
M8	AUG 1958	13.00
M9	NOV 1958	13.00

The 3s. booklet dated NOVEMBER 1958, DECEMBER 1958 and JANU-
ARY 1959 exist both as listed and with mixed St. Edward's Crown and
Crowns wmks.

B. *Wmk crowns (Nos. 570/2 and 575) or graphite lines (Nos. 587/9 and 592).*

M10	DEC 1958	13.00
M11	JAN 1959	13.00
M12	FEB 1959	13.00
M13	AUG 1959	13.00
	g. With graphite lines	£160
M14	SEPT 1959	13.00
	g. With graphite lines	£160

II. Brick-red cover as Type C. Wmk Crowns (Nos. 570/2 and 575), graphite lines (Nos. 587/9 and 592) or phosphor (Nos. 610/12 and 615).

M15	OCT 1959	13.00
	g. With graphite lines	£160
M16	NOV 1959	13.00
M17	DEC 1959	13.00
M18	JAN 1960	13.00
M19	FEB 1960	13.00
	g. With graphite lines	£160
M20	MAR 1960	13.00
	g. With graphite lines	£160
M21	APR 1960	13.00
	g. With graphite lines	£160
M22	MAY 1960	13.00

M23	JUNE 1960	13.00
M24	JULY 1960	13.00
M25	AUG 1960	13.00
	p. With phosphor bands	22.00
M26	SEPT 1960	13.00
M27	OCT 1960	13.00
M28	NOV 1960	13.00
	p. With phosphor bands	40.00

III. Brick-red cover as Type D. Wmk Crowns (Nos. 570/2 and 575) or phosphor (Nos. 610/12 and 615).

M29	DEC 1960	13.00
	p. With phosphor bands	40.00
M30	JAN 1961	13.00
M31	FEB 1961	13.00
M32	MAR 1961	13.00
M33	APR 1961	13.00
	p. With phosphor bands	22.00
M34	MAY 1961	13.00
M35	JUNE 1961	13.00
M36	JULY 1961	13.00
	p. With phosphor bands	22.00
M37	AUG 1961	13.00
	p. With phosphor bands	22.00
M38	SEPT 1961	13.00
	p. With phosphor bands	22.00
M39	OCT 1961	13.00
	p. With phosphor bands	22.00
M40	NOV 1961	13.00
M41	DEC 1961	13.00
M42	JAN 1962	13.00
M43	FEB 1962	13.00
	p. With phosphor bands	22.00
M44	MAR 1962	13.00
	p. With phosphor bands	23.00
M45	APR 1962	13.00
	p. With phosphor bands	22.00
M46	MAY 1962	13.00
	p. With phosphor bands	23.00
M47	JUNE 1962	13.00
	p. With phosphor bands	22.00
M48	JULY 1962	13.00
M49	AUG 1962	13.00
	p. With phosphor bands	22.00
M50	SEPT 1962	13.00
	p. With phosphor bands	23.00
M51	OCT 1962	13.00
	p. With phosphor bands	23.00
M52	NOV 1962	13.00
	p. With phosphor bands	22.00
M53	DEC 1962	13.00
	p. With phosphor bands	24.00
M54	JAN 1963	13.00
M55	FEB 1963	13.00
	p. With phosphor bands	22.00
M56	MAR 1963	13.00
	p. With phosphor bands	22.00
M57	APR 1963	13.00
	p. With phosphor bands	23.00
M58	MAY 1963	13.00
	p. With phosphor bands	23.00
M59	JUNE 1963	13.00
	p. With phosphor bands	22.00
M60	JULY 1963	13.00
	p. With phosphor bands	22.00
M61	AUG 1963	13.00
	p. With phosphor bands	22.00
M62	SEPT 1963	13.00
M63	OCT 1963	13.00
M64	NOV 1963	13.00
	p. With phosphor bands	22.00

M65	DEC 1963	13.00
	p. With phosphor bands	23.00
M66	JAN 1964	13.00
	p. With phosphor bands	22.00
M67	MAR 1964	13.00
	p. With phosphor bands	23.00
M68	MAY 1964	13.00
	p. With phosphor bands	22.00
M69	JULY 1964	13.00
	p. With phosphor bands	23.00
M70	SEPT 1964	13.00
	p. With phosphor bands	23.00
M71	NOV 1964	13.00
	p. With phosphor bands	22.00
M72	JAN 1965	13.00
	p. With phosphor bands	22.00
M73	MAR 1965	13.00
	p. With phosphor bands	22.00
M74	MAY 1965	13.00
	p. With phosphor bands	22.00

3s. 9d. Booklets

1953–57. *Red cover as Type B. Pages of six stamps:* 18 × 2½d.
A. *Wmk Tudor Crown (No. 519b)*

G 1	NOV 1953	15.00
G 2	JAN 1954	15.00
G 3	MAR 1954	14.00
G 4	DEC 1954	14.00
G 5	FEB 1955	14.00
G 6	APR 1955	15.00
G 7	JUNE 1955	15.00
G 8	AUG 1955	15.00

3s. 9d. booklets dated OCTOBER and DECEMBER 1955 exist both as listed and with the two wmks mixed.

G 9	OCT 1955	16.00
G10	DEC 1955	16.00

Wmk St. Edward's Crown (No. 544b).
B. *Same composition but with interleaving pages between each pane of stamps.*

G12	FEB 1956	7.50
G13	APR 1956	7.50
G14	JUNE 1956	7.50
G15	AUG 1956	7.50
G16	OCT 1956	7.50
G17	DEC 1956	7.50
G18	FEB 1957	7.50
G19	APR 1957	7.50
G20	JUNE 1957	6.50
G21	AUG 1957	14.00

4s. 6d. Booklets

1957–65. *Pages of six stamps:* 18 × 3d.

I. Purple cover as Type B.
A. *Wmk St. Edward's Crown (No. 545).*

L1	OCT 1957	10.00
L2	DEC 1957	10.00
L3	FEB 1958	10.00
L4	APR 1958	10.00
L5	JUNE 1958	10.00
L6	OCT 1958	10.00
L7	DEC 1958	10.00

B. *Wmk Crowns (No. 575).*

L8	DEC 1958	22.00

II. Purple cover as Type C. Wmk Crowns (No. 575) or graphite lines (No. 592).

L9	FEB 1959	11.00
L10	JUNE 1959	11.00
L11	AUG 1959	11.00
	g. With graphite lines	12.00
L12	OCT 1959	11.00
L13	DEC 1959	11.00

III. Violet cover as Type C. Wmk Crowns (No. 575), graphite lines (No. 592) or phosphor (No. 615).

L14	FEB 1959	11.00
L15	APR 1959	11.00
	g. With graphite lines	12.00
L16	JUNE 1959	11.00
	g. With graphite lines	12.00
L17	DEC 1959	11.00
L18	FEB 1960	14.00
	g. With graphite lines	12.00
L19	APR 1960	14.00
	g. With graphite lines	12.00
L20	JUNE 1960	14.00
L21	AUG 1960	14.00
	p. With phosphor bands	25.00
L22	OCT 1960	14.00

IV. Violet cover as Type D. Wmk Crowns (No. 575) or phosphor (No. 615).

L23	DEC 1960	14.00
L24	FEB 1961	14.00
	p. With phosphor bands	17.00
L25	APR 1961	14.00
	p. With phosphor bands	17.00
L26	JUNE 1961	14.00
L27	AUG 1961	14.00
	p. With phosphor bands	17.00
L28	OCT 1961	14.00
	p. With phosphor bands	17.00
L29	DEC 1961	14.00
L30	FEB 1962	14.00
	p. With phosphor bands	17.00
L31	APR 1962	14.00
	p. With phosphor bands	17.00
L32	JUNE 1962	14.00
	p. With phosphor bands	17.00
L33	AUG 1962	14.00
	p. With phosphor bands	17.00
L34	OCT 1962	14.00
	p. With phosphor bands	55.00
L35	DEC 1962	14.00
	p. With phosphor bands	17.00
L36	FEB 1963	14.00
	p. With phosphor bands	17.00
L37	APR 1963	14.00
	p. With phosphor bands	17.00
L38	JUNE 1963	14.00
	p. With phosphor bands	17.00
L39	AUG 1963	14.00
	p. With phosphor bands	17.00
L40	OCT 1963	14.00
	p. With phosphor bands	17.00
L41	NOV 1963	14.00
	p. With phosphor bands	17.00
L42	DEC 1963	14.00
	p. With phosphor bands	55.00
L43	JAN 1964	14.00
L44	FEB 1964	14.00
	p. With phosphor bands	17.00
L45	MAR 1964	14.00
	p. With phosphor bands	17.00

L46	APR 1964	14.00
	p. With phosphor bands.................................	17.00
L47	MAY 1964	14.00
	p. With phosphor bands.................................	17.00
L48	JUNE 1964...	14.00
	p. With phosphor bands.................................	17.00
L49	JULY 1964	14.00
	p. With phosphor bands.................................	17.00
L50	AUG 1964...	14.00
	p. With phosphor bands.................................	17.00
L51	SEPT 1964	14.00
	p. With phosphor bands.................................	17.00
L52	OCT 1964	14.00
	p. With phosphor bands.................................	17.00
L53	NOV 1964...	14.00
	p. With phosphor bands.................................	17.00
L54	DEC 1964...	11.00
	p. With phosphor bands.................................	17.00
L55	JAN 1965	11.00
	p. With phosphor bands.................................	17.00
L56	FEB 1965	11.00
	p. With phosphor bands.................................	17.00
L57	MAR 1965	11.00
	p. With phosphor bands.................................	70.00
L58	APR 1965	8.50

1965 (26 July)–**67.** *New composition. Pages of six stamps. 12 × 4d.,
6 × 1d. Slate-blue cover as Type D. Wmk Crowns (Nos. 571 and 576a)
or phosphor (Nos. 611 and 616a).*

L59	JULY 1965	8.50
	p. With phosphor bands.................................	14.00
L60	SEPT 1965	8.50
	p. With phosphor bands.................................	14.00
L61	NOV 1965	8.50
	p. With phosphor bands.................................	15.00
L62	JAN 1966	8.50
	p. With phosphor bands.................................	15.00
L63	MAR 1966	8.00
	p. With phosphor bands.................................	7.00
L64	JAN 1967	8.50
	p. With phosphor bands.................................	7.00
L65	MAR 1967	8.50
	p. With phosphor bands.................................	7.00
L66p	MAY 1967. With phosphor bands	6.50
L67p	JULY 1967. With phosphor bands	7.00
L68p	SEPT 1967. With phosphor bands	6.50
L69p	NOV 1967. With phosphor bands	6.50
L70p	JAN 1968. With phosphor bands	6.50
L71p	MAR 1968. With phosphor bands	6.50

4s. 6d. Booklets with Machin type stamps

1968–70. *Slate-blue cover as Type D. Pages of six stamps: 12 × 4d.,
6 × 1d. PVA gum (Nos. 724, 731Ev).*

LP45	MAY 1968	4.50

Type LP46
Ships Series with GPO Cypher

(Des S. Rose)

Blue cover as Type LP46. Ships Series. Composition as last.

LP46	JULY 1968 (*Cutty Sark*)	1.25

Same composition but change to one centre phosphor band (No. 732).

LP47	SEPT 1968 (*Golden Hind*).............................	1.25
LP48	NOV 1968 (*Discovery*)	1.25

*Same composition but change to 4d. bright vermilion with one centre
phosphor band (No. 733).*

LP49	JAN 1969 (*Queen Elizabeth 2*)	1.25
LP50	MAR 1969 (*Sirius*)	1.25
LP51	MAY 1969 (*Sirius*)	1.50
LP52	JULY 1969 (*Dreadnought*)............................	2.00
LP53	SEPT 1969 (*Dreadnought*)	3.00
LP54	NOV 1969 (*Mauretania*)	2.25
LP55	JAN 1970 (*Mauretania*)	2.25
LP56	MAR 1970 (*Victory*).................................	2.25
LP57	MAY 1970 (*Victory*).................................	5.00

Type LP58
Ships Series with Post Office
Corporation Crown Symbol

(Des S. Rose)

As last but cover changed to Type LP58.

LP58	AUG 1970 (*Sovereign of the Seas*)...................	2.25
LP59	OCT 1970 (*Sovereign of the Seas*)..................	5.00

5s. Booklets

1953–57. *Buff cover. Pages of six stamps. 12 × 2½d., 6 × 2d., 6 × 1½d.,
6 × 1d., 6 × ½d.*

*I. Composite booklets containing stamps of King George VI and Queen
Elizabeth II.*

*A. K.G.VI ½d., 1d. and 2d. (Nos. 503/4 and 506) and Q.E.II 1½d. and 2½d.
(Nos. 517 and 519b). Cover as Type A. No interleaving pages.*

H1	MAY 1953	18.00
H2	JULY 1953	18.00

*B. Same composition but with addition of two interleaving pages, one
at each end. Cover as Type A.*

H3	SEPT 1953	20.00

C. *Same composition and with interleaving pages but cover as Type B.*

H4	NOV 1953	20.00
H5	JAN 1954	20.00

D. *New composition: K.G.VI 1d. and 2d. (Nos. 504 and 506) and Q.E.II ½d., 1½d. and 2½d. (Nos. 515, 517 and 519b).*

H6	MAR 1954	60.00

E. *New composition: K.G.VI 2d. (No. 506) and Q.E.II ½d., 1d., 1½d. and 2½d. (Nos. 515/17 and 519b).*

H7	MAR 1954	60.00

II. *Booklets containing only Queen Elizabeth II stamps. Buff cover as Type B. Two interleaving pages as before.*

A. *Wmk Tudor Crown (Nos. 515/18 and 519b).*

H8	MAR 1954	20.00
H9	MAY 1954	18.00
H10	JULY 1954	18.00
H11	SEPT 1954	18.00
H12	NOV 1954	18.00

B. *Same composition but with interleaving pages between each pane of stamps.*

H13	JAN 1955	18.00
H14	MAR 1955	18.00
H15	MAY 1955	18.00
H16	JULY 1955	18.00

5s. booklets dated SEPTEMBER and NOVEMBER 1955 and JANUARY 1956 exist both as listed and with the two watermarks mixed. There are so many different combinations that we do not list them separately, but when in stock selections can be submitted.

C. *Wmk St. Edward's Crown (Nos. 540/3 and 544b).*

H17	SEPT 1955	16.00
H18	NOV 1955	17.00
H19	JAN 1956	17.00
H20	MAR 1956	17.00
H21	MAY 1956	17.00
H22	JULY 1956	17.00
H23	SEPT 1956	17.00
H24	NOV 1956	18.00
H25	JAN 1957	22.00

D. *Same watermark. Introduction of 2d. light red-brown (No. 543b) in place of No. 543.*

H26	JAN 1957	16.00
H27	MAR 1957	17.00
H28	MAY 1957	17.00
H29	JULY 1957	17.00
H30	SEPT 1957	17.00
H31	NOV 1957	17.00

1958–65. E. *New composition. Pages of six stamps: 12 × 3d. (No. 545), 6 × 2½d. (No. 544b), 6 × 1d. (No. 541), 6 × ½d. (No. 540). Wmk St. Edward's Crown.*

H32	JAN 1958	17.00
H33	MAR 1958	17.00
H34	MAY 1958	17.00
H35	JULY 1958 (11.58)	17.00
H36	NOV 1958	17.00

5s. booklets dated JULY 1958, NOVEMBER 1958 and JANUARY 1959 exist with mixed watermarks.

F. *Blue cover as Type C. Wmk Crowns (Nos. 570/1, 574/5), graphite lines (Nos. 587/8 and 591/2) or phosphor (Nos. 610/11, 614 and 615).*

H37	JAN 1959	17.00
H38	MAR 1959	18.00

H39	JULY 1959	17.00
	g. With graphite lines	60.00
H40	SEPT 1959	17.00
H41	NOV 1959	17.00
H42	JAN 1960	17.00
H43	MAR 1960	18.00
	g. With graphite lines	60.00
H44	MAY 1960	17.00
H45	JULY 1960	18.00
H46	SEPT 1960	17.00
	g. With graphite lines	60.00
	p. With phosphor bands	42.00
H47	NOV 1960	18.00

G. *As last but blue cover as Type D. Same composition.*

I. *Phosphor has two bands.*

H48	JAN 1961	17.00
H49	MAR 1961	17.00
	p. With phosphor bands	38.00
H50	MAY 1961	17.00
H51	JULY 1961	17.00
	p. With phosphor bands	38.00
H52	SEPT 1961	17.00
	p. With phosphor bands	38.00
H53	NOV 1961	17.00
H54	JAN 1962	17.00
	p. With phosphor bands	38.00

II. *Phosphor has one band.*

H55	MAR 1962	17.00
	p. With phosphor bands	38.00
H56	MAY 1962	17.00
	p. With phosphor bands	38.00
H57	JULY 1962	17.00
	p. With phosphor bands	38.00
H58	SEPT 1962	17.00
	p. With phosphor bands	38.00
H59	NOV 1962	17.00
	p. With phosphor bands	38.00
H60	JAN 1963	17.00
	p. With phosphor bands	38.00
H61	MAR 1963	17.00
	p. With phosphor bands	38.00
H62	MAY 1963	17.00
	p. With phosphor bands	38.00
H63	JULY 1963	17.00
	p. With phosphor bands	38.00
H64	SEPT 1963	17.00
	p. With phosphor bands	38.00
H65	NOV 1963	17.00
	p. With phosphor bands	38.00
H66	JAN 1964	17.00
	p. With phosphor bands	38.00
H67	MAR 1964	17.00
	p. With phosphor bands	38.00
H68	MAY 1964	17.00
	p. With phosphor bands	38.00
H69	JULY 1964	17.00
	p. With phosphor bands	38.00
H70	SEPT 1964	17.00
	p. With phosphor bands	38.00
H71	NOV 1964	17.00
	p. With phosphor bands	38.00
H72	JAN 1965	17.00
	p. With phosphor bands	38.00
H73	MAR 1965	17.00
	p. With phosphor bands	38.00
H74	MAY 1965	17.00
	p. With phosphor bands	38.00

5s. Booklets with Machin type stamps

Type HP26
English Homes Series with
GPO Cypher

(Des S. Rose)

1968 (27 Nov)–**70.** *Cinnamon cover as Type HP26 (English Homes Series). Pages of six stamps:* 12 × 5d. *(No. 735).*

HP26	DEC 1968 (Ightham Mote)	1.10
HP27	FEB 1969 (Little Moreton Hall)	1.10
HP28	APR 1969 (Long Melford Hall)	1.25
HP29	JUNE 1969 (Long Melford Hall)	1.50
HP30	AUG 1969 (Long Melford Hall)	1.50

Type HP31
English Homes Series with Post
Office Corporation Crown Symbol

(Des S. Rose)

As last but cover change to Type HP31.

HP31	OCT 1969 (Mompesson House)	1.40
HP32	DEC 1969 (Mompesson House)	2.10
HP33	FEB 1970 (Cumberland Terrace)	1.75

STAMP MONTHLY

Finest and most informative magazine for all collectors. Obtainable from your newsagent or by postal subscription – details on request

Type HP34

(Des Peter Gauld)

As last but cover change to Type HP34 (special edition to advertise "Philympia" International Philatelic Exhibition, London, September 1970).

HP34	(no date) (3.3.70)	1.00

As last but cover changed to Type HP31.

HP35	JUNE 1970 (The Vineyard, Saffron, Walden)	1.75
HP36	AUG 1970 (The Vineyard, Saffron, Walden)	1.75
HP37	OCT 1970 (Mereworth Castle)	1.75
HP38	DEC 1970 (Mereworth Castle)	2.25

6s. Booklets

1965 (21 June)–**67.** *Containing stamps of 1960–68.*

Pages of six stamps: 18 × 4d.
Claret cover as Type D. Wmk Crowns (No. 576a) or phosphor (No. 616a).

Q 1	JUNE 1965	13.00
	p. With phosphor bands	15.00
Q 2	JULY 1965	13.00
	p. With phosphor bands	15.00
Q 3	AUG 1965	13.00
	p. With phosphor bands	17.00
Q 4	SEPT 1965	13.00
	p. With phosphor bands	13.00
Q 5	OCT 1965	13.00
	p. With phosphor bands	13.00
Q 6	NOV 1965	13.00
	p. With phosphor bands	13.00
Q 7	DEC 1965	13.00
	p. With phosphor bands	13.00
Q 8	JAN 1966	13.00
	p. With phosphor bands	13.00
Q 9	FEB 1966	13.00
	p. With phosphor bands	13.00
Q10	MAR 1966	13.00
	p. With phosphor bands	13.00
Q11	APR 1966	13.00
	p. With phosphor bands	13.00
Q12	MAY 1966	13.00
	p. With phosphor bands	13.00
Q13	JUNE 1966	13.00
	p. With phosphor bands	13.00
Q14	JULY 1966	13.00
	p. With phosphor bands	13.00
Q15	AUG 1966	13.00
	p. With phosphor bands	13.00
Q16	SEPT 1966	13.00
	p. With phosphor bands	13.00
Q17	OCT 1966	13.00
	p. With phosphor bands	13.00

Q18	NOV 1966	13.00
	p. With phosphor bands........................	13.00
Q19	DEC 1966	13.00
	p. With phosphor bands........................	13.00
Q20	JAN 1967	13.00
	p. With phosphor bands........................	13.00
Q21	FEB 1967	13.00
	p. With phosphor bands........................	13.00
Q22	MAR 1967	13.00
	p. With phosphor bands........................	13.00
Q23	APR 1967	13.00
	p. With phosphor bands........................	13.00
Q24p	MAY 1967. With phosphor bands..............	13.00
Q25p	JUNE 1967. With phosphor bands.............	13.00
Q26p	JULY 1967. With phosphor bands	13.00
Q27p	AUG 1967. With phosphor bands	13.00

6s. Booklets with Machin type stamps

1967–70. *Claret cover as Type D. Pages of six stamps: 18 × 4d. Two phosphor bands. Gum arabic (No. 731).*

QP28	SEPT 1967	27.00
QP29	OCT 1967	27.00
QP30	NOV 1967	27.00
QP31	DEC 1967	27.00
QP32	JAN 1968	27.00
QP33	FEB 1968 (No. 731*Ea*)........................	27.00
QP34	MAR 1968 (No. 731*Ea*).......................	27.00
QP35	APR 1968 (No. 731*Ea*)........................	27.00
QP36	MAY 1968 (No. 731*Ea*).......................	13.00

Change to PVA gum (No. 731Ev).

QP37	MAY 1968	£160

Type QP38
Birds Series with GPO Cypher

(Des S. Rose)

Orange-red cover as Type QP38 (Birds Series). Same composition. Two phosphor bands. PVA gum (No. 731Ev).

QP38	JUNE 1968 (Kingfisher) (4.6.68)	1.25
QP39	JULY 1968 (Kingfisher)	4.50
QP40	AUG 1968 (Peregrine Falcon)	1.25

Change to one centre phosphor band (No. 732).

QP41	SEPT 1968 (Peregrine Falcon) (16.9.68)	1.25
QP42	OCT 1968 (Pied Woodpecker).................	1.25
QP43	NOV 1968 (Pied Woodpecker).................	1.60
QP44	DEC 1968 (Great Crested Grebe)	1.60
QP45	JAN 1969 (Barn Owl)...........................	1.60

Change to 4d. bright vermilion with one centre phosphor band (No. 733).

QP46	FEB 1969 (Barn Owl) (20.2.69)	1.60

QP47	MAR 1969 (Jay)	2.00
QP48	MAY 1969 (Jay)	1.60
QP49	JULY 1969 (Puffin)	1.60
QP50	SEPT 1969 (Puffin)	2.00

Type QP51
Birds Series with Post Office
Corporation Crown Symbol

(Des S. Rose)

As last but cover change to Type QP51.

QP51	NOV 1969 (Cormorant)	2.00
QP52	JAN 1970 (Cormorant)	2.00
QP53	APR 1970 (Wren)	2.00
QP54	AUG 1970 (Golden Eagle)	2.25
QP55	OCT 1970 (Golden Eagle)	2.25

10s. Booklets

1961 (10 Apr–Oct). *Green cover as Type D. Pages of six stamps: 30 × 3d., 6 × 2d., 6 × 1½d., 6 × 1d., 6 × ½d. Wmk Crowns (Nos. 570/3 and 575).*

X1	No date..	38.00
X2	OCT 1961	38.00

1962–64. *New composition. Pages of six stamps: 30 × 3d., 6 × 2½d., 6 × 1½d., 6 × 1d. (Nos. 571/2 and 574/5).*

X3	APR 1962	27.00
X4	AUG 1962	27.00
X5	MAR 1963	27.00
X6	JULY 1963	27.00
X7	DEC 1963	27.00
X8	JULY 1964	27.00
X9	DEC 1964	27.00

1965 (23 Aug)**–66.** *Ochre cover as Type D. Pages of six stamps: 24 × 4d., 6 × 3d., 6 × 1d. Wmk Crowns (Nos. 571, 575, 576a).*

X10	AUG 1965	19.00
X11	DEC 1965	18.00
X12	FEB 1966	18.00
X13	AUG 1966	15.00
X14	NOV 1966	12.00

1967–68. *Ochre cover as Type D. Pages of six phosphor stamps: 24 × 4d., 6 × 3d., 6 × 1d. Wmk Crowns (Nos. 611, 615c (one side phosphor band), 616a).*

X15p	FEB 1967	8.00

Composition as No. X15p. Wmk Crowns (Nos. 611, 615e (one centre phosphor band) 616a).

X16p	AUG 1967	7.50
X17p	FEB 1968	5.50

10s. Booklets with Machin type stamps

Type XP4
Explorers Series with GPO Cypher

(Des S. Rose)

1968 (25 Mar–Aug). *Bright purple cover as Type XP4 (Explorers Series). Pages of six stamps: 24 × 4d., 6 × 3d., 6 × 1d. PVA gum (Nos. 724, 729Ev, 731Ev).*
XP4   MAY 1968 (Livingstone)........................... 4.50
XP5   AUG 1968 (Livingstone) 4.50

1968 (16 Sept)–**70.** *Yellow-green covers as Type XP4 (Explorers Series). New composition. Pages of six stamps: 12 × 5d. (with two phosphor bands), 12 × 4d. (with one centre phosphor band) and pane comprising 4 × 1d. se-tenant with vert pair of 4d. (each with one centre phosphor band). PVA gum (Nos. 725, 732 and 735).*
XP6   SEPT 1968 (Scott) 2.25

Change to 4d. bright vermilion (one centre band) but se-tenant pane comprises 1d. with two phosphor bands and 4d. with one left side phosphor band (Nos. 724 and 733/4).
XP 7   FEB 1969 (Mary Kingsley) (6.1.69) 2.25
XP 8   MAY 1969 (Mary Kingsley) 3.50
XP 9   AUG 1969 (Shackleton) 3.50
XP10   NOV 1969 (Shackleton)........................... 3.50

Type XP11
Explorers Series with Post Office
Corporation Crown Symbol

(Des S. Rose)

As last but cover change to Type XP11.
XP11   FEB 1970 (Frobisher) 3.50
XP12   NOV 1970 (Captain Cook) 3.50

£1 Booklet with Machin type stamps

Type ZP1

1969 (1 Dec). *"Stamps for Cooks". Type ZP1 (150 × 72 mm) with full colour pictorial cover showing "Baked, Stuffed Haddock". Contains 12 recipes on interleaving pages and on se-tenant label attached to booklet panes. PVA gum. Stapled.*
ZP1   £1 containing panes of fifteen stamps (5 × 3): 15 × 5d. (No. 735), 30 × 4d. (No. 733) and pane comprising 6 × 4d. (three each of Nos. 734 and 734Eb) se-tenant with 6 × 1d. (No. 724) and 3 × 5d. (No. 735)........... 70.00
ZP1a   As last but booklet is sewn with thread instead of being stapled 13.00

II. Decimal Booklets, 1971–86.

A. Stitched Booklets.

The 25p., 30p., 35p., 45p. and 50p. booklets have pictorial covers (except for the 35p. and 45p.) without the design inscription.
This was no longer necessary as the designs and background information were given on the inside of the front cover. Each series was numbered.

10p. Booklets

Type DN46
British Pillar Box Series

(Des R. Maddox)

1971 (15 Feb)–**74.** *British Pillar Box Series. Orange-yellow cover as Type DN46. Pages of four stamps: 2 × 2p. se-tenant vertically with 2 × ½p. and 2 × 1p. se-tenant vertically with 2 × 1½p. (Nos. X841, X844 and X848/9).*
DN46   FEB 1971 (No. 1 1855 type) 1.10
DN47   APR 1971 (No. 1 1855 type) (19.3.71) 1.10
DN48   JUNE 1971 (No. 2 1856 type) (1.6.71) 1.10
DN49   AUG 1971 (No. 2 1856 type) (14.7.71) 2.00

DN50	OCT 1971 (No. 3 1857–9 type) (27.8.71)	2.00
DN51	DEC 1971 (No. 3 1857–9 type) (6.10.71)......................	2.00
DN52	FEB 1972 (No. 4 1866–79 type) (8.12.71)	1.75
DN53	APR 1972 (No. 4 1866–79 type) (24.2.72).....................	1.75
DN54	JUNE 1972 (No. 5 1899 type) (12.4.72)........................	1.75
DN55	AUG 1972 (No. 5 1899 type) (8.6.72)...........................	1.75
DN56	OCT 1972 (No. 6 1968 type) (2.8.72)	1.75
DN57	DEC 1972 (No. 6 1968 type) (30.10.72)	1.75
DN58	FEB 1973 (No. 7 1936 type) (5.1.73)	1.75
DN59	APR 1973 (No. 7 1936 type) (2.4.73)..........................	2.00
DN60	JUNE 1973 (No. 8 1952 type) (18.4.73)........................	1.75
DN61	AUG 1973 (No. 8 1952 type) (4.7.73)...........................	11.00
DN62	OCT 1973 (No. 9 1973 type) (16.8.73)	2.00
DN63	DEC 1973 (No. 9 1973 type) (12.11.73)	2.00
DN64	FEB 1974 (No. 9 1973 type) (17.12.73)	2.00
DN65	APR 1974 (No. 10 1974 type) (22.2.74)........................	1.40
DN66	JUNE 1974 (No. 10 1974 type) (23.4.74)	1.40

In No. DN47 the pillar box is slightly reduced in size.

In Nos. DN49 onwards the values are arranged *se-tenant* horizontally instead of vertically.

Type DN67
Postal Uniforms Series

(Des C. Abbott)

1974 (23 July)–**76.** *Postal Uniforms Series. Orange-yellow cover as Type* DN67. *Contents unchanged.*

DN67	AUG 1974 (No. 1 1793 type)	1.40
DN68	OCT 1974 (No. 1 1793 type) (27.8.74)	1.40
DN69	DEC 1974 (No. 2 1837 type) (25.10.74)	1.40
DN70	FEB 1975 (No. 2 1837 type) (12.12.74)	1.40
DN71	APR 1975 (No. 3 1855 type) (26.3.75)	1.40
DN72	JUNE 1975 (No. 3 1855 type) (21.5.75).........................	90
DN73	AUG 1975 (No. 3 1855 type) (27.6.75).........................	90
DN74	OCT 1975 (No. 3 1855 type) (3.10.75)	45
DN75	JAN 1976 (No. 3 1855 type) (16.3.76)	55

**HAVE YOU READ THE NOTES AT THE
BEGINNING OF THIS CATALOGUE?**

These often provide answers to the enquiries we receive.

25p. Booklets

Type DH39
Veteran Transport Series

(Des D. Gentleman)

1971 (15 Feb). *Veteran Transport Series. Dull purple cover as Type* DH39. *Pages of six stamps:* 5 × 2½p. *with one printed label,* 4 × 2½p. *with two printed labels,* 5 × ½p. *with one printed label (Nos.* X841 *and* X851).

DH39	FEB 1971 (No. 1 Knife-board omnibus)........................	5.00

Type DH40

1971 (19 Mar). *Issued to publicise the National Postal Museum Exhibition of 80 Years of British Stamp Booklets. Dull purple cover as Type* DH40.

DH40	APR 1971	5.00

1971 (11 May)–**73.** *Dull purple cover as Type* DH39. *Veteran Transport Series continued.*

DH41	JUNE 1971 (No. 2 B-type omnibus).............................	5.00
DH42	AUG 1971 (No. 2 B-type omnibus) (17.9.71)	7.00
DH43	OCT 1971 (No. 3 Showman's Engine) (22.11.71)..........	6.00
DH44	FEB 1972 (No. 4 Mail Van) (23.12.71)	5.00
DH45	APR 1972 (No. 4 Mail Van) (13.3.72)	7.00
DH46	JUNE 1972 (No. 5 Motor Wagonette) (24.4.72)	5.50
DH47	AUG 1972 (No. 5 Motor Wagonette) (14.6.72).............	8.00
DH48	OCT 1972 (No. 6 Taxi Cab) (17.7.72)	5.50
DH49	DEC 1972 (No. 6 Taxi Cab) (19.10.72)	6.00
DH50	DEC 1972 "Issue S" (No. 6 Taxi Cab) (6.11.72)	5.50
DH51	FEB 1973 (No. 7 Electric Tramcar) (26.2.73)................	8.00

Nos. DH42/52 contain panes showing the label imperf in the margin.

Type DH52

1973 (7 June). *Dull mauve cover as Type DH52.*
DH52   JUNE 1973... 7.00

30p. Booklets

Type DQ56
British Birds Series

(Des H. Titcomb)

1971 (15 Feb). *British Birds Series. Bright purple cover as Type DQ56. Pages of six stamps: 2 panes of 5 × 3p. with one printed label (No. X855).*
DQ56   FEB 1971 (No. 1 Curlew) 3.50

1971 (19 Mar). *Bright purple cover as Type DH40.*
DQ57   APR 1971 .... 3.50

1971 (26 May)–**73.** *Bright purple cover as Type DQ56. British Birds Series continued.*
DQ58   JUNE 1971 (No. 2 Lapwing) 3.50
DQ59   AUG 1971 (No. 2 Lapwing) (23.7.71) 3.50
DQ60   OCT 1971 (No. 3 Robin) (1.10.71)............................. 5.00
DQ61   DEC 1971 (No. 3 Robin) (10.11.71)............................ 5.00
DQ62   FEB 1972 (No. 4 Pied Wagtail) (21.12.71) 3.75
DQ63   APR 1972 (No. 4 Pied Wagtail) (9.2.72)....................... 3.75
DQ64   JUNE 1972 (No. 5 Kestrel) (12.4.72) 3.75
DQ65   AUG 1972 (No. 5 Kestrel) (8.6.72)............................. 4.50
DQ66   OCT 1972 (No. 6 Black Grouse) (31.7.72)................... 3.75
DQ67   DEC 1972 (No. 6 Black Grouse) (30.10.72).................. 3.75
DQ68   DEC 1972 "Issue S" (No. 6 Black Grouse) (6.12.72) 3.75
DQ69   FEB 1973 (No. 7 Skylark) (29.1.73)............................ 3.75
DQ70   APR 1973 (No. 7 Skylark) (2.4.73) 5.00
DQ71   JUNE 1973 (No. 8 Oyster-catcher) (8.5.73) 5.00
DQ72   AUG 1973 (No. 8 Oyster-catcher) (7.6.73) 5.50
DQ72a   As DQ72 but buff cover (10.8.73)* 5.00
Nos. DQ59/72a have the label imperf in the margin.
*No. DQ72a was printed with a buff cover because of a shortage of the original purple-coloured card.

1974 (30 Jan). *Red cover similar to Type DH52. Make-up as before but with No. X856.*
DQ73   SPRING 1974 .... 3.50

1974 (21 June). *Red cover similar to Type DT9. Make-up as before.*
DQ74   JUNE 1974.. 3.50

35p. Booklets

Type DP1
British Coins Series

(Des P. Gauld)

1973 (12 Dec)–**74.** *British Coins Series. Blue cover as Type DP1. Pages of six stamps: 2 pages of 5 × 3½p. with one blank label (No. X858£a).*
DP1   AUTUMN 1973 (No. 1 Cuthred's Penny) 2.50
DP2   APR 1974 (No. 1 Cuthred's Penny) (10.4.74) 4.50
DP3   JUNE 1974 (No. 2 Silver Groat) (4.7.74)...................... 2.50

1974 (23 Oct). *Blue cover as Type DT9. Make-up as before but with No. X859.*
DP4   SEPT 1974 .... 2.50

45p. Booklets

1974 (9 Oct–26 Nov). *British Coins Series continued. Yellow-brown cover as Type DP1. Pages of six stamps: 2 pages of 5 × 4½p. (No. X865) with one blank label.*
DS1   SEPT 1974 (No. 3 Elizabeth Gold Crown) 4.50
DS2   DEC 1974 (No. 3 Elizabeth Gold Crown) (1.11.74) 5.00
DS2a   As DS2 but orange-brown cover (26.11.74)* 6.00
*No. DS2a was printed with an orange-brown cover because of a shortage of the original yellow-brown card.

50p. Booklets

Type DT1

(Des Rosalie Southall)

1971 (15 Feb)–72. *British Flowers Series. Turquoise-green cover as Type DT1. Pages of six stamps: 6 × 3p., 4 × 3p. se-tenant horizontally with 2 × 2½p. (side band), 5 × 2½p. (centre band) with one printed label and 5 × ½p. with one printed label (Nos. X841 and X851/2, X855).*

DT1	FEB 1971 (No. 1 Large Bindweed)	7.00
DT2	MAY 1971 (No. 2 Primrose) (24.3.71)	7.00
DT3	AUG 1971 (No. 3 Honeysuckle) (28.6.71)	7.00
DT4	NOV 1971 (No. 4 Hop) (17.9.71)	8.00
DT5	FEB 1972 (No. 5 Common Violet) (23.12.71)*	7.50
DT6	MAY 1972 (No. 6 Lords-and-Ladies) (13.3.72)	7.00
DT7	AUG 1972 (No. 7 Wood Anemone) (31.5.72)	6.50
DT8	NOV 1972 (No. 8 Deadly Nightshade) (15.9.72)	6.50

Nos. DT3/8 have the label imperf in the margin.

*Although generally released on 24 December, this booklet was put on sale at the London E.C.1 Philatelic Counter and also at one other Philatelic Counter on the 23 December.

Type DT9

1973 (19 Jan–June). *Turquoise-green cover as Type DT9.*

DT9	FEB 1973	6.50
DT10	APR 1973 (26.2.73)	6.50
DT11	MAY 1973 (2.4.73)	7.50
DT12	AUG 1973 (14.6.73)	12.00

1973 (14 Nov)–74. *Moss-green cover similar to Type DT9. Pages of six stamps: 2 pages of 5 × 3½p. with one blank label (No. X858Ea) and 1 page of 5 × 3p. (centre band) with one blank label (No. X856).*

DT13	AUTUMN 1973	5.50
DT14	MAR 1974 (18.2.74)	3.50

85p. Booklet

1974 (13 Nov). *Purple cover similar to Type DT9.*

DW1   Containing 3 pages of 5 × 4½p. (No. X865) with one blank label and 1 page of 5 × 3½p. (No. X859) with one blank label 7.50

Sponsored Booklets

Type DX1

(Des J. Wallis)

1972 (24 May). *"The Story of Wedgwood". Full colour pictorial cover, Type DX1 (150 × 72 mm). Containing information and illustrations on interleaving panes and on se-tenant label attached to booklet panes.*

DX1   £1 containing 12 × 3p. (No. X855) and booklet panes X851n, X841o and X841p 55.00

Type DX2

(Des J. Wallis)

1980 (16 Apr). *"The Story of Wedgwood". Multicoloured cover, Type DX2 (163 × 97 mm) showing painting "Josiah Wedgwood and his Family" by George Stubbs. Booklet contains text and illustrations on the labels attached to panes and on interleaving pages.*

DX2   £3 containing booklet panes Nos. X849n, X849o, X888l and X895l 7.00

No. DX2 is inscribed "January 1980".

Type DX3

(Des B. Dedman)

1982 (19 May). *"Story of Stanley Gibbons". Multicoloured cover, Type DX3 (163 × 97 mm) showing early envelope design on front and stamp album with text on back. Booklet contains text and illustrations on labels attached to panes and on interleaving pages.*

DX3   £4 containing booklet panes Nos. X849p, X899m and X903l/m 11.00

No. DX3 is inscribed "February 1982".

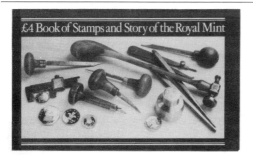

Type DX4

(Des B. West)

1983 (14 Sept). *"Story of the Royal Mint". Multicoloured cover, Type DX4 (163 × 97 mm) showing current coins, die and tools. Booklet contains text and illustrations on labels attached to panes and on interleaving pages.*

DX4   £4 containing booklet panes Nos. X899m × 2, X918l and X933l 12.00

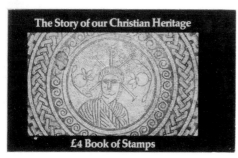

Type DX5

(Des P. Miles)

1984 (4 Sept). *"The Story of our Christian Heritage". Multicoloured cover, Type DX5 (163 × 97 mm) showing mosaic of Christ from Hinton St. Mary Roman villa. Booklet contains text and illustrations on labels attached to panes and on interleaving pages.*

DX5   £4 containing booklet panes Nos. X886l, X901m ×2 and X936l 11.00

Type DX6

(Des D. Driver)

1985 (8 Jan). *"Story of the Times" (newspaper). Multicoloured cover, Type DX6 (163 × 95 mm) showing "Waiting for the Times" (painting by Haydon). Booklet contains text and illustrations on labels attached to panes and on interleaving pages.*

DX6   £5 containing booklet panes Nos. X864l, X900l, X936l and X936m......................... 13.00

Type DX7

(Des Trickett and Webb Ltd)

1986 (18 Mar). *"The Story of British Rail". Multicoloured cover, Type DX7 (162 × 95mm) showing diesel locomotive. Booklet contains text and illustrations on labels attached to panes and on interleaving pages.*

DX7   £5 containing booklet panes Nos. X896l, X897m, X936l and X936m......................... 13.00

Type DX8

(Des Aitken Blakeley Designers)

1987 (3 Mar). *"The Story of P & O". Multicoloured cover, Type DX8 (162 ×95 mm) showing the "William Fawcett". Booklet contains text and illustrations on labels attached to panes and on interleaving pages.*

DX8   £5 containing booklet panes Nos. X847m, X900l, X900m and X939l 12.00

STAMP MONTHLY

Finest and most informative magazine for all collectors. Obtainable from your newsagent or by postal subscription – details on request

Type DX9

(Des The Partners Limited)

1988 (9 Feb). *"The Story of the Financial Times" (newspaper). Multi-coloured cover, Type* DX9 *(162 × 97 mm). Booklet contains text and illustrations on labels attached to the panes and on interleaving pages.*

DX9   £5 containing booklet panes Nos. X977ba,
          X977cb, X977da and X977db 7.50

B. Folded Booklets.

NOTE. All panes are attached to the covers by the selvedge.

10p. Booklets

Type FA1

(Des Post Office artist)

1976 (10 Mar)–77.   *Cover as Type* FA1 *printed in dull rose on very pale lavender. Containing booklet pane* X841r.
FA1   NOV 1975 60
FA2   MAR 1976 (9.6.76) 80
FA3   JUNE 1977 (13.6.77) 70

Type FA4

(Des N. Battershill)

1978 (8 Feb)–79.   *Farm Buildings Series. Bistre-brown and turquoise-blue covers as Type* FA4, *containing booklet pane No.* X843m.
FA4   Design No. 1, Oast Houses 70
FA5   Design No. 2, Buildings in Ulster (3.5.78) 60
FA6   Design No. 3, Buildings in Yorkshire (9.8.78) 60
FA7   Design No. 4, Buildings in Wales (25.10.78) 70
FA8   Design No. 5, Buildings in Scotland (10.1.79) 60
FA9   Design No. 6, Buildings in Sussex (4.4.79) 60
    Nos. FA4/5 are inscribed "January 1978", FA6 "July 1978", FA7 "October 1978", FA8 "December 1978" and FA9 "March 1979".

Type FA10

(Des Hamper and Purssell)

1979 (17 Oct)–80.   *"London 1980" International Stamp Exhibition. Red and blue cover as Type* FA10 *showing Post Office exhibition stand and containing No.* X845l.
FA10   Inscr "August 1979" 40
FA11   Inscr "January 1980" (12.1.80) 40

50p. Booklets

Type FB1

1977 (26 Jan).   *Cover as Type* FB1 *printed in maroon and pale blue.*
FB1A   Containing booklet pane X841s 2.50
FB1B   Containing booklet pane X841sa 2.00

1977 (13 June).   *Cover as Type* FB1. *Printed in chestnut and stone.*
FB2A   Containing booklet pane X844n 4.00
FB2B   Containing booklet pane X844na 2.00

Type FB3

(Des J. Ireland)

1978 (8 Feb)–79.   *Commercial Vehicles Series. Olive-yellow and grey covers as Type* FB3. A. *Containing booklet pane No.* X844n. B. *Containing booklet pane No.* X844na.

		A	B
FB3	Design No. 1, Clement Talbot van	4.00	2.00
FB4	Design No. 2, Austin taxi (3.5.78)	4.00	2.00
FB5	Design No. 3, Morris Royal Mail van (9.8.78)......	4.50	2.00
FB6	Design No. 4, Guy Electric dustcart (25.10.78)....	4.50	2.00
FB7	Design No. 5, Albion van (10.1.79)	5.00	2.00
FB8	Design No. 6, Leyland fire engine (4.4.79)	3.75	2.00

Nos. FB3/4 are inscribed "January 1978", FB5 "July 1978", FB6 "October 1978", FB7 "December 1978" and FB8 "March 1979".

1979 (28 Aug).   *Contents changed.* A. *Containing booklet pane No.* X849l. B. *Containing booklet pane No.* X849la.

		A	B
FB9	Design No. 6 Leyland fire engine....................	1.75	1.75

Type FB10

(Des B. Smith)

1979 (3 Oct)–**81.** *Veteran Cars Series. Orange-red and reddish lilac covers as Type FB10. A. Containing booklet pane No. X849l. B. Containing booklet pane No. X849la.*

	A	B
FB10 Design No. 1, 1907 Rolls-Royce Silver Ghost......	1.90	1.90

No. FB10 is inscribed "August 1979".

Contents changed. A. Containing booklet pane No. X849m. B. Containing booklet pane No. X849ma.

	A	B
FB11 Design No. 2, 1908 Grand Prix Austin (4.2.80)	1.90	1.90
FB12 Design No. 3, 1903–5 Vauxhall (25.6.80)	1.90	1.90
FB13 Design No. 4, 1897–1900 Daimler (24.9.80)	1.90	1.90

No. FB11 is inscribed "January 1980", No. FB12 "May 1980" and No. FB13 "July 1980".

Contents changed. A. Containing No. X841t. B. Containing No. X841ta.

	A	B
FB14 Design No. 5, 1896 Lanchester (26.1.81)...........	1.75	1.75
FB15 Design No. 6, 1913 Bull-nose Morris (18.3.81)	1.75	1.75

Nos. FB14/15 are inscribed "January 1981".

Type FB16

(Des R. Downer)

1981 (6 May)–**82.** *Follies Series. Brown and orange-brown covers as Type FB16. A. Containing No. X841t. B. Containing No. X841ta.*

	A	B
FB16 Design No. 1, Mugdock Castle, Stirlingshire	1.75	1.75

No. FB16 is inscribed "January 1981".

Contents changed. A. Containing No. X854l. B. Containing No. X854la.

	A	B
FB17 Design No. 1, Mugdock Castle, Stirlingshire (26.8.81)	3.50	5.50
FB18 Design No. 2, Mow Cop Castle, Cheshire-Staffs border (30.9.81)..	3.50	3.75

Nos. FB17/18 are inscribed "January 1981".

Contents changed. A. Containing No. X841u. B. Containing No. X841ua.

	A	B
FB19 Design No. 3, Paxton's Tower, Llanarthney, Dyfed (1.2.82)	1.90	1.90
FB20 Design No. 4, Temple of the Winds, Mount Stewart, Northern Ireland (6.5.82).........................	1.90	1.90
FB21 Design No. 5, Temple of the Sun, Stourhead, Wilts (11.8.82)	1.90	1.90
FB22 Design No. 6, Water Garden Cliveden, Bucks (6.10.82)	1.90	1.90

Nos. FB19/22 are inscribed "February 1982".

Type FB23

(Des H. Titcombe)

1983 (16 Feb–26 Oct). *Rare Farm Animals Series. Bright green and black covers as Type FB23. A. Containing booklet pane No. X841u. B. Containing booklet pane No. X841ua.*

	A	B
FB23 Design No. 1, Bagot Goat...............................	1.90	1.90

Contents changed. Containing No. X845n.

FB24 Design No. 2, Gloucester Old Spot Pig (5.4.83)..........	4.50
FB25 Design No. 3, Toulouse Goose (27.7.83)	4.50
FB26 Design No. 4, Orkney Sheep (26.10.83)	4.50

No. FB23 is inscribed "February 1982" and Nos. FB24/6 "April 1983".

Type FB27

(Des P. Morter)

1984 (3 Sept)–**85.** *Orchids Series. Yellow-green and lilac covers as Type FB27. Containing booklet pane No. X845p.*

FB27 Design No. 1, Dendrobium nobile and Miltonia hybrid	1.75
FB28 Design No. 2, Cypripedium calceolus and Ophrys apifera (15.1.85)	1.75
FB29 Design No. 3, Bifrenaria and Vanda tricolour (23.4.85) .	1.75
FB30 Design No. 4, Cymbidium and Arpophyllum (23.7.85)..	1.75

Nos. FB27/30 are inscribed "September 1984".

Type FB31

(Des M. Thierens Design Ltd)

1985 (4 Nov). *Cover as Type* FB31 *printed in black and bright scarlet. Containing booklet pane No.* X905l.

FB31 Pillar box design 1.40
No. FB31 is inscribed "November 1985" and was sold at a discount of 1p. off the face value of the stamps it contained.

Type FB32

(Des P. Morter)

1986 (20 May–29 July). *Pond Life Series. Emerald and dull blue covers as Type* FB32. *Containing booklet pane No.* X905l.

FB32 Design No. 1, Emperor Dragonfly, Four-spotted Libel-
lula and Yellow Flag 1.40
FB33 Design No. 2, Common Frog, Fennel-leaved Pondweed and Long-stalked Pondweed (29.7.86) 1.40
No. FB33 was originally issued with double-lined blue stars printed on the reverse over the gum. It was subsequently issued, on 12 August, with this underprint omitted.

Nos. FB32/33 are inscribed "November 1985" and were each sold at a discount of 1p. off the face value of the stamps.

Type FB34

(Des N. Battershill)

1986 (29 July). *Roman Britain Series. Brown-ochre and Indian red cover as Type* FB34. *Containing booklet pane No.* X845q.

FB34 Design No. 1, Hadrian's Wall 1.40
No. FB34 is inscribed "November 1985".

1986 (20 Oct)–**87**. *Pond Life Series continued. Blue and green cover as Type* FB32. *Containing booklet pane. No.* X845s.

FB35 Design No. 3, Moorhen and Little Grebe................. 1.40
FB36 Design No. 4, Giant Pond Snail (27.1.87) 1.40
No. FB36 is inscribed "October 1986".

1986 (20 Oct)–**87**. *Roman Britain Series continued. Brown-ochre and Indian red cover as Type* FB34. *Containing booklet pane No.* X847l.

FB37 Design No. 2, Roman Theatre of Verulamium, St.
Albans 1.40
FB38 Design No. 3, Portchester Castle, Hampshire (27.1.87) 1.40
No. FB38 is inscribed "October 1986".

Type FB39

(Des Patricia Howes)

1987 (14 Apr)–**88**. *Bicentenary of Marylebone Cricket Club Series. Brown and dull ultramarine cover as Type* FB39. *Containing booklet pane No.* X847l *attached by the selvedge.*

FB39 Design No. 1, Father Time weathervane 75
FB40 Design No. 2, Ashes urn and embroidered velvet bag
(14.7.87) 75
FB41 Design No. 3, Lord's Pavilion and wrought iron deco-
ration on roof (29.9.87) 75
FB42 Design No. 4, England team badge and new
stand at Lord's (26.1.88) 75
Nos. FB39/42 are inscribed "October 1986".

Type FB43

(Des G. Evernden)

1987 (14 Apr)–**88**. *Botanical Gardens Series. Covers as Type* FB43. *Containing booklet pane No.* X845s (FB43/4) *or* X845sa (FB45/6) *attached by the selvedge.*

FB43 Design No. 1 (cover in ultramarine and rose-red),
Rhododendron "Elizabeth", Bodnant 75
FB44 Design No. 2 (cover in deep ultramarine and cobalt),
Gentiana sino-ornata, Edinburgh (14.7.87) 75
FB45 Design No. 3 (cover in dull ultramarine and orange-
yellow), Lilium auratum and "Mount Stuart" (incor-
rect inscr) (29.9.87) 75
a. With corrected spelling "Mount Stewart" (30.10.87) . 75
FB46 Design No. 4 (cover in dull ultramarine and yellow-
orange), Strelitzia reginae, Kew (26.1.88) 75
Nos. FB43/6 are inscribed "October 1986".
The panes from Nos. FB45/6 have imperforate vertical sides.

65p. Booklet

1976 (14 July). *Cover as Type FB1, but larger (90 × 49 mm). Printed in turquoise-blue and pale buff. A. Selvedge at left. B. Selvedge at right.*

		A	B
FC1	Containing ten 6½p. (No. X872)	7.50	5.00

70p. Booklets

1977 (13 June). *Cover as Type FB1, but larger (90 × 49 mm). Printed in purple-brown and dull rose. A. Selvedge at left. B. Selvedge at right.*

		A	B
FD1	Containing ten 7p. (No. X875)	5.00	4.50

Type FD2

(Des E. Stemp)

1978 (8 Feb)–**79**. *Country Crafts Series. Grey-green and red-brown covers as Type FD2 (90 × 49 mm). Containing ten 7p. (No. X875). A. Selvedge at left. B. Selvedge at right.*

		A	B
FD2	Design No. 1, Horse-shoeing	9.00	4.00
FD3	Design No. 2, Thatching (3.5.78)	42.00	3.75
FD4	Design No. 3, Dry-stone-walling (9.8.78)	90.00	3.75
FD5	Design No. 4, Wheel-making (25.10.78)	6.00	5.00
FD6	Design No. 5, Wattle fence-making (10.1.79)	12.00	5.50

Nos. FD2/3 are inscribed "January 1978", FD4 "July 1978", FD5 "October 1978" and FD6 "December 1978".

Type FD7

(Des F. Wegner)

1979 (5 Feb). *Official opening of Derby Mechanised Letter Office. Pale yellow-green and lilac cover as Type FD7 (90 × 49 mm). Containing ten 7p. (No. X875). A. Selvedge at left. B. Selvedge at right.*

		A	B
FD7	Kedleston Hall	7.00	7.00

No. FD7 is inscribed "December 1978".

On sale only in the Derby Head Post Office area to promote postcode publicity and also at the Philatelic Bureau and philatelic sales counters.

1979 (4 Apr). *Country Crafts Series continued. Grey-green and red-brown covers as Type FD2 (90 × 49 mm). A. Selvedge at left. B. Selvedge at right.*

		A	B
FD8	Design No. 6, Basket-making	4.50	4.50

No. FD8 is inscribed "March 1979".

80p. Booklet

Type FE1

(Des P. Hutton)

1979 (3 Oct). *Military Aircraft Series. Blue and grey cover as Type FE1 (90 × 49 mm). Containing ten 8p. (No. X879) attached by the selvedge. A. Selvedge at left. B. Selvedge at right.*

		A	B
FE1	Design No. 1, BE2B, 1914, & Vickers Gun Bus, 1915	2.50	2.50

No. FE1 is inscribed "August 1979".

85p. Booklet

1976 (14 July). *Cover as Type FB1 but larger (90 × 49 mm). Printed in light yellow-olive and brownish grey. A. Selvedge at left. B. Selvedge at right.*

		A	B
FF1	Containing ten 8½p. (No. X881)	5.50	5.50

90p. Booklets

1977 (13 June). *Cover as Type FB1, but larger (90 × 49 mm). Printed in deep grey-blue and cobalt. A. Selvedge at left. B. Selvedge at right.*

		A	B
FG1	Containing ten 9p. (No. X883)	4.50	5.50

Type FG2

(Des R. Maddox)

1978 (8 Feb)–**79**. *British Canals Series. Yellow-olive and new blue cover as Type FG2 (90 × 49 mm). Containing ten 9p. (No. X883). A. Selvedge at left. B. Selvedge at right.*

		A	B
FG2	Design No. 1, Grand Union	15.00	5.00
FG3	Design No. 2, Llangollen (3.5.78)	4.00	£200
FG4	Design No. 3, Kennet & Avon (9.8.78)	9.00	8.00
FG5	Design No. 4, Caledonian (25.10.78)	4.50	5.50
FG6	Design No. 5, Regents (10.1.79)	12.00	7.00

Nos. FG2/3 are inscribed "January 1978", FG4 "July 1978", FG5 "October 1978" and FG6 "December 1978".

(Des F. Wegner)

1979 (5 Feb). *Official Opening of Derby Mechanised Letter Office. Violet-blue and rose cover as Type FD7 (90 × 49 mm). Containing ten 9p. (No. X883). A. Selvedge at left. B. Selvedge at right.*

		A	B
FG7	Tramway Museum, Crich	8.00	8.00

No. FG7 is inscribed "December 1978".

On sale only in the Derby Head Post Office area to promote postcode publicity and also at the Philatelic Bureau and philatelic sales counters.

1979 (4 Apr). *British Canals Series continued. Yellow-olive and new blue cover as Type FG2. A. Selvedge at left. B. Selvedge at right.*

		A	B
FG8	Design No. 6, Leeds & Liverpool	3.50	3.50

No. FG8 is inscribed "March 1979".

£1 Booklets

Type FH1

(Des N. Battershill)

1979 (3 Oct). *Industrial Archaeology Series. Red and green cover as Type FH1 (90 × 49 mm). Containing ten 10p. (No. X887). A. Selvedge at left. B. Selvedge at right.*

		A	B
FH1	Design No. 1, Ironbridge, Telford, Salop	3.75	3.50

No. FH1 is inscribed "August 1979".

1980 (4 Feb–24 Sept). *Military Aircraft Series continued. Blue and grey cover as Type FE1 (90 × 49 mm). Containing ten 10p. (No. X888). A. Selvedge at left. B. Selvedge at right.*

		A	B
FH2	Design No. 2, Sopwith Camel & Vickers Vimy	3.50	3.50
FH3	Design No. 3, Hawker Hart* & Handley Page Heyford (25.6.80)	3.50	3.75
FH4	Design No. 4, Hurricane & Wellington (24.9.80)	3.75	3.75

No. FH2 is inscribed "January 1980", No. FH3 "May 1980" and No. FH4 "July 1980".

*On the booklet cover the aircraft is wrongly identified as a Hawker Fury.

Type FH5

(Des M. Newton and S. Paine)

1986 (29 July)–**87**. *Musical Instruments Series. Scarlet and black covers as Type FH5. Containing six 17p. (X936).*

FH5	Design No. 1, Violin	3.00

No. FH5 is inscribed "November 1985" and was sold at a discount of 2p. off the face value of the stamps.

Contents changed. Containing No. X901n.

FH6	Design No. 2, French horn (20.10.86)	3.00
FH7	Design No. 3, Bass clarinet (27.1.87)	3.00

No. FH7 is inscribed "October 1986". These booklets were sold at a discount of 3p. off the face value of the stamps.

Type FH8

(Des A. Davidson)

1987 (14 Apr)–**88**. *Sherlock Holmes Series. Bright scarlet and grey-black cover as Type FH8. Containing booklet pane No. X901n (FH8/9) or X901na (FH10/11) attached by the selvedge.*

FH8	Design No. 1, *A Study in Scarlet*	1.50
FH9	Design No. 2, *The Hound of the Baskervilles* (14.7.87)	1.50
FH10	Design No. 3, *The Adventure of the Speckled Band* (29.9.87)	1.50
FH11	Design No. 4, *The Final Problem* (26.1.88)	1.50

Nos. FH8/11 are inscribed "October 1986".

The panes from Nos. FH10/11 have imperforate vertical sides.

£1.15 Booklets

1981 (26 Jan–18 Mar). *Military Aircraft Series continued. Blue and grey cover as Type FE1 (90 × 49 mm). Containing ten 11½p. (No. X893). A. Selvedge at left. B. Selvedge at right.*

	A	B
FI1 Design No. 5, Spitfire & Lancaster	3.50	3.50
FI2 Design No. 6, Lightning & Vulcan (18.3.81)	3.50	3.50

Nos. FI1/2 are inscribed "January 1981".

Type FI3
(Des R. Maddox)

1981 (6 May–30 Sept). *Museums Series. Blue and turquoise-green cover as Type FI3 (90 × 49 mm). Containing ten 11½p. (No. X893). A. Selvedge at left. B. Selvedge at right.*

	A	B
FI3 Design No. 1, Natural History Museum (British Museum), London	3.50	3.50
FI4 Design No. 2, National Museum of Antiquities of Scotland (30.9.81)	3.50	3.50

Nos. FI3/4 are inscribed "January 1981".

£1.20 Booklets

1980 (4 Feb–24 Sept). *Industrial Archaeology Series continued. Red and green cover as Type FH1 (90 × 49 mm). Containing ten 12p. (No. X927). A. Selvedge at left. B. Selvedge at right.*

	A	B
FJ1 Design No. 2, Beetle Mill, Ireland	3.75	3.75
FJ2 Design No. 3, Tin mines, Cornwall (25.6.80)	3.75	4.00
FJ3 Design No. 4, Bottle Kilns, Gladstone, Stoke-on-Trent (24.9.80)	3.75	3.75

No. FJ1 is inscribed "January 1980", No. FJ2 "May 1980" and No. FJ3 "July 1980".

1986 (14 Jan). *Pillar box "Write Now" cover as Type FB31 (90 × 49mm), printed in yellow-green and pale red. Containing ten 12p. (No. X896). A. Selvedge at left. B. Selvedge at right.*

	A	B
FJ4 "Write Now" (Pillar box design) (no imprint date)	3.50	3.50

Type FJ5

(Des R. Maddox)

1986 (29 Apr). *National Gallery cover as Type FJ5 (90 × 49mm), printed in magenta and blue-green. Containing ten 12p. (No. X896). A. Selvedge at left. B. Selvedge at right.*

	A	B
FJ5 National Gallery design	3.50	3.50

No. FJ5 is inscribed "November 1985".

Type FJ6
(Des Trickett and Webb Ltd)

1986 (29 July). *Handwriting cover as Type FJ6 (90 × 49 mm), printed in bright orange and bright blue. Containing ten 12p. (No. X896). A. Selvedge at left. B. Selvedge at right.*

	A	B
FJ6 "Maybe"...	3.50	3.50

No. FJ6 is inscribed "November 1985".

£1.25 Booklets

1982 (1 Feb–6 Oct). *Museums Series continued. Blue and turquoise-green cover as Type FI3 (90 × 49 mm). Containing ten 12½p. (No. X898). A. Selvedge at left. B. Selvedge at right.*

	A	B
FK1 Design No. 3, Ashmolean Museum, Oxford	3.50	3.50
FK2 Design No. 4, National Museum of Wales, Cardiff (6.5.82)	3.50	3.50
FK3 Design No. 5, Ulster Museum, Belfast (11.8.82) .	3.50	3.50
FK4 Design No. 6, Castle Museum, York (6.10.82) ...	3.50	3.50

Nos. FK1/4 are inscribed "February 1982".

Type FK5
(Des S. Paine)

1983 (16 Feb–26 Oct). *Railway Engines Series. Red and blue-green cover as Type FK5 (90 × 49 mm). Containing ten 12½p. (No. X898). A. Selvedge at left. B. Selvedge at right.*

	A	B
FK5 Design No. 1, GWR *Isambard Kingdom Brunel* .	3.50	3.50
FK6 Design No. 2, LMS Class 4P Passenger Tank Engine (5.4.83)	3.50	3.50

FK7 Design No. 3, L.N.E.R. *Mallard* (27.7.83) 3.50 3.75
FK8 Design No. 4, SR/BR *Clan Line* (26.10.83) 3.50 3.50
    No. FK5 is inscribed "February 1982" and Nos. FK6/8 "April 1983".

£1.30 Booklets

Type FL1

(Des J. Gibbs)

1981 (6 May–30 Sept). *Postal History Series. Cover as Type* FL1 *(90 × 49 mm). Containing No. X894I. A. Selvedge at left. B. Selvedge at right.*

	A	B
FL1 Design No. 1, Penny Black (red & black cover) ..	5.50	4.50
FL2 Design No. 2, The Downey Head, 1911 (red & green cover) (20.9.81)	7.50	18.00

    No. FL1 is inscribed "April 1981" and No. FL2 "September 1981".

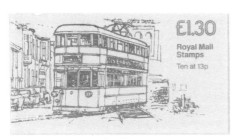

Type FL3

(Des J. Thirsk)

1984 (3 Sept). *Trams Series. Yellow-orange and purple cover as Type* FL3 *(90 × 49 mm). Containing ten 13p. (No. X900). A. Selvedge at left. B. Selvedge at right.*

	A	B
FL3 Design No. 1, Swansea/Mumbles Railway Car No. 3	3.75	3.75
FL4 Design No. 2, Glasgow Car No. 927 & Car No. 1194 (15.1.85)	3.75	3.75
FL5 Design No. 3, Car No. 717, Blackpool (23.4.85) .	3.75	3.75
FL6 Design No. 4, Car No. 120 & "D" Class Car, London (23.7.85)	3.75	3.75

    Nos. FL3/6 are inscribed "September 1984".

Type FL7

(Des Anne Morrow)

1986 (20 Oct). *Books for Children. Cover as Type FL7 (89 ×48 mm) printed in rose-red and lemon. Containing ten 13p. (No. X900). A. Selvedge at left. B. Selvedge at right.*

	A	B
FL7 Teddy bears design	3.75	3.75

Type FL8

(Des Trickett and Webb Ltd)

1987 (27 Jan). *"Keep in Touch" cover as Type FL8 (90 × 49 mm), printed in light green and bright blue. Containing ten 13p. (No. X900). A. Selvedge at left. B. Selvedge at right.*

	A	B
FL8 Handclasp and envelope design	3.75	3.75

    No. FL8 is inscribed "October 1986".

Type FL9

(Des Hannah Firmin)

1987 (14 Apr). *"Ideas for your Garden". Cover as Type FL9 (90 × 49 mm) printed in bistre and orange-brown. Containing ten 13p. stamps (No. X900). A. Selvedge at left. B. Selvedge at right.*

	A	B
FL9 Conservatory design	2.00	2.00

    No. FL9 is inscribed "October 1986".

Type FL10

(Des Trickett and Webb Ltd)

1987 (14 July). *"Brighter Writer". Cover as Type FL10 (90 × 48 mm) printed in orange and bright reddish violet. Containing ten 13p. stamps (No. X900). A. Selvedge at left. B. Selvedge at right.*

	A	B
FL10 Flower design	2.00	2.00

No. FL10 is inscribed "October 1986".

Type FL11

(Des E. Stemp)

1987 (29 Sept). *"Jolly Postman". Cover as Type FL11 (90 × 49 mm) printed in pale blue and deep blue. Containing ten 13p. stamps (No. X900). A. Selvedge at left. B. Selvedge at right.*

	A	B
FL11 Boy drawing design	2.00	2.00

No. FL11 is inscribed "October 1986".

Type FL12

(Des E. Hughes)

1988 (26 Jan). *Bicentenary of Linnean Society. Cover as Type FL12 (90 × 49 mm) printed in blue and claret. Containing ten 13p. stamps (No. X900). A. Selvedge at left. B. Selvedge at right.*

	A	B
FL12 Mermaid, fish and insect (from "Hortus Sanibatis", 1497)	2.00	2.00

No. FL12 is inscribed "October 1986".

£1.40 Booklets

1981 (26 Jan–18 Mar). *Industrial Archaeology Series continued. Red and green cover as Type FH1 (90 × 49 mm). Containing ten 14p. (No. X930). A. Selvedge at left. B. Selvedge at right.*

	A	B
FM1 Design No. 5, Preston Mill, Scotland	3.75	3.75
FM2 Design No. 6, Talyllyn Railway, Tywyn (18.3.81)	3.75	3.75

Nos. FM1/2 are inscribed "January 1981".

Type FM3

(Des E. Stemp)

1981 (6 May–30 Sept). *19th-century Women's Costume Series. Claret and blue cover as Type FM3 (90 × 49 mm). Containing ten 14p. (No. X930). A. Selvedge at left. B. Selvedge at right.*

	A	B
FM3 Design No. 1, Costume, 1800–15	3.75	4.50
FM4 Design No. 2, Costume, 1815–30 (30.9.81)	3.75	3.75

Nos. FM3/4 are inscribed "January 1981".

£1.43 Booklets

1982 (1 Feb–6 May). *Postal History Series continued. Cover as Type FL1 (90 × 49 mm). Containing No. X899l. A. Selvedge at left. B. Selvedge at right.*

	A	B
FN1 Design No. 3, James Chalmers (postal reformer) (orange & turquoise-blue cover)	4.00	4.00
FN2 Design No. 4, Edmund Dulac (stamp designer) (brown & red cover) (6.5.82)	4.00	4.00

Type FN3

(Des J. Gardner)

1982 (12 July). *"Holiday Postcard Stamp Book". Purple and turquoise-blue cover as Type* FN3 *(90 × 49 mm). Containing No.* X899l. A. *Selvedge at left.* B. *Selvedge at right.*

		A	B
FN3	*Golden Hinde* on front, postcard voucher on back	4.00	4.00

1982 (21 July)–**83**. *Postal History Series continued. Cover as Type* FL1 *(90 × 49 mm). Containing No.* X899l. A. *Selvedge at left.* B. *Selvedge at right.*

		A	B
FN4	Design No. 5, "Forces Postal Service" (grey & violet cover)	4.00	5.00
FN5	Design No. 6, The £5 Orange (orange & black cover) (6.10.82)	4.00	4.00
FN6	Design No. 7, Postmark History (brt scarlet & dp dull blue cover) (16.2.83)	4.00	4.00

Nos. FN1/6 are inscribed "February 1982".

£1.46 Booklets

1983 (5 Apr–26 Oct). *Postal History Series continued. Cover as Type* FL1 *(90 × 49 mm).* A. *Containing No.* X899n. B. *Containing No.* X899na.

		A	B
FO1	Design No. 8, Seahorse High Values (blue & green cover)	9.00	9.00
FO2	Design No. 9, Parcel Post Centenary (turquoise-blue & carmine cover) (27.7.83)......................	9.00	9.00
FO3	Design No. 10, Silver Jubilee of Regional Stamps (dull green & reddish violet) (26.10.83)	9.00	9.00

No. FO1 is inscribed "March 1983", No. FO2 "May 1983" and No. FO3 "June 1983".

£1.50 Booklets

1986 (14 Jan). *Pillar box "Write Now" cover as Type* FB31 *(90 × 49mm), printed in ultramarine and red.* A. *Containing No.* X897l. B. *Containing No.* X897la.

		A	B
FP1	"Write Now" (Pillar box design)	4.00	4.00

No. FP1 shows no imprint date.

1986 (29 Apr). *National Gallery cover as Type* FJ5 *(90 × 49mm), printed in violet and vermilion.* A. *Containing No.* X897l. B. *Containing No.* X897la.

		A	B
FP2	National Gallery design	4.00	4.00

No. FP2 is inscribed "November 1985".

1986 (29 July). *Handwriting cover as Type* FJ6 *(90 × 49 mm), printed in blue-green and bright blue.* A. *Containing No.* X897l. B. *Containing No.* X897la.

		A	B
FP3	"No"	4.00	4.00

No. FP3 is inscribed "November 1985".

£1.54 Booklets

1984 (3 Sept). *Postal History Series continued. Reddish purple and pale blue cover as Type* FL1 *(90 × 49 mm).* A. *Containing No.* X901l. B. *Containing No.* X901la.

		A	B
FQ1	Design No. 11, Old & new Postage Dues	4.50	4.50
FQ2	Design No. 12, Queen Victoria embossed stamps (yellow-green & blue cover) (15.1.85)	4.50	4.50
FQ3	Design No. 13, Queen Victoria surface-printed stamps (blue-green & carmine cover) (23.4.85) ..	4.50	4.50
FQ4	Design No. 14, 17th-century mounted & foot messengers (dp brown & orange-red cover) (23.7.85)	4.50	4.50

No. FQ1 is inscribed "July 1984" and Nos. FQ2/4 are inscribed "September 1984".

£1.55 Booklets

1982 (1 Feb–6 Oct). *19th-century Women's Costume Series continued. Claret and blue cover as Type* FM3 *(90 × 49 mm). Containing ten 15½p. (No.* X932). A. *Selvedge at left.* B. *Selvedge at right.*

		A	B
FR1	Design No. 3, Costume, 1830–50	4.25	4.25
FR2	Design No. 4, Costume, 1850–60 (6.5.82)	4.25	4.25
FR3	Design No. 5, Costume, 1860–80 (11.8.82)	4.25	4.25
FR4	Design No. 6, Costume, 1880–1900 (6.10.82)	4.25	4.25

Nos. FR1/4 are inscribed "February 1982".

£1.60 Booklets

Type FS1

(Des Carol Walklin)

1983 (5 Apr). *"Birthday Box" Design. Magenta and red-orange cover as Type* FS1 *(90 × 49 mm). Depicting birthday cake and associated items.* A. *Selvedge at left.* B. *Selvedge at right.*

		A	B
FS1	Containing ten 16p. (No. X933) (no imprint date) .	4.50	4.50
	a. Rates altered and "February 1983" imprint date	10.00	25.00

Type FS2

(Des R. Maddox)

1983 (10 Aug). *British Countryside Series. Special Discount Booklet (sold at £1.45). Greenish blue and ultramarine cover as Type FS2 (90 × 49 mm). Containing ten* 16p. *stamps (No. X933Eu). A. Selvedge at left. B. Selvedge at right.*

	A	B
FS2 Design No. 1, Lyme Regis, Dorset	6.50	6.50

Stamps from No. FS2 show a double-lined "D" printed in blue on the reverse, over the gum.
No. FS2 is inscribed "April 1983".

1983 (21 Sept). *British Countryside Series continued. Dull green on violet cover as Type FS2 (90 × 49 mm). Containing ten* 16p. *stamps (No. X933). A. Selvedge at left. B. Selvedge at right.*

	A	B
FS3 Design No. 2, Arlington Row, Bibury, Gloucestershire	4.25	4.25

No. FS3 is inscribed "April 1983".

Type FS4

(Des M. Newton)

1984 (14 Feb). *"Write it" Design. Vermilion and ultramarine cover as Type FS4 (90 × 49 mm). Containing ten* 16p. *stamps (No. X933). A. Selvedge at left. B. Selvedge at right.*

	A	B
FS4 Fountain pen	4.00	4.00

No. FS4 is inscribed "April 1983".

£1.70 Booklets

Type FT1

(Des G. Hardie)

1984 (3 Sept). *Social Letter Writing Series. Rose and deep claret cover as Type FT1 (90 × 49 mm). Containing ten* 17p. *(No. X936). A. Selvedge at left. B. Selvedge at right.*

	A	B
FT1 Design No. 1, "Love Letters"	4.50	4.50

No. FT1 is inscribed "September 1984".

1985 (5 Mar). *Social Letter Writing Series continued. Special Discount Booklet (sold at £1.55). Turquoise-blue and deep claret cover as Type FT1 (90 × 49 mm). Containing ten* 17p. *(No. X936Eu). A. Selvedge at left. B. Selvedge at right.*

	A	B
FT2 Design No. 2, "Letters abroad"	6.00	6.00

Stamps from No. FT2 show a double-lined "D" printed in blue on the reverse, over the gum.
No. FT2 is inscribed "September 1984".

1985 (9 Apr). *Social Letter Writing Series continued. Bright blue and deep claret cover as Type FT1 (90 × 49 mm). Containing ten* 17p. *(No. X936). A. Selvedge at left. B. Selvedge at right.*

	A	B
FT3 Design No. 3, "Fan letters"	4.50	4.50

No. FT3 is inscribed "September 1984".

Type FT4

(Des B. Smith)

1985 (30 July). *350 Years of Royal Mail Public Postal Service. Special Discount Booklet (sold at £1.53). Cover Type FS4 (90 × 60 mm), printed in rosine and bright blue. Containing ten* 17p. *(No. 1290Eu) with selvedge at top.*

FT4 Datapost Service design		6.00

The stamps from this booklet show double-lined letters "D" printed on the reverse over the gum.
No. FT4 is inscribed "September 1984".

1985 (8 Oct). *Social Letter Writing Series continued. Black and bright scarlet cover as Type FT1 (90 × 49 mm). Containing ten* 17p. *(No. X936). A. Selvedge at left. B. Selvedge at right.*

	A	B
FT5 Design No. 4, "Write Now" (Pillar box)	4.50	4.50

1986 (29 Apr). *National Gallery cover as Type FJ5 (90 × 49mm), printed in blue-green and blue. Containing ten* 17p. *(No. X936). A. Selvedge at left. B. Selvedge at right.*

	A	B
FT6 National Gallery design	4.50	4.50

No. FT6 is inscribed "November 1985".

1986 (29 July). *Handwriting cover as Type FJ6 (90 × 49 mm) printed in red and bright blue. Containing ten* 17p. *(No. X936). A. Selvedge at left. B. Selvedge at right.*

	A	B
FT7 "Yes"	4.50	4.50

No. FT7 is inscribed "November 1985".

£1.80 Booklet

1986 (20 Oct). *Books for Children. New blue and orange-brown cover as Type FL7. Containing ten 18p. (No. X939). A. Selvedge at left. B. Selvedge at right.*

	A	B
FU1 Rabbits design	4.75	4.75

1987 (27 Jan). *"Keep in Touch" cover as Type FL8 printed in magenta and bright blue. Containing ten 18p. (No. X939). A. Selvedge at left. B. Selvedge at right.*

	A	B
FU2 Handclasp and envelope design	4.75	4.75

No. FU2 is inscribed "October 1986".

1987 (14 Apr). *"Ideas for your Garden". Claret and brown-olive cover as Type FL9 (90 × 49 mm). Containing ten 18p. stamps (No. X939). A. Selvedge at left. B. Selvedge at right.*

	A	B
FU3 Garden path design	2.75	2.75

No. FU3 is inscribed "October 1986".

1987 (14 July). *"Brighter Writer". Turquoise-green and reddish orange cover as Type FL10 (90 × 48 mm). Containing ten 18p. stamps (No. X939). A. Selvedge at left. B. Selvedge at right.*

	A	B
FU4 Berries and leaves design	2.75	2.75

No. FU4 is inscribed "October 1986".

1987 (29 Sept). *"Jolly Postman". Cover as Type FL11 (90 × 49 mm) printed in deep blue and claret. Containing ten 18p. stamps (No. X939). A. Selvedge at left. B. Selvedge at right.*

	A	B
FU5 Girl drawing design	2.75	2.75

No. FU5 is inscribed "October 1986".

1988 (26 Jan). *Bicentenary of Linnean Society. Cover as Type FL12 (90 × 49 mm) printed in dull yellow-green and dull claret. Containing ten 18p. stamps (No. X939). A. Selvedge at left. B. Selvedge at right.*

	A	B
FU6 Wolf and birds (from "Hortus Sanitatis", 1497)	2.50	2.50

Christmas Booklets

Type FX1

(Des J. Matthews)

1978 (15 Nov). *"Christmas Greetings". Cover Type FX1 (90 × 49 mm). Printed in rose-red and sage-green.*

FX1	£1.60, containing booklet pane No. X875l attached by the selvedge	3.75

No. FX1 is inscribed "August 1978".

Type FX2

(Des P. Sharland)

1979 (14 Nov). *"Christmas Greetings". Red and green cover as Type FX2 (90 × 49 mm), showing Christmas cracker.*

FX2	£1.80, containing booklet pane No. X879l	4.50

No. FX2 is inscribed "October 1979".

Type FX3

(Des E. Fraser)

1980 (12 Nov). *Christmas. Red and blue cover as Type FX3 (90 × 49 mm), showing Nativity scene.*

FX3	£2.20, containing booklet pane No. X888m	6.00

No. FX3 is inscribed "September 1980".

Type FX4

(Des W. Sanderson)

1981 (11 Nov.). Christmas. Red and blue cover as Type FX4 (90 × 49 mm), showing skating scene.
FX4   £2.55, containing booklet pane No. X893I 8.00
No. FX4 is inscribed "January 1981".

Type FX5

(Des A. Davidson)

1982 (10 Nov). Christmas. Red and green cover as Type FX5 (90 × 49 mm), showing Christmas Mummers.
FX5   £2.50, containing booklet pane No. X898I 9.00
No. FX5 is inscribed "February 1982" and was sold at a discount of 30p. off the face value of the stamps.
Each stamp in the pane has a blue star printed on the reverse over the gum.

Type FX6

(Des Barbara Brown)

1983 (9 Nov). Christmas. Brown-lilac and yellow cover as Type FX6 (90 × 49 mm), showing pantomime scenes.
FX6   £2.50, containing twenty 12½p. (No. X898Eua) 6.50
No. FX6 is inscribed "April 1983" and was sold at a discount of 30p. off the face value of the stamps.
Each stamp in the pane has a double lined blue star printed on the reverse over the gum.

Type FX7

(Des Yvonne Gilbert)

1984 (20 Nov). Christmas. Light brown and red-orange cover as Type FX7 (90 × 60 mm), showing Nativity scene.
FX7   £2.60, containing twenty 13p. (No. 1267Eu) 6.50
No. FX7 is inscribed "September 1984" and was sold at a discount of 30p. off the face value of the stamps.
The stamps from this booklet show double-lined blue stars printed on the reverse over the gum.

Type FX8

(Des Adrian George)

1985 (19 Nov). Christmas. Bright blue and rose cover as Type FX8 (90 × 60 mm), showing The Pantomime.
FX8   £2.40, containing twenty 12p. (No. 1303Eu) 5.75
The stamps from this booklet show double-lined blue stars printed on the reverse over the gum.

Type FX9

(Des Lynda Gray)

1986 (2 Dec). *Christmas. Red and dull blue-green cover as Type* FX9 (91 × 48 mm), *showing Shetland Yule cakes. A. Selvedge at left. B. Selvedge at right.*

		A	B
FX9	£1.30, containing ten 13p. (No. X900Eu)	4.50	4.00

No. FX9 is inscribed "October 1986" and was sold at a discount of 10p. off the face value of the stamps.

Each stamp in the pane has a blue star printed on the reverse over the gum.

C. Window Booklets

These were produced for sale in selected areas through post offices and commercial outlets.

NOTE: All panes are attached to the covers by the selvedge.

52p. Booklet

Type GA1

1987 (4 Aug). *Laminated cover Type* GA1 *(75 × 60 mm) printed in scarlet, lemon and black.*

GA1	Containing booklet pane No. X900n	80

No. GA1 is inscribed "20 October 1986".

72p. Booklet ·

1987 (4 Aug). *Laminated cover as Type* GA1 *(75 × 60 mm) printed in scarlet, lemon and black.*

GB1	Containing booklet pane No. X939m	1.10

No. GB1 is inscribed "20 October 1986".

£1.04 Booklet

1987 (4 Aug). *Laminated cover as Type* GA1 *(75 × 60 mm) printed in scarlet, lemon and black.*

GC1	Containing booklet pane No. X948l	1.50

No. GC1 is inscribed "20 October 1986".

£1.30 Booklet

1987 (4 Aug). *Laminated cover similar to Type* GA1, *but 98 × 60 mm, printed in scarlet, lemon and black.*

GD1	Containing booklet pane No. X900o	2.00

No. GD1 is inscribed "20 October 1986".

£1.80 Booklet

1987 (4 Aug). *Laminated cover similar to Type* GA1, *but 98 × 60 mm, printed in scarlet, lemon and black.*

GE1	Containing booklet pane No. X939n	2.75

No. GE1 is inscribed "20 October 1986".

Notes

Notes

STANLEY GIBBONS
FOR
ALBUMS
CATALOGUES
HANDBOOKS
ACCESSORIES

The following pages give details
of selected items from the
Stanley Gibbons Publications range

A complete listing with current prices
is available from your local stockist
or direct from

Stanley Gibbons Publications Limited.
Unit 5 Parkside,
Christchurch Road,
Ringwood,
Hampshire BH24 3SH.
or telephone 042 54 2363

A CHOICE OF ALBUMS
FOR THE GB COLLECTOR

For the collector who requires a quality printed album in which to house a straightforward Great Britain Collection: Stanley Gibbons has a fine range from which to choose.

THE WINDSOR POPULAR

Popular with collectors since 1925, this is our most detailed GB album with spaces for all those special items such as se-tenant strips and panes, sideways watermarks and shades. A spring-back album with superb quality printed leaves providing a clearly identified space for every stamp and on the facing page an illustrated catalogue giving details and SG catalogue numbers for easy reference.

Item 5240	Windsor Popular Volume 1 1840–1970
Item 5242	Windsor Popular Volume 2 1970–1981
Item 5428	Windsor Popular Volume 3 1982–date

THE WINDSOR SOVEREIGN

Details as for the Windsor Popular but bound in tan leather finish PVC with a matching slip case. This luxury album is the perfect setting for that special GB Collection.

Item 5244	Windsor Sovereign Volume 1 1840–1970
Item 5246	Windsor Sovereign Volume 2 1970–1981
Item 5483	Windsor Sovereign Volume 3 1982–date

THE GREAT BRITAIN ONE COUNTRY ALBUM

This elegant 4-ring album provides the perfect home for any straightforward GB collection. Housed in rich burgundy leather effect binders with gold tooling on the cover and spine, the high quality cartridge leaves are laid out and written up to ensure that your collection is attractively displayed whatever its stage of development. Every stamp illustrated and identified by its SG catalogue number.

| Item 5250 | Great Britain One Country Volume 1 1840–1970 |
| Item 5252 | Great Britain One Country Volume 2 1970–date |

STANLEY GIBBONS GREAT BRITAIN LUXURY HINGELESS ALBUM

This impressive album represents the very ultimate in luxury convenience and style, its padded binders are covered in navy blue leatherette rexine and decorated with the country's crest in traditional heraldic colours. The leaves are of the highest quality, tastefully laid out to give a superbly attractive display with a crystal clear mount already affixed in each space for the immediate insertion of your stamps. Each album is presented in its own matching slip case for added protection.

| Item 5284 | Great Britain Luxury Hingeless Album Volume 1 1840–1970 |
| Item 5285 | Great Britain Luxury Hingeless Album Volume 2 1970–date |

THE DAVO STANDARD GREAT BRITAIN ALBUM

A superior album attractively emblazoned with the country's crest on the cover and spine and incorporating solid brass screw peg fittings for exceptional convenience and security. It is covered in fine navy canvas and contains high quality cartridge leaves laid out with a printed space for each stamp. The high capacity and large page size of this album enables all GB issues to be accommodated in a single volume – it therefore represents excellent value for money. Supplied in slip case.

| Item 5285ST | Davo Standard Great Britain Album complete 1840–date |

An illustrated colour brochure giving details and prices of these and all other Stanley Gibbons Publications products available by post from

**Stanley Gibbons Publications Ltd
5 Parkside, Christchurch Road
Ringwood, Hampshire BH24 3SH
Telephone 042 54 2363**

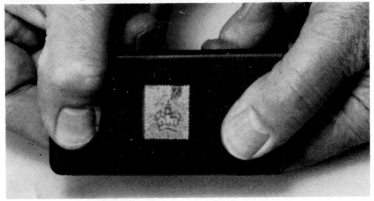

PEG-FITTING
BLANK LOOSE-LEAF ALBUMS

Stanley Gibbons blank albums give you the freedom and flexibility you need to arrange your collection exactly as you want it.

All those items which can add real interest to a collection: shades, inverted watermarks, gum variations, cylinder blocks, unusual cancellations, etc. can be easily accommodated and there is no need to be frustrated by empty spaces perpetually reminding you of the stamps you do not hae.

Peg-fitting albums represent the very peak of Stanley Gibbons range – albums which have stood the test of time from the Devon, now in its 30th year of production to the Philatelic which has been housing the great collections of the world for over a century!

The Devon
A strong elegant, large-capacity binder containing 100 fine quality cartridge leaves ($10\frac{3}{8} \times 9\frac{1}{3}$ in.). Choice of maroon, green, black or blue. Ideal for collections where that extra capacity is required. Transparent interleaving available, boxed.

The Exeter
A quality binder in a choice of red, blue or green containing 40 leaves ($10\frac{3}{8} \times 9\frac{1}{3}$ in.) of fine white cartridge. All leaves are double linen-hinged with transparent facing so that leaves lie flat when the album is opened and damaging friction is minimised.

The Plymouth
Maroon, black, green or blue, a connoisseur's album in a strong matching slip-case. Supplied with 40 double linen-hinged leaves ($10\frac{3}{8} \times 9\frac{1}{3}$ in.) with glassine facing for additional protection.

The Philatelic
The largest album in the Stanley Gibbons range, it not only accommodates more stamps per page than other albums but also allows sheets, blocks, etc., to be arranged and mounted on its $12\frac{7}{8} \times 10\frac{1}{3}$ in. leaves. Bound in handsome deep green cloth with leather corners and spine, supplied with 80 double linen-hinged, transparent faced leaves and presented in a sturdy deep green slip-case.

The Oriel
Supreme among luxury blank albums, the Oriel will enhance the very finest collection. Half bound in rich red leather with gold tooling, each album contains 50 superior gilt-edged double linen-hinged leaves ($10\frac{3}{8} \times 9\frac{3}{8}$ in.) with transparent facings and is supplied in a luxury matching slip-case.

The most prestigious home for your stamps.

Additional binders and leaves are available for all Stanley Gibbons peg-fitting albums.

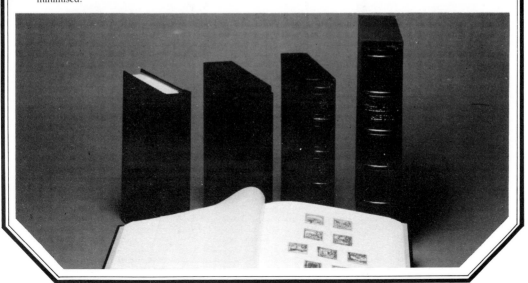

BLANK SPRINGBACK ALBUMS

The fine albums give the more advanced collector the freedom and flexibility he needs to arrange his collection exactly as he wants it.

All leaves are finely printed with a feint quadrille and most have side and centre markings to aid arrangement. Many have transparent interleaving to reduce friction between stamps and facing pages – interleaving sheets are available for those albums which are not supplied with this.

There are six very popular, value-for-money albums in the Stanley Gibbons springback range.

1. Tower (Item 0331)
A choice of red, green, or black gold-blocked binder with 100 leaves of white cartridge $11\frac{1}{8}'' \times 9\frac{7}{8}''$. Boxed.

2. Senator Medium (Item 0384)
A very popular 'first' blank leaved album for many years now. 50 leaves $10\frac{3}{8}'' \times 8\frac{3}{4}''$, a choice of three binder colours; black, green or red.

3. Senator Standard (Item 0386)
As the Senator Medium but with 100 larger sized leaves ($11\frac{1}{8}'' \times 9\frac{7}{8}''$). One of our best selling albums!

4. Simplex Medium (Item 3810)
Fifty leaves of high quality cream paper with a subtle decorative border ($10\frac{3}{8}'' \times 8\frac{3}{4}''$). Binder choice of green or red with gold blocking on the spine.

5. Simplex Standard (Item 3812)
100 larger sized leaves ($11\frac{1}{8}'' \times 9\frac{7}{8}''$), otherwise the same style as the Simplex Medium. Boxed. Popular with generations of stamp collectors!

6. Utile (Item 3821)
25 white cartridge special double linen-hinged transparent faced leaves ($11\frac{1}{8}'' \times 9\frac{7}{8}''$) designed to lie flat when album is opened. Attractive binder in choice of green or red.

Transparent Interleaving. Fine quality glazed transparent paper in packs of 100 sheets for Tower, Senator, Simplex or similar types of loose-leaf springback albums.
Item 3310 Standard size $11'' \times 9\frac{5}{8}''$.
Item 3311 Medium size $10'' \times 8\frac{1}{4}''$.

For further details visit your favourite stamp shop or, in case of difficulty, write to:
Stanley Gibbons Publications Ltd.,
5 Parkside, Christchurch Road,
Ringwood, Hampshire BH24 3SH
Telephone 042 54 2363

COVER ALBUMS

With cover collecting growing in popularity all the time we are proud to offer a comprehensive range of albums to meet the needs of first day cover collector and postal historian alike. All leaves have black card inserts to set off your covers to best advantage.

1. The New Pioneer Cover Album
A fully padded PVC Binder in a choice of black, green or red. Holds up to 40 covers in a high capacity, low priced album, ideal for the beginner.

2. The Protector Cover Album
The luxury padded binder comes in deep blue, brown or maroon with gold blocking on the spine and a secure 4-ring arch mechanism. The album contains 19 double and 1 single-pocket leaves, the former being specifically designed to house the current standard British Post Office first day covers. The leaves are made from 'Polyprotec' a material which does not crease or tear easily, will not degrade and offers considerable protection against that and ultra violet light. Holds up to 78 covers.

3. The Malvern Cover Album
Another great value album suitable for collectors at all levels. The 4-ring arch fitting binder contains 19 double-pocket leaves, 1 single-pocket leaves and holds up to 78 covers in all. Available in blue, green, red or black.

4. The New Classic Cover Album
A compact de-luxe album with 20 crystal clear leaves offering full protection for up to 40 covers and two clear fly leaves to hold an index of notes. Available in black, red or blue and supplied in a protective slip box.

5. The SG Major Cover Album
(Not illustrated)
A luxury album recommended for that really special collection. The fully padded, leather grained PVC binder has peg fittings and comes with 13 crystal clear leaves (12 double-pocket and 1 single pocket) and two clear fly leaves in which to insert notes. Available in dark red, deep blue, brown or black – the top of the range.

6. The Universal Cover Album
The cover album which allows stamps, booklets and presentation packs to be housed all together – see page 200 for details.

IMPORTANT MESSAGE TO G.B. COLLECTORS!

You know how important it is to have the very latest edition of the Stanley Gibbons Concise Catalogue with its listings of all the new issues, up to date information on earlier stamps and of course prices accurately set by experts with their fingers on the pulse of the current international stamp market.

If you would like us to notify you of the next edition of Concise all you have to do is complete the form below and post it to:

The Advance Information Service,
Stanley Gibbons Publications Ltd.,
5 Parkside, Christchurch Road,
Ringwood, Hampshire BH24 3SH.

For similar information on other Great Britain catalogues as listed on page v, please indicate title of interest on the form.

ADVANCE INFORMATION WITHOUT OBLIGATION!

To: **The Advance Information Service,**
Stanley Gibbons Publications Ltd.,
5 Parkside, Christchurch Road,
Ringwood, Hampshire BH24 3SH.

Please notify me of publication dates of new editions

of . . . .

Name: . . . .

Address: . . . .

. . . .

. . . .